MEDICAL ILLUSTRATIONS IN
MEDIEVAL MANUSCRIPTS

MEDICAL ILLUSTRATIONS IN MEDIEVAL MANUSCRIPTS

BY

LOREN MacKINNEY

PART I

EARLY MEDICINE IN ILLUMINATED MANUSCRIPTS

PART II

MEDICAL MINIATURES IN EXTANT MANUSCRIPTS: A CHECKLIST
COMPILED WITH THE ASSISTANCE OF

THOMAS HERNDON

UNIVERSITY OF CALIFORNIA PRESS

Berkeley and Los Angeles

1965

PUBLISHED IN THE UNITED STATES OF AMERICA
BY THE UNIVERSITY OF CALIFORNIA PRESS
BERKELEY AND LOS ANGELES, CALIFORNIA

THIS WORK IS ALSO PUBLISHED IN THE UNITED KINGDOM
BY THE WELLCOME HISTORICAL MEDICAL LIBRARY, LONDON

Printed in Great Britain

PREFACE

The present volume is neither a popular picture book for lay readers nor a medical history for professional physicians and surgeons. It aims to satisfy both the medical man who appreciates history and the intellectual layman who is interested in the age-old struggle against human ailments. It makes use of both the pictorial and textual records of our remote past in presenting some of the more prominent aspects of the early healing art. The author is aware of the pitfalls that beset the Ph.D. who writes medical history without benefit of formal medical training. He is also aware of the fact that the medical practices encountered in manuscripts make more demands on paleographical, iconographical and linguistic, than on medical, competencies. This conclusion is the result of thirty years of research, and the writing of thirty-two articles and two books in the field of early medical history.

In this connection personal acknowledgement is due for the generous technical assistance of professionals in the above-mentioned research realms: in paleography to Augusto Beccaria (Milan), Neil Ker (Oxford), Elias Lowe (Princeton), A. N. L. Munby (Cambridge), S. A. J. Moorat (Wellcome Library), Mrs. Charles Singer, and my colleagues, B. L. Ullman and John G. Kunstmann; in iconography to Mme. Zofia Ameisenowa (Cracow), Walter Artelt (Frankfort), Otto Bettman and Harry Bober (New York City), A. Süheyl Unver (Istanbul) and Kurt Weitzmann (Princeton); in linguistics to numerous colleagues in the departments of Classics and Germanic and Romance Languages of our University; and in medicine, likewise at our University, Drs. J. B. Bullitt, Loren G. MacKinney, Warner Wells and Nathan Womack. Other medical men have read our articles and made constructive criticisms. Also thanks are due to Professor Augusto Beccaria and Astrik L. Gabriel who first convinced us of the importance of pictorial sources. Dr. William Sharpe's critical reading of the completed typescript enabled us to amend many a faulty passage. We pay final tribute to the ever-inspiring influence as well as advice on specific problems that we were privileged to receive through the years from those three great masters of medical history, John Fulton, Henry Sigerist and Charles Singer.

PREFACE

The background of research on which the book rests also evokes the acknowledgement of a debt extending over thirty years of investigation of medical (as well as non-medical) manuscripts in European and American collections. The principal repositories of manuscripts in the USA, Canada, Great Britain, Belgium, Holland, France, Spain, Italy, the Germanies, Hungary, Yugoslavia, Poland, Russia and the Scandinavian countries, were surveyed with the invaluable assistance of Mrs. MacKinney during six summers and two academic years. For the financial subsidies that made it possible to examine and microfilm hundreds of manuscripts in these widely scattered centres, grateful acknowledgement is made to the following institutions: The American Philosophical Society, The National Institutes of Health, the Kenan Fund, the Research Council and the Smith Fund of the University of North Carolina, the Medical Center of the University of California at Los Angeles and the Wellcome Trust of London. For their courtesy in providing access to manuscripts and their patience in satisfying the needs of the researchers, the administrators and staffs of the manuscript centres that were visited have our lasting gratitude. Most of the libraries in the checklist (Part II, *below*) were visited but special demands were made on the time and patience of the following persons, to whom we express our appreciation and thanks. In Europe: Drs. Helmut Boase, Jurgen Mau and J. Irmscher in East Berlin; Mme. Helena Ostromecka and Dr. Walter in Breslau (Wroclaw); Dr. Helga Hajdu in Budapest; Dr. Zofia Ameisenowa in Cracow; Dr. Wege in Dessau; Dr. J. D. H. Widdess in Dublin; Dr. C. P. Finlayson in Edinburgh; Dr. Stroebel in Erfurt; Dr. R. O. MacKenna in Glasgow; Dr. Goetz in Leipzig; Ditward Murray, S. A. J. Moorat and Dr. F. N. L. Poynter in London; Drs. Albert Boeckle, Karl Dachs and Bernhard Bischoff in Munich; R. W. Hunt in Oxford; Drs. Thérèse d'Alverny, M. Ouy and Emile Van Moe in Paris; C. Angelis in Rome; Dr. Alexander Gela in Warsaw; Dr. Parnika in Weimar. In America: Dr. Dorothy Schullian in Cleveland; Dr. Henry Viets in Boston; Dr. W. W. Francis and Cecile Desbarats in Montreal; Dr. Gertrude Annan in New York City; Dr. J. A. Benjamin in Rochester (N. Y.); Madeline Stanton and Elizabeth Thomson in New Haven; Drs. L. J. Daly and Charles Ermatinger of the Vatican Microfilm Library at St. Louis University; Nicholas Heer of Harvard University.

In the final processing of the manuscript, typescript and photoreproductions we have been ably assisted by Mr. Thomas Herndon, who also had much to do with solving earlier paleographical, iconographical and linguistic problems, as well as

PREFACE

with the arduous task of checking references, reading proofs, and the like. Mr. Samuel Boone has rendered expert service in providing photoreproductions. Finally, to Dr. F. N. L. Poynter of the Wellcome Historical Medical Library we are indebted for encouragement and technical assistance through the years of research and writing and through the final editing of the volume, and to the Wellcome Trust for financing the earlier researches in Great Britain and the final publication.

Loren MacKinney

Chapel Hill
April 1963

TABLE OF CONTENTS

LIST OF MINIATURES

LIST OF MINIATURES

LIST OF MINIATURES

LIST OF MINIATURES

INTRODUCTION

THE present volume is the outcome of illustrated lectures that have been given by the author over a period of years, before groups of both medical and non-medical historians both locally and in national and international meetings, also before academies of medicine, hospital staffs and societies of medical, pharmaceutical and liberal-arts students, and at college lecture series, and dinner meetings of professors and businessmen. With these varying classes of auditors and viewers, the method of permitting the manuscript illustrations and texts to speak for themselves has met with marked success. Surprise at the variety and practicalness of many of the methods employed by early physicians and surgeons has been matched by amusement at the forthright primitive objectivity and colourful beauty of the miniatures. Many have commented as favourably on the refreshing realism of the miniatures as they have unfavourably on the over-sophisticated modernization of medical scenes by illustrators of our day, especially in the increasingly popular pharmacy displays. Truly the contrast between these two types of portrayal of early medicine is noteworthy. The miniatures are realistic sometimes to an extreme of crudity, whereas the modern pictorial (as expressed by one of its protagonists) aims at 'a contemporary art expression that is compatible with the practice of twentieth-century medicine.' One who prefers objectivity might suggest that the modernizers who are intent on the super-idealization of past medicine for the delectation of present-day tastes might insert in the corner of each lavishly imaginary portrayal a small exact reproduction of a similar scene from a miniature with the caption, 'This is the way they really practised in by-gone days.' Thus, by a touch of fidelity to the originals, the present age could pay tribute to truth as well as goodness and beauty in reproducing the past.

The present volume also represents a more pedantically scholarly programme than mere illustrated lectures reproducing past medical practice. It involves the endless procedure of checklisting manuscript miniatures of early medicine. Obviously, the multiplicity of extant manuscripts in collections throughout the civilized world precludes examination of all of them, even those that contain illustrations.

INTRODUCTION

Our aim has been to examine all *illustrated medical* manuscripts. For Europe, this has been accomplished with relative thoroughness since most illustrated manuscripts are now in the great museums and libraries of the Western World. A number of illustrated medical manuscripts in private or outlying libraries have escaped notice or have been examined in photoreproduction. Nevertheless, our coverage gives an accurate idea of the quantity and quality of illustration in pre-modern medical manuscripts. As for medical miniatures in *non*-medical manuscripts (for example, the famous operations by Saints Cosmas and Damian, in ecclesiastical manuscripts), only a few important items that have come to our notice have been included. These suggest rich possibilities in the realm of non-medical manuscripts as yet little explored by medical historians. In the near future we plan to investigate it intensively.

Meanwhile, in Part II, we present a checklist of medical miniatures in Early Western manuscripts (including not only those written in Latin, but also in Greek, and the vernaculars); Islamic and other Eastern manuscripts, with a few notable exceptions, are beyond our purview.

Recently a group of American historians, after discussing the problems inherent in chronological epochs, came to one tentative conclusion that met with wide approval: the traditional triad of ancient, medieval and modern histories is obsolete. It was generally agreed that all human civilizations before the industrial-technological revolution that was under way by 1800, should be designated as 'ancient'; all since that change, as 'modern' or 'contemporary.' Whatever the defects in this sweeping shift in chronological nomenclature, involving the elimination of 'Ancient History' (to *c.* A.D. 500), 'Medieval History' (*c.* 500 to *c.* 1500) and 'Modern History' (*c.* 1500 to the present), the thought pattern of uninterrupted evolution is basic in our survey of medical practice. This underlying theme is present throughout, even though we occasionally use the traditional terms, and even though our data is presented through the medium of manuscripts, chiefly from the thirteenth, fourteenth and fifteenth centuries, the outstanding period of manuscript illumination.

Incidentally, the miniatures presented are select examples from a collection of about 4000 microfilm frames obtained during years of search in manuscript collections in Eastern and Western Europe and America. The approximately 100 selections are representative of medical practice, not only in the 'Middle Ages,' during which period most of the manuscripts were copied, but also in ancient Greece and Rome, whence came, in somewhat degraded form, much of the medical practice, as well as many of the original illustrations from which the miniatures were copied. Later, the printers of the early 'modern' period took over, with some adaptations, the treatises and miniatures that they found in medical manuscripts for reproduction in medical books. Thus, in manuscript miniatures it is possible to see Western medicine in cross-section as it emerged from the declining classical world to leaven the rough Christian-Germanic society and eventually, during the late 'Middle Ages' and 'Renaissance,' to evolve into so-called 'Modern' medical 'Science.' It is noteworthy that the Greeks called their medicine an 'Art' rather than a science. Much of the basic medical practice of 'ancient-medieval' Europe persisted on the Continent and in America until the nineteenth century, notably cautery, bloodletting, herbal medicines and crude forms of surgery. To be sure, early 'modern' physicians (*c.* 1500 to *c.* 1800) improved some of the traditional techniques; on the other hand, some physicians and many of their patients continued to rely on those superstitions of early folk medicine that we often refer to as 'medieval,' as though they were invented and monopolized by our early European ancestors. Manuscript miniatures and texts, we believe, reflect the breadth and depth of the healing art as practised in the West during the ages before the nineteenth-century technological revolution. They reflect it neither at its 'Dark-Age' worst (few medical manuscripts were created during this era), nor at its 'Classical' or 'Enlightenment' best; rather, at its late 'medieval' period of vigorous growth. For better as well as for worse, in the miniatures and accompanying texts we can see how our remote and recent forbears handled, and mishandled, the ever-present problems of healing.

Part One

EARLY MEDICINE IN ILLUMINATED MANUSCRIPTS

I. HOSPITALS AND CLINICS[1]

INSTITUTIONALIZED medical service was conspicuously rare in most pre-modern civilizations. The temple healing of ancient Egypt and the Greek Aesculapion more closely resemble the treatment at modern shrines such as Lourdes than that in hospitals of our day. Likewise, Roman *sanatoria* and military hospitals, and most medieval guest-houses (*xenodochia*), monastic *infirmaria* and 'hospices' of the Hospitallers provided little that resembles modern clinical treatment.

This was especially true of the earlier medieval centuries. The so-called 'hospitals' of the West provided only a semi-medical type of practical nursing adjusted to the *care* rather than to the *cure* of sick, crippled, old and indigent inmates. 'God's poor,' as they were called, obtained hospitality, rather than healing, in guest houses or 'hospices' staffed by monks, nuns and, occasionally, secular clerics. *Leprosaria* were for the confinement of incurables. *Infirmaria* were chiefly for members of the restricted orders of clerics.

Early medieval manuscripts have more of textual than of pictorial evidence concerning such institutions. One of the most interesting written descriptions shows that in sixth-century Spain a *xenodochium* established by the Bishop of Merida had physicians (*medici*) in addition to the usual attendants. Furthermore, couches, litters and food were provided 'for God's poor,' whether they were 'ambulatory or sedentary' patients, 'slave or free,' 'Christian or Jew.' An eleventh-century *xenodochium* in Rome also had physicians (*medici*), 'beds with blankets,' and 'necessities . . . for the sick and destitute.' A similarly rare, and less impressive, example comes from the pen of the poet-theologian Alcuin, who described a medical centre in Charlemagne's realm as follows:

[1] Under the topic 'hospitals' we include institutionalized care of the sick, especially bed-patients. 'Clinics' we interpret as institutionalized or semi-institutionalized out-patient care of ambulatory patients. This violates the philological origin of the term ('pertaining to a bed') but seems closer to modern usage which tends to consider as clinical any type of collective out-patient treatment. We avoid the rather common usage of clinical for any practical bedside treatment that stresses experimental rather than theoretical medicine. There are, of course, cases that defy any such rigid classification.

3

> Physicians flock to the Hippocratic halls
> This one opens veins; that one mixes herbs in a pot
> Another cooks a broth, still another mixes a potion.
> Nevertheless, O Physicians, give thanks for everything
> So that Christ's blessing may attend your labours.

Noteworthy, in this account, are the references to bloodletting and pharmaceutical activities in a 'Hippocratic' establishment, which may well have been largely a figment of clerical-poetical imagination. Nevertheless, such evidence cannot be disregarded. Furthermore, there is supporting evidence of a pictorial nature from a manuscript written later in the same ninth century. Sketched in the manuscript is a plan of the monastery of St. Gall showing rooms captioned for bloodletting, purging and bathing; also for toilets and separate quarters for sick monks, 'very sick' monks, physicians and the infirmary administrator (*domus magistri eorum*). This plan may have been, like Alcuin's poem, merely an ideal, but it presents objectively in black and white the actual parts of a *cella infirmorum* such as was described in chapter thirty-six of the Benedictine Rule.

During the same period in the Moslem Near East, institutionalized medical service developed more rapidly and flourished to a much higher degree. As early as the ninth century in the great cities of Islam, there were veritable medical hospitals with endowments, trustees and well-organized staffs of physicians. Some of them, such as the Bagdad *bimaristan* headed by Rhazes until his death (*c.* 932), were actual teaching hospitals. Not until the thirteenth century could Western Europe approach this type of institution, even in outstanding centres. There were San Spirito, established in Rome by Pope Innocent III, the Hôtel-Dieu in Paris and the famous St. Bartholomew's Hospital in London. From then on there are ample pictorial and textual evidences for the steady advance of medical service in Western eleemosynary institutions. Patients are pictured and described in innumerable manuscripts in the process of being diagnosed and treated by one or by several physicians in settings that would be called 'out-patient departments' or 'diagnostic clinics' or hospitals today. There are also examples of specialized treatment; ensuing pages will picture and describe special quarters for surgical patients undergoing bloodletting or operations of various kinds. In the later centuries large towns had hospitals staffed with administrators, usually medical men, lay or clerical physicians and surgeons, and nursing brothers or sisters. Generally, the 'hospital' of this period seems to have been a large hall divided into cubicles, like a modern 'ward,' with private side-rooms for special patients and services. The modern medical hospital was emerging.

1. A Byzantine Diagnostic-Pharmaceutical Clinic

(In a Greek manuscript from fourteenth-century Byzantium: Paris, BN,
MS Greek 2243, folio 10v. At the beginning of Nicolaus Myrepsus'
alphabetical antidotary.[1])

Unlike many medieval medical scenes, this colourful miniature from a late Greek manuscript portrays diagnosis, preparation of medicines and treatment all in the same clinical establishment. At left is the head physician, clad in long garments topped by a curious pyramid-shaped hat. Above him is inscribed the Greek title for 'The Physician.' He holds aloft a uroscopy flask for inspection. Immediately to the right, below an inscription for 'The Patient,' is a man covered with sores, holding two crutches. Further to the right is an assistant, clothed like the physician but in drab colours, holding the basket-carrier for the uroscopy flask. Still further to the right, seated on the ground, is a mother holding a mature-looking child and pointing to her own head as if in sorrow or pain. Still further to the right stands another long-robed, pyramid-hatted physician. In his right hand he holds a medical case filled with medical receptacles; in his left, either a book or possibly an abacus. To the extreme right on shelves are a variety of containers for medicines. Below them an apprentice compounds medicine, wielding two pestles simultaneously. Such double-pestle action is unusual in medical illustration, not only ancient and medieval, but also modern. A number of examples, comprising the only ones known to medical historians, are found in thirteenth- and fourteenth-century manuscripts.[2] The Byzantine miniature under consideration is also noteworthy for its bright colouring and intricate border decoration.

2. A Western Out-Patient Clinic

(In a manuscript from fifteenth-century France: London, BM, Royal,
15.E.2, folio 165; Bartholomaeus Anglicus, *De proprietatibus rerum*, in
French, at the beginning of book XII.)

This miniature provides one of the best known medieval pictures of what might be called an 'out-patient clinic.' Although limited in size, the room accommodates two

[1] Unless otherwise stated (e.g., Greek, German, etc.) all manuscripts cited are in Latin. Folio numbers with a suffix 'v' are for the verso side. Book and chapter numbers are those in the manuscript or in standard editions of the treatises.

[2] See Loren MacKinney, 'Double-Pestle Action in Medieval Miniatures,' with six photo-reproductions, in *Journal of the American Pharmaceutical Association*, March, 1961, N.S.I., 160–161.

physicians and four patients. At the left a physician examines a patient's elbow that has been badly cut or fractured. One of the modern interpretations of this action as bloodletting can be rejected on comparison with numerous existing illustrations of bloodletting, a simple surgical operation usually at the elbow. Here the utensils on the table and below the room are pharmaceutical, not surgical. The physician seems to be preparing to dress a wound. The other physician is performing a uroscopy in the usual fashion, apparently for the patient to the right who awaits the diagnosis in troubled anticipation. Outside the door two more patients approach; one of them, whose foot has been amputated, hobbles on a peg leg with the aid of a crutch. The other, with a bandaged leg, uses a staff.

The ornate border and background of the miniature were executed with an aesthetic touch unusual in medical manuscripts. In fact, it is not from a specifically medical treatise, but a de luxe French version of the popular encyclopaedic handbook of Bartholomaeus Anglicus, *On the Properties of Things*, (*De proprietatibus rerum*). The manuscript was made for King Edward IV of England, at Bruges in 1482 (as noted on folio 77v). It contains a number of colourful illustrations, among them another clinical scene (on folio 77v). Both pictures are representations of general medical practice rather than specific illustrations of accompanying texts. Other manuscripts of the same treatise (e.g., Cambridge, Fitzwilliam Museum, MS 251, folios 54v, 106) have clinical scenes in which patients timidly approach pompously enthroned physicians. There are many such pictorial evidences of the high status of professorial physicians and surgeons in the later medieval centuries.

3. A THREE-BED HOSPITAL

(In a manuscript from fifteenth-century Ferrara: Florence, Laurentian, Gaddian, MS 24, folio 247v. Avicenna, *Canon*, beginning of book IV.)

Here we have one of the best extant miniatures of what might be termed a hospital in the modern sense of the word, that is, with nurses and physicians, also out-patients as well as bed-patients. The lower part of the picture portrays activities that we call an 'out-patient clinic,' that is, one or more physicians treating various types of ailments. At left is a physician wearing an unusual type of headdress with a turban-like veil reaching to his shoulders. He greets an incoming patient who walks with the aid of a staff, his arm in a sling. To the right, another physician, similarly clothed, seems to be probing or cleansing an ugly-looking shin wound or sore; the anxious patient sits on a stool holding his crutch.

The upper portion of the picture portrays a three-bed hospital; however, this number of beds does not mean that medieval hospitals were thus limited. In the bed to the left is a worried patient. The patient in the middle bed is being attended by a physician who gives instructions, at the same time apparently about to take the pulse. In the bed at right is a patient to whom an attendant is bringing a bowl of food on a tray. On the wall to the left of this bed hangs a basket-carrier for a uros-copy flask. The patients are probably afflicted with fever, the subject matter of the succeeding text. It is noteworthy that the beds are higher at the heads than at the feet; probably a vagary of the illustrator, attempting to present a better view of the patients, but possibly an evidence of a feature in hospital furnishings unmentioned in contemporary texts.

The lower part of the miniature seems to be intended as an illustration for the accompanying text concerning a variety of ailments. The occupants of the three beds in the upper portion may pertain to the accompanying text concerning fever patients.

4. PRELIMINARY EXAMINATIONS IN SURGEON'S OFFICE-CLINIC

(In a manuscript from fifteenth-century France: Paris, BN, French, MS 396, folio 66. Guy de Chauliac, *Chirurgia*, in French, IV, 1.)

Medieval medical illustrations sometimes combine in one picture, at the beginning of a treatise, some of the ailments a medical man might meet in his practice. Here we have a representation of three kinds of ulcers that a surgeon like Guy de Chauliac would be expected to recognize in his preliminary examinations. The picture comes at the beginning of Treatise IV of his *Surgery* and illustrates in a clinical setting the ailments of Doctrine II; ch. 2 (ulcers of the eye, 'bound with a silk bandage'), ch. 4 (ulcers of the 'shoulders and arms') and ch. 7 (ulcers of the 'penis and pouch of the testicles').

Guy sits at the right, clad in a long robe and a tight-fitting surgeon's cap; beside him on a lectern is his book. Passing in review, as it were, are three ambulatory patients who illustrate the three texts mentioned above: at right, a badly ulcerated arm; at centre, a bandaged eye with bloody discharge showing under the bandage;

and, at left, ulcerated genitalia. With the help of Guy's book any surgeon might diagnose and treat these ailments.

Other miniatures illustrate other treatises of the *Surgery*. The frontispiece, depicting Guy lecturing to five students, illustrates the prologue in which (along with other things) Guy refers to lectures and how each generation learns from past accumulations of knowledge, so that we are 'as children standing on a giant's shoulders.' Treatise I, concerning anatomy, has a clinical illustration of four surgeons cutting open the chest of a cadaver; treatises II and III have no introductory illustrations; treatise IV, on ulcers, has the one described above; treatise V, on fractures, has an illustration of a surgeon and two assistants setting a fractured elbow, while another surgeon attends to a fractured leg; treatise VI, on special maladies such as arthritis of the joints, has a somewhat damaged miniature showing a surgeon and an assistant treating three patients, one with a bandaged knee, one with a bandaged arm and a third with an ailment of the thigh; treatise VII has no illustration. A possible explanation of the lack of illustrations for treatises II (on apostema and pustules), III (on wounds) and VII (the antidotary) is that in the sixteenth century the manuscript was restored and rebound, with paper folios substituted for a number of the original vellum folios; the lost folios may have contained illustrations.

II. DIAGNOSIS AND PROGNOSIS: (A) BY UROSCOPY; (B) BY PULSE-READING; (C) BY ASTROLOGY, ETC.

RATIONAL analysis of ailments, estimation of their probable course and prescribed treatment were characteristic of ancient Greek medicine and had much influence in later Western practice. But, whereas Greek methods of analysis (diagnosis) and estimation (prognosis) were highly rational, many Roman and medieval physicians in the West tended to mystical or magical procedures which our age considers pure superstition. Modern writers, until comparatively recent times, have over-publicized these so-called 'medieval' aspects of early medicine, overlooking the fact that much 'medieval superstition' was derived from the Graeco-Roman era. The first-century *Natural History* of Pliny is a veritable storehouse of superstitious folk-medicine which he derived from earlier classical works, both Roman and Greek, and from which medieval practitioners and writers borrowed freely. Inasmuch as the Middle Ages and early-modern era followed the superstitious legacy of their classical predecessors far more assiduously than they did the scientifically rational heritage, the latter of these trends is often overlooked. For example, the pulse and urine were considered important as indicators of ailments and pathological conditions.

Cassiodorus, the intelligent Christian chancellor of Theodoric, Ostrogothic conqueror and ruler of Italy, in a letter written to the royal physicians in the sixth century, gave evidence concerning the prevalence of these two methods of diagnosis as follows:

For a skilled physician the pulsing of the veins reveals [to his fingers] the patient's ailment just as the appearance of the urine indicates it to his eyes.[1]

During the ensuing centuries, uroscopy and pulse-reading were mentioned briefly but often in medical instructions found in early manuscripts.[2]

[1] MGH Auct. Antiq., XII, 191 f.; Latin text and translation quoted in Loren MacKinney, *Early Medieval Medicine* (Baltimore, 1937), pp. 47, 48, 163 ff.
[2] Loren MacKinney, 'Medical Ethics and Etiquette in the Early Middle Ages,' *Bulletin of the History of Medicine*, 1952, *26*, 24, 26.

Both of these methods of diagnosis seem to have been derived, either directly or indirectly, from Galenic-Hippocratic treatises, which in turn may have derived them from Egyptian, Hindu and Chinese traditions. According to Sarton's *Introduction to the History of Science* (Baltimore, 1931, II, 75–76), the pulse lore of these oriental peoples is deeper rooted than that of the occident. Western European manuscripts from the ninth century onward contain short treatises,[1] which seem to be epitomes of seventh-eighth-century Greek works such as Theophilus-Philaretus, *Pulses and Urines*.[2] Latin translations of the two works, usually under the names Philaretus and Theophilus respectively, appeared often in late-medieval manuscripts, and sections based on their works concerning urine and pulse diagnosis are to be found in many of the popular Western handbooks on medicine.

(A) UROSCOPY[3]

Uroscopy was practised assiduously for both diagnosis and prognosis. It was thought that colour, texture, clarity, odour and even taste of a patient's urine (see quotation below, fig. 14) revealed something of the nature of the ailment, its stage of development and probable outcome. The various qualities of the urine indicated the condition of the humours and the digestion with special reference to the liver. Variants on the basis of the time of day the sample was taken, the patient's age, sex, eating habits, etc., were taken into consideration, and precautions were laid down as to the method, etc., of collecting urine. Dr. O. C. Gruner, eminent Arabist, sees much of practical value in the urine data as presented by Avicenna in the *Canon*, which circulated widely in the West, in some respects even rivalling Galen's works.[4] In the late Middle Ages a rare, but curiously similar method of diagnosis appeared.

---

[1] Among the earliest and most important of these manuscripts are those from ninth-century Lorsch, the ninth-century Loire valley, ninth-century Reichenau, and tenth-century Chartres. See Loren MacKinney, 'Medical Ethics . . . ,' pp. 19–22.

[2] See Sarton, *Introduction* . . . , II, 175, on the confusion of Theophilus and Philaretus; and for details on these authors; also Owsei Temkin, 'Geschichte des Hippokratismus im ausgehenden Altertum.' In *Kyklos*, 1932, 4, 1–80.

[3] For early medical practice we prefer the term 'uroscopy' (the examination of urine) to 'urinalysis' which carries the modern connotation of chemical analysis.

[4] See especially the *Canon*, 1, 2.3.2, for details. Gruner's translation and commentary (*A Treatise on the Canon of Medicine of Avicenna*, London, 1930, I, especially pp. 330 ff.) has valuable and interesting data on uroscopy. For example, occasionally patients played tricks on their physicians, such as eating saffron or some other herb to colour the urine (also see quotation below, fig. 9). Physicians, on the other hand, were so confident of their techniques that they claimed to detect coitus from threads floating in the urine.

As noted in Castiglioni, *History of Medicine* (p. 380), occasionally attention was given to the blood; its colour, density and odour. The condition of the patient's stools and sputum were also taken into account.

5. BYZANTINE UROSCOPY

(In a manuscript from fifteenth-century Byzantium: Bologna, University, MS 3632, folio 51. Theophilus Protospatharius, *On urines*, in Greek.)

Throughout the Middle Ages, according to the evidence of manuscript miniatures, there were rows of urine flasks in physicians' offices and in clinics, as there are today in diagnostic clinics and hospitals.

The picture portrays uroscopy in a Greek setting. Seated at top left is a famous seventh-century Greek expert on urology, Theophilus, whose treatise *On urines* was much used in the Greek East and in the Latin West (in translation). Handing Theophilus a urine flask that has been taken from a carrier-basket is his assistant, Posos (according to the Greek caption above him). Both men are clad in long robes and curious bonnet-like caps distinctly Eastern in style. Below, are rows of uroscopy flasks, twenty-one in number. Over each flask is a caption indicating the type of urine therein (the text of the treatise describes in detail the various textures and colours of urines, and their significance). Noteworthy in our illustration is the shape of the flasks, very different from those depicted in Western manuscripts, which are round-bottomed and large-necked. A later folio of the manuscript (134v) shows a flask similar in shape to that handed to Theophilus but somewhat taller. It is held aloft for examination by Isaac, whose head-dress and robe is similar to those in folio 51. Incidentally, the number of flasks (on folio 51) exemplifying the various types of urine is one more (twenty-one) than in most Western Latin manuscripts.

6. WESTERN UROSCOPY CHART

(In a manuscript from the fifteenth century: Oxford, Bodley, Ashmole, MS 789, folio 364v. Anon, *On uroscopy*. Fifteenth century, Oxford, Bodley, Ashmole, MS 391, folio 10 has an almost identical chart.)

In sharp contrast to the preceding picture of a Greek uroscopy chart (twenty-one flat-sided flasks in rows) is this Western-style circular chart of twenty bulging, round-bottomed, large-necked flasks. At the centre of the chart-circle is the caption, 'A table of analysis of urines by colours.' Around this in smaller circles are seven captions describing urines by groups. For example, in the small circle at 1–2 o'clock position is the caption, 'These four urines signify excess of digestion.'[1] The other captions signify 'excessive burning,' 'mortification,' 'indigestion,' 'beginning of digestion,' 'medium digestion' and 'perfect digestion.' The captions, around the outer rim, for each separate flask, describe the colours of the urines; e.g., the light-yellow urine at the 1 o'clock position is captioned, '*subrubeus* colour of urine, or of occidental crocus.' The urine colours around the circle run, from *subrubeus*, in clockwise fashion as follows: red (*rubeus*), ruddy (*rubicundus*), green (*viridis*), black (*niger*), white (*albus*), milk (*lacteus*), etc. The circles at the top of the page are eclipse diagrams.

There are Western manuscripts in which each flask has a separate picture, with captions that include the disease and the cure (e.g., Cambridge, Trinity, MS 922).

7. DELIVERING A URINE FLASK AT A DIAGNOSTIC CLINIC

(In a manuscript from fifteenth-century Flanders: Glasgow, Hunter, MS 9, folio 84. Avicenna, *Canon*, I, 2.3.2., ch. 2.)

Many of the manuscript miniatures of uroscopy picture the delivery of the patient's urine sample to the physician in the characteristic flask, usually carried in a basket container. Here is a colourful representation of such a scene. At left is a woman (perhaps pregnant) who, after handing the flask to one of the four physicians, makes an explanation concerning it. In her hand she holds the flask-carrier (which, incidentally, seems too small for the somewhat oversized uroscopy flask). The flask is about to take its place on the shelf along with five others. One of the physicians (all of whom are clad in ermine-trimmed robes and academic birettas) points to a flask on the shelf, making comments to one of his colleagues. The picture illustrates a section in Avicenna's *Canon* concerning the 'Significance of the colour of urine.'

8. CONSTANTINUS AFRICANUS DOES UROSCOPY FOR WOMEN AND MEN

(In a manuscript from the fifteenth century: Oxford, Bodley, MS Rawl. C.328, folio 3. Twelve anonymous illustrations of uroscopy and cautery, preceding Albucasis, *Chirurgia*, etc.)

---

[1] Here the term 'digestion' is probably of broader significance than today. Like the Greek term κρασες, it implies a balance of the humours, and not merely gastric digestion.

The fame of Constantinus Africanus, monk of Monte Cassino, in late Western medicine was comparable to Galen's in Rome, Theophilus's in Byzantium and Avicenna's in Islam. This picture, the first in a series of twelve preceding Albucasis' *Surgery* and other medical works, is dedicated to Constantine, who translated many medical works from Arabic into Latin, thereby winning greater fame than he deserved as an originator of scientific medicine.

The text above the picture reflects the exaggerated merits attributed to him even to the present day. It reads as follows:

This is Constantinus, monk of Monte Cassino, who is as it were the fount of that science of long standing concerning the diagnosis of urines (*iudiciis urinarum*) and all ailments. In this book and many others he has set forth the true cure. To him come women with urine so that he may tell the ailment in the case.

The illustrator skilfully depicted the famous monk, seated with what doubtless was intended to represent one of his books, which he explains to the patients approaching with their urine-filled flasks. First comes a woman, presenting her flask with a hopeful expression on her face. She is followed by a man with his flask and by one other person. The other eleven illustrations present in similarly dramatic fashion figures representing cautery (see below figs. 47, 48 for two of them).

9. A PHYSICIAN MAKES A CAREFUL INSPECTION OF URINE

(In a Paduan manuscript of the year 1434: Munich, MS 25, folio lv. Bartholomaeus de Montagnano, *Consilia Medica*, frontispiece.)

Most medieval scenes of uroscopy portray the physician merely holding the flask up to the light to obtain a general idea of its colour and texture. In this picture Bartholomaeus de Montagnano, a prominent Paduan physician, carefully inspects a flask of urine. Before him on the lectern and shelf are two open books. They may be Theophilus *On urines*, or the section of Isaac Judaeus' or of Avicenna's works which treat of urines in detail. On such books Westerners relied heavily. At times, however, they tested their physicians' efficiency by playing tricks, such as the following:

A famous monastic physician of St. Gall during the tenth century . . . was about to examine [the urine of] the Duke of Bavaria. As a trick to test Notker, the Duke substituted for his own urine that of a woman who was pregnant. But Notker, after making his examination, without any apparent sign of suspicion made the solemn announcement that: 'God is about to bring to pass an unheard of event; within thirty days the Duke will give birth to a child.' Whereupon the Duke was said to have blushed . . . (from Mac-Kinney, *Early Medieval Medicine* . . . , pp. 45–46).

At the top of our miniature, which is the frontispiece to Bartholomaeus' *Consilia*, is a maxim that reads as follows:

One physician is scarcely more worthy than another; Homer was the most illustrious poet.

However, Dr. Bartholomaeus began his treatise on the opposite page with six lines of poetry which urges those who would become physicians to read his book of case studies.

10. UROSCOPY IN A CLINIC

(In a French manuscript from fifteenth-century France: Cambridge, Fitzwilliam Museum, MS 251, folio 54v. Bartholomaeus Anglicus, *De proprietatibus rerum*, V, 1, in French.)

This is one of the most dramatic of the numerous medieval miniatures concerning uroscopy and clinical patients; first, in the variety of ailments portrayed, second, in the tense attitudes of the five patients, and third, in the authoritative attitude of the physician. Clad in the usual splendid robes of a physician, and wearing a skull cap, he explains the uroscopy diagnosis apparently for the patient on the floor, who is afflicted with dropsy. The other patients present an ailing leg, a head and an arm (in a sling), a hand and a chest, respectively. The beautifully executed miniature appears at the beginning of book V of a French version of the *De proprietatibus rerum* of Bartholomaeus Anglicus, in a section concerned with the parts of the body. The text above the miniature explains that 'properties in general, and then in particular,' will be considered next; the text below explains that 'According to Avicenna the members [of the body] are organs composed of the primary combination of humours.' The French version, done in 1372 by Jean Corbechon for King Charles V, is only one of several translations; e.g., into Provençal (before 1391), into Spanish (fifteenth century) and into English (1397–1398).

(B) DIAGNOSIS BY THE PULSE

Pulse-reading was perhaps the most popular method of diagnosis in pre-modern times. Some medieval writers asserted that it was more important than uroscopy. For example, in the introduction to a pulse treatise in a fourteenth-century manuscript (Paris, Arsenal, MS 1024, folio 16v), the anonymous compiler explained that the urine indicated the condition of the liver, the pulse that of the heart; therefore, since the heart was more important than the liver, pulse-reading was more important than uroscopy. More influential, probably, than such logic was the practical factor of the simplicity of taking the pulse. The pulse beat could be detected by feeling any place where an artery passed over a bony prominence. The favourite place was the radial artery, which was handy, close to the surface and to the heart. Furthermore, as some medieval writers pointed out, it was a location where a woman's pulse could be taken without embarrassment or moral danger (a not unimportant factor in view of ancient, medieval and even modern attitudes toward the medical profession). Details on this point, and on the position to be taken by the physician, the placing of his fingers, etc., can be seen in the pulse pictures and explanations thereof (to be presented below). By palpation the skilful physician (as today) noted the duration and pauses in heart beat, variations in the succession of beats, their rhythm and consistency, also the condition between beats. In addition to the differentiation of diastole and systole, various types of beat were classified; for example, simple, compound, regular, irregular, sluggish, continuous, recurrent, undulatory ('bounding'), flickering, spasmodic, hard, soft, harsh, feeble ('formicant'), chord-like, creeping ('vermicular'), jerky ('gazelle-like') and fading.[1]

Intelligent interpretation of the pulse beat was supposed to indicate to the physician not only the type of ailment but also the stage of its progress and the patient's general bodily condition. In this complicated procedure marginal factors also were considered: the seasons, the patient's sex, age, emotional condition, and his case history including habits of eating, drinking, sleeping, exercise, bathing and the like. Some supposed experts stressed the differentiation of a left-side from a right-side pulse. In general, there was an intelligent and professional approach to the problem. After

[1] O. C. Gruner's *A Treatise on the Canon of Medicine of Avicenna* (I, 286 ff.) presents charts of complicated medieval data on the pulse. The Greeks are said to have differentiated fifteen kinds of pulse, the Chinese twenty-seven, and a fifth-century Christian forty. Ernest Wickersheimer has shown that Constantinus of Monte Cassino (c. 1100) devised a method of recording by heavy and light dots the differences between strong and feeble pulse beats. ('Note sur les œuvres médicales d'Alphane, Archevêque de Salerne,' *Janus*, 1930, *34*, 273–278.)

analysing the various aspects of a fourteenth-century pulse treatise, Dr. Ernest Wickersheimer (in the above-cited note) concluded that 'Although I do not know whose advice this was, I know that it was that of a true physician.' Perhaps this could be said more often than it is, of medieval medical men.

II. TAKING THE PULSE OF A BED-PATIENT

(In a manuscript from fifteenth-century Flanders: Glasgow, Hunter, MS 9, folio 76. Avicenna, *Canon*, I, 2.3.1)

Most pulse miniatures show the physician standing at the bedside. Here we see an emaciated patient anxiously watching the physician's fingers on his wrist. Noteworthy is the clear portrayal of the physician's four fingers on the inner side of the wrist, a method still taught medical students. However, the artist misrepresented, or the physician failed to use, the best ancient and medieval technique; viz., to grasp with his *right* hand the *right* hand of the patient, thus bringing the tips of the four fingers to bear on the radial artery where the beat is strongest. (Incidentally, an ancient Hindu treatise advised taking men's pulses on the right hand, women's on the left). Ancient and medieval writers, when instructing young physicians on pulse techniques, invariably advised grasping the patient's right arm with the physician's right. They also advised the physician to take a position at the foot of the bed where he could see the patient's face. If the patient should become unduly alarmed by this, the physician should stand at the head of the bed, but under no circumstances should he sit on the bed itself. Celsus, Galen and others gave detailed advice on these matters.[1] Some physicians went so far as to make a marked beat of the pulse on the forefinger an indication of head ailment: on the second finger, stomach trouble; on the third, intestinal ailment; on the little finger, trouble with the feet.

From as early as the ninth century young physicians were reading the following suggestions concerning the technique of pulse-taking:

Learn how to take the pulse so that you can do it standing or seated. . . . If you are holding the right hand below the wrist with your right hand, let the fingers be uppermost. . . . Let two fingers, the index and middle fingers, be placed together inside on the upper part of the artery. Hold the pulse for a long time so that you can detect the up and down beat. . . .[2] These instructions would place the tips of the fingers on the approved place, the radial artery, an even better position than the picture shows.

[1] See MacKinney, 'Medical Ethics . . . ,' pp. 19 ff.; and B. F. Horine, 'An Epitome of Ancient Pulse Lore,' *Bulletin of History of Medicine*, 1941, *10*, 209–249.

[2] Paris, BN, MS Lat. 11219, folio 13. See also the articles cited in the preceding note.

Minor details in the miniature are the garb of the physician and his associate: birettas and splendid academic robes with the enlarged ends of ties showing underneath the capes. In the background two women and a man await the diagnosis of their ailments.

12. TAKING THE PULSE AT THE BRACHIAL ARTERY

(In a manuscript from France in the year 1345: Chantilly, Musée Condé, MS 334(569), folio 260v. Guido de Vigevano, *Anothomia*, fig. 18.)

Although medieval physicians taking the pulse usually were portrayed with fingers on the wrist, the texts indicate that it could be taken elsewhere, on the arm, the foot, the neck, even behind the ear. Our miniature indicates pulse-taking high on the arm at the brachial artery. At first glance it might seem that the physician's grip on the patient's wrist was for pulse-taking at the radial artery, but the position of the four fingers at the wrist is wrong for pulse-taking, while that of the fingers on the upper arm is correct.

The text captions give no information on this point, and little at all on procedure. The caption at upper left reads as follows:

This, the last figure [of eighteen anatomical miniatures], shows how the pulse should be taken; but at the outset the physician ought to know the condition of the body before taking the pulse. [The text, above at right, merely ends the picture series as follows:] And this ends the anatomy of all the bodily members. . . .

The series of eighteen illustrations accompanies the *Anatomy* of Guido de Vigevano, an Italian-trained surgeon who became French royal physician and dedicated his treatise to King Philip VII of France.

13. TAKING A WOMAN'S PULSE

(In a manuscript from fifteenth-century Germany: Edinburgh, Royal Observatory, MS Crawford 9.14.5, folio 84. Heinrich's miscellany on health, in German.)

The ninth-century text (from which we quoted in fig. 11) concerning the technique of pulse-taking has an additional bit of advice which reads as follows:

17

When a female lies before you and you are about to take her pulse, look neither at the top of her head nor the bottom of her feet, but at the hand you are holding. By taking the pulse you determine the inner ailment. [The text continues as in no. 11, and then adds the following:] When taking the pulse have your hands warm lest the touch of cold hands upset the warm pulse and make it impossible to determine the true condition [of the patient].

Above the miniature presented here is a much briefer text in German. The top eight lines contain general comments concerning sweating and the pulse; the last ten lines (six of them in red script) discuss the actual taking of the pulse, as follows:

One must be on his guard against applying hands out of cold or salty water, which bring about contraction of the arteries and rheumatic ailments. Here is how you hold the pulse and how you detect a well or sick person, also the inner developments that it is necessary to know.

Obviously the picture would have been a better illustration for the ninth-century manuscript-text than for this. However, such as it is, it portrays a 'female,' though somewhat more exposed than was considered proper medieval bedside technique.[1] The physician may be following the tenth-century instructions 'to look neither at the top of her head nor the bottom of her feet,' but he is not looking 'at the hand.' Nor is he 'holding' it; he seems to be taking the pulse at the brachial artery, with four fingers on the upper arm. As we noted (in fig. 12) this was an approved, but rather unusual place for taking the pulse.

Our miniature and text are from an astrological-medical manuscript, by an unidentifiable German named Heinrich who included in the treatise data concerning constellations, the zodiac, the four temperaments, bathing, uroscopy and bloodletting.[2]

14. GALEN DOES A WOMAN'S UROSCOPY AND PULSE

(In a manuscript from fifteenth-century Flanders: Dresden, MS Db. 92–93, folio 293v. Pseudo-Galen, *De pulsibus et urinis*, 2.)

Occasionally, manuscript miniatures, in order to emphasize the two principal types of diagnosis, depicted a physician checking both urine and pulse at the same time.

---

[1] The Oriental custom of always taking the pulse at the wrist, thought to be for the purpose of preventing undue exposure of women patients, is also the handiest method.

[2] For assistance in the difficulties presented by this manuscript text, in both figs. 13 and 17, I am indebted to my colleague, Professor John Kunstmann, head of the German Department.

Here, the physician in the person of Galen, clad in splendid ermine-trimmed robes and ermine head-dress, holds a uroscopy flask in one hand while with the other he takes a lady's pulse. Incidentally, his pulse technique is badly represented; his thumb rests on the side of her wrist far down toward her thumb, an impossible point for pulse-taking. In the background are the lady's boy and girl attendants.

The illustration is one of several hundred done expertly in colour with elaborate decorations in a manuscript of various Galenic works. Partly water-damaged during World War II, fortunately it survived. A photofacsimile, with several folios in colour, was published by E. G. Van Leersum and W. Martin, *Codices Graeci et Latini . . .*, (Leiden, 1910). From this our reproductions were made, inasmuch as it was impossible to obtain colour microfilms at Dresden in 1960. The text accompanying the picture reads in part as follows:

Of these diversities of pulses I have already written. . . . Ch. 2. Concerning the pulse and urine in ephemeral fever. The pulse in ephemeral fevers is simple, not especially unequal, nor sluggish, nor difficult. If the taste of the urine is anaemic and the patient has a headache . . . [various aspects of diagnosis follow].[1]

It was obvious that it was the reference to both pulse and urine that led the illustrator to show Galen doing both pulse and uroscopy at the same time. Other manuscripts have similar double-action pictures.

15. A MEDIEVAL COMIC: THE APE DOCTORS A MAN

(In a manuscript from France in the year 1316: Cambridge, Fitzwilliam Museum, MS 298, folio 25. Metz Pontifical.)

The prevalence of humour in the literature, manuscript texts and miniatures of the Middle Ages is well-known to medievalists. Although less known to medical historians, it is present in miniatures from both medical (see below, figs. 26, 35, 36, 37) and non-medical manuscripts. The ape-physician in our illustration is unusually interesting because he is found in a religious manuscript, the famous Metz Pontifical, and at a comparatively early date, about 1316. He is pictured in the margin of the manuscript and is one of many 'drolleries' therein that portray everyday scenes, many of them involving animals. Here the ape plays the role of physician doing a

---

[1] Hans Pohl published the text from St. Gall MS 44, under the title *Ein Pseudo-Galen-Text aus dem frühen Mittelalter* (Leipzig University dissertation, 1922).

double diagnosis—pulse and urine simultaneously—on a man, who leans on a crutch exposing his genitalia and abdomen.

The scene seems not so much for the purpose of ridiculing physicians as of playing up animals; note the highly professional air of the ape.[1] Incidentally, apes were popular in medieval illustrations, appearing in the marginal drolleries of liturgical manuscripts such as this, and in medical and animal treatises. In another margin of the same manuscript (folio 81) is an ape-physician doing a pulse-urine diagnosis on a crane. A bestiary (Cambridge, University, MS G.6.5, folio 13) pictures five apes, one of them holding a uroscopy flask. A fifteenth-century Book of Hours (Edinburgh University, Db. 3.30, folio 25v) has a marginal miniature of a dog-physician doing a urinalysis of a cat reclining in bed wearing a nightcap.

(C) PROGNOSIS AND DIAGNOSIS BY ASTROLOGY AND BIRD LORE

Much that moderns consider superstitious was accepted as science in ancient and medieval times. The most prominent of such practices was astrology, which was predicated on the tradition that the stars of the macrocosmos, or outer world, constantly influenced the body and soul of man, the microcosmos. Throughout the early centuries, as George Sarton expressed it (*op. cit.*, II, 790):

It would not have occurred to any medieval physician to question these principles [of medical astrology] any more than to a modern one to doubt the indications of a good thermometer. . . . Astrology became a brand of medical propaedeutics as important as physiology.

As early as A.D. 600 Isidore of Seville, in his *Etymologiae* (IV, 13), wrote:

It is necessary for a medical man to know . . . astronomy by which he may calculate the stars and change of seasons; for a physician has said that our bodies are affected by their qualities. . . .

A paraphrase of this, found in manuscripts from the ninth century onward, asserts that a physician 'must know the science of the stars since our bodies change along with these, and since human illnesses are affected by their normality and abnormality.' The idea of astral influences on health, survival and life in general prevailed

---

[1] An interesting, and little-known, example of modern ape-drolleries, can be seen in the walls of a restaurant bar opposite the entrance of the Cook County Hospital in Chicago. In a fresco extending around all sides of the bar-room, about twenty years ago an unknown artist pictured a wide variety of medical activities, realistically and in colour. Some members of the Hospital staff detect in the faces of the apes the features of certain physicians and surgeons of the Hospital.

throughout the Middle Ages and is still a prominent feature in some otherwise intelligent segments of modern society.

In pre-modern times the most eminent physicians recommended and practised astrology for the prevention of ailments, for diagnosis, for treatment and for prognostication of the outcome. Ancient and Moslem medical writers were cited by medieval physicians in support of medical astrology. Complete handbooks, or sections thereon, were written by famous men such as Aetius, Rhazes, Michael Scot, Petrus de Abano, Raymundus Lullius, Roger Bacon, Petrus Hispanus, Thadeus de Parma, Guy de Chauliac, Cecco d'Ascoli, Petrus de Argellata and Jean Sanivet. Titles such as the following were used: 'What a Physician Needs to Know of Astrology,' 'The Doctor's Friend, A Directory of Astrological Medicine,' 'Astronomical Physics for the Greater Security of the Exercise of the Art of Medicine,' etc. Calendars and almanacs noted lucky and unlucky ('Egyptian') days for bloodletting, purging, operations and even for sexual intercourse as well as other non-medical activities. Many small, folding almanacs of this sort, with illustrations, are conserved in manuscript form in libraries. In formal medical manuscripts, similar illustrations were included, showing constellation- and zodiac-figures on men's bodies. These indicated the relationship of the stars to ailments of various parts of the body. Even John Arderne, practical-minded English surgeon, operated on various parts of the body at the times indicated by zodiac readings. Epidemics such as the Black Death were predicted, treated and avoided by resorting to the signs of the zodiac and other astrological factors. Guy de Chauliac, who doubted the efficacy of lucky and unlucky days, was forced to observe them in bloodletting to give his patients confidence. In 1437, at Paris, astrological observances for bloodletting and purging were questioned, but approved. As late as the seventeenth century a handbook of medical astrology, compiled by an astro-philosopher and dedicated to Lord Ashmole of Oxford, was lauded as 'an indispensable adjunct to the equipment of the wise physician.' Prognosis of the recovery or death of a patient was often based on astral readings.

However, the stars had a rival in the curious lore of the caladrius bird. Based on a legend associated with Alexander the Great, the procedure involved the placing of the bird on the patient's bed; it prophesied his recovery by looking *at* him, his death by looking *away*. The great da Vinci, in his notebooks, cited similar powers for the goldfinch. It should be remembered, however, that early physicians also used methods more convincing to the modern mind, notably the pulse and the urine.

16. PROGNOSIS OF DEATH BY THE CALADRIUS BIRD

(In a manuscript from the twelfth century: Cambridge, Corpus Christi,
MS 22, folio 166. *Physiologus, 5.*)

Among the magical methods of prognosticating the fate of a patient, that most
often found in manuscript illustrations was the use of a caladrius bird. As related in
the text below the miniature,

There is a bird called the caladrius which is completely white. It is found in royal courts. If
a man is sick unto death the caladrius will show whether he will live or die. If he is to die it
turns its face away. . . . If he is to live it turns toward him.

In our miniature, which is one of the earliest of Western illustrations of the caladrius,
the patient is begging the caladrius to look at him. Miniatures in other manuscripts
show the caladrius looking away, and in some there are two birds, one looking
toward the patient, the other away. A somewhat different use of a bird is illustrated
below in fig. 33; in treating the bite of a mad dog a cock was given grains of wheat;
if it ate them, the patient was supposed to recover.

The caladrius legend appears often in later medieval bestiaries, encyclopaedias and
also in certain romances of Alexander, who was supposed to have found caladrius-
like birds at the court of Xerxes. The legend seems to have originated in the Middle
East. In the third century B.C. Aelian, in his *History of Animals* (XVII, 13), using the
spelling *charadrius*, told how its gaze cured jaundice. Later Eastern writers reported
similarly. In the West, by way of the moralized bestiary *Physiologus*, the bird took
on religious connotations: viz., it is found in Jerusalem; after it looks at a person
'as if it would take all his illness upon itself, it flies toward the sun, as it were burning
up his infirmities'; it typifies 'our Saviour, all white'; like Him, 'it turns its face
toward us.'

17. DIAGNOSIS-PROGNOSIS BY ASTROLOGY

(In a manuscript from Germany in the year 1464: Edinburgh, Royal
Observatory, MS Crawford 9.14.5, folio 37. Anonymous work on
astrology and medicine, in German.)

In both medical and astronomical manuscripts one finds illustrations of professors
gazing at the stars. This type of miniature often appears as the frontispiece of health

books such as Aldobrandino's treatise on health. Our miniature is a typical representation of medical astrology; a physician studies the sky, consulting his book for the diagnostic-prognostic interpretation. On the book one can make out only a few letters, apparently in roughly scribbled Latin. Below is the following anonymous explanation in German of the divine origin of astrology:

The following presents several points concerning the uses of the firmament and the heavens. This should be remembered: God commanded Abraham to look at the sky and its embellishments [*Genesis* 15:5: 'He said "Look now toward the heaven, and tell the stars, if thou be able to number them." And He said unto him "So shall thy seed be"']. And also remember God's almightyness. The twelve signs [of the zodiac] provide valuable information . . . [The text continues with instructions concerning the medical uses of astrology].

III. MATERIA MEDICA

BY far the greater part of medieval healing was by means of medicines. These were compounded chiefly from herbs, secondarily from animals and rarely from minerals (until the time of Paracelsus). Drugs were used either externally or internally, and either as simples (i.e., by themselves) or in compounds. The collecting, compounding and applying of medicines, along with surgery, seems to have been carried on indiscriminately by physicians, surgeons and folkhealers throughout most of the Classical and Middle Ages. Not until the thirteenth century was there much evidence of separation of the professions of pharmacists and surgeons from that of general physician-practitioners. Whether the medieval healer was a physician (*medicus*), surgeon (*cirurgicus*), pharmacist (*apothecarius*) or merely an intelligent non-professional practitioner, he relied on handbooks (called *De simplicibus*, *antidotaria*, etc.) that described, and often illustrated, the materia medica supposed to be effective. This information was based on classical Graeco-Roman works such as Theophrastus' *Medical botany* and the famous *Materia medica* of Dioscorides, compiled in the first century A.D. This book, with its descriptions and illustrations of the simple substances from which medicines were made, along with explanations of their various uses, provided the basis for Greek, Roman, Moslem and Western pharmacopoeiae. To its almost 400 plant-animal-mineral illustrations additions were made, notably by Moslems such as Avicenna (d. 1037), whose writings increased Western pharmacopoeia to well over 700 items, and Ibn al-Baitar (d. 1248), who described some 1400 simples (300 of which were new items, including some foods). By the fourth century the Greek Dioscorides was alphabetized, and the Latin versions by 1200.

Since such works were too expensive for most medical practitioners, there were innumerable abbreviated handbooks, often illustrated with simple or stereotyped sketches copied from classical Greek works. Crude though the sketches were, they helped amateur collectors in the identification of materia medica, doubtless saving many a patient from poisoning. One of the most popular and best-illustrated of these handbooks was the fourth- or fifth-century Pseudo-Apuleius herbal entitled

Herbarium Apulei Platonici. Often this was accompanied by a materia medica of animals, entitled *Sextus Placitus Papyriensis Liber medicinae ex animalibus pecoribus et bestiis vel avibus*, and occasionally by a third work attributed to Dioscorides and entitled *De herbis femininis*. We present a number of illustrations from medieval manuscript-copies of these popular works. Without discussing the many late compilations and translations of *Materia medica* by Westerners (such as Macer Floridus, Rufinus, Pseudo-Albertus Magnus and Simon of Genoa), by Greeks (such as Simon Seth) and by Moslems (such as Rhazes and Hunain), and books on stones (such as Marbode's *Liber lapidum*), we conclude by mentioning an outstandingly realistic illustrator of herbs, in fifteenth-century Venice, Rinius, who compiled a book of simples (*Liber de simplicibus*) that marks the dawn of modern portrayals of medical botany. Books of this sort, in manuscript and print, along with the increasingly popular publications called *Hortus sanitatis*, *Garth der Gesundheit*, etc., brought about the eventual eclipse of Dioscorides.

18. THE FATHERS OF THE WESTERN PHARMACOPOEIA AT WORK

(In a fifteenth-century copy of a Greek manuscript from sixth-century Constantinople: Vatican, Chigi, Greek, MS F.VII.159, folio 236v. At the end of Dioscorides, *Materia medica*.)

The Western world has come to think of Dioscorides, first century Graeco-Roman, as synonymous with materia medica. As a matter of fact, he was neither the founder of pharmacognosy nor the contributor of all the pharmaceutical products that appeared in his own book. His famous *Materia medica* was itself based on earlier handbooks, notably those of Theophrastus (*c.* 300 B.C., Athens) and Cratevas (an Asia Minor Greek, first century B.C.), with the addition of bird lore and excellent illustrations thereof from Dionysius of Philadelphia's *Ornithiaca*. However, Dioscorides picked up much data while accompanying Roman armies in expeditions to the Eastern Mediterranean. Little is known about his life except that he was born near Tarsus in Asia Minor, probably shortly after the time of Paul, another famous native of the region.

The original version of the *Materia medica* probably comprised five books, concerned with (1) spices, salves and oils, (2) animal products and some plants, (3) additional plants, (4) trees and (5) wines and stones. Most of the illustrations were of plants, some of which were copied, along with the descriptions, from Cratevas.

A century after Dioscorides, Galen criticized the book, but used it. In the sixth century Cassiodorus urged monks to use 'the herb book of Dioscorides.' In ensuing centuries it was amended and revised to such an extent that probably none of the medieval Greek, Latin or Islamic versions are much like the original. Its history is that of a practical, evolving compendium.

The oldest existing manuscript (Vienna, NB, Med. Greek, 1) is thought to be an early sixth-century copy of an Alexandrian archetype that originated in Asia Minor (a church at Bawit has sixth-century mural decorations similar to the border designs of the opening folios of the Vienna manuscript). The manuscript was copied and illustrated at Constantinople for presentation to Juliana Anicia, daughter of Olybrius, one of the last emperors at Rome. It was lavishly illustrated, with many full-page coloured miniatures (still in fairly good condition) picturing the presentation scene, groups of physicians and medical botanists, and the discovery of mandragora (mandrake) plant and its incorporation into the book. This last-mentioned scene is clearly portrayed in the miniature, taken from a fifteenth-century copy that is an almost exact (but clearer) reproduction of folio 5v of the Vienna manuscript. Here, in an elaborate Byzantine or Alexandrian architectural background, (at centre) the haloed goddess of wisdom, Sophia, shows a mandragora plant to the illustrator and to the author. The illustrator (thought to represent Cratevas), with painting equipment on his bench, is finishing a picture of the plant. A bearded Dioscorides writes the description of the famous mandragora. The face of Dioscorides resembles some of the Christian portrayals of the bearded Peter and others of the Disciples, and the physicians in two other miniatures are thought by some scholars to be related to Roman mosaics of seven wise men, or to portraits in a manuscript of *De hebdomadibus* ('Sevens'). Whatever the validity of identifications of these and of the *pictor* in the mandragora miniature, here is a vivid representation of the process of bookmaking in the case of the most famous corpus of materia medica known to the Western world.

19. A CROWDED PAGE FROM A PICTORIAL MATERIA MEDICA

(In a manuscript from the fifteenth century: Vatican, Chigi, MS F.VII.158, folio 88v. A pictorial-alphabetical Dioscorides, *Materia medica*.)

This is one of the more closely packed pages of the alphabetical Latin version of Dioscorides. As early as the fourth century, the Greek Dioscorides had been alphabetized; the Latin version remained in its original non-alphabetical form probably until the thirteenth century. Nevertheless, it became what Lynn Thorndike has referred to as 'the most widely disseminated handbook of pharmacy of the whole later middle ages.' This may have been due to its emphasis on the pictorial, as is well exemplified by our sample page. Whereas in most versions each illustration was accompanied by the name of the item, its synonyms, a brief description and a list of its medical uses, the version from which our miniature comes has only the name (in red script), a synonym and (added by a later hand) a reference to a source of detailed information (usually Dioscorides).

The page shown, from the 'T' section of the alphabet, exemplifies not only a lively, realistic type of illustration, but also the predominance of herbal over animal and mineral substances. Here are pictured three herbs: at right, the shrub (*tetrait*); 'secundum Avicenna, herba judaica'; at left, a tree (*terbentina*), at the foot of which a man ('Vegetius,' the author of a Roman veterinary treatise) collects turpentine with a dipper and pours it into a keg (*salix*); at top right, *testiculus canis*, with a reference to Dioscorides, in whose original treatise (III, 142) the herb was described. The outlines of this herb indicate the appropriateness of the name 'dog testicles.' Only two animals are pictured on the page: at bottom right, a tortoise (*testudo terrena*); and, at left centre, the popular medieval creature called *tassus*, with a reference to Sextus Placitus, whose treatise on animal substances was usually prefaced by a short account of the *tassus*. The one mineral substance on the page (at top centre) is the famous 'Lemnian Earth' (*terra sigillata*). Above the illustration is a reference to Dioscorides, who described it (IV, 113). Galen also (*De simplici medicina*, IX, 2) gave a detailed account, including his effort to obtain a supply. It was said to consist of red earth from a cavern on the isle of Lemnos, mixed with goat's blood, moulded into pellets which were stamped with the figure of a goat, and sold as an antidote. According to tradition, other stamps have been used, including numbers, dates (according to the Christian calendar), figures of Diana and the like. Priestly control of the manufacture and sale of the pellets continued even under Turkish rule. Modern efforts to make of the pellets an early example of 'trade-mark' pills seem gratuitous. However, there is a possible relationship with the 'clay eating' of negroes and 'poor whites' in some parts of present-day America; medical men see a possible therapeutic value in certain types of clay that may have been discovered by chance in any age.

The manuscript, with 216 pages of illustrations such as we see in our sample page, indicates the importance of pictures, however crude, for identifying materia medica in an age when few people could read.

20. COLLECTING MEDICINAL HERBS

(In a manuscript from Germany of about the year 1200: Eton College, MS 204, folio Iv. Pseudo-Musa, *De herba vettonica*, etc.)

In this, the first of several miniatures representing the actual preparation of medicines, we have a colourful frontispiece from an early manuscript of treatises attributed to various authors (Musa, Apuleius, Sextus Placitus, etc.). It was copied at about the year 1200, probably somewhere in Germany. The illustrator's portrayal seems to be more artistically imaginative than precise. The tree resembles a tropical palm. The herbs held by the youth and one of the old men are less like betony (the description of which follows immediately) than gladiola or the madonna lily as they appear in other manuscripts. Some modern commentators have suggested that the crutches held by the old men are 'special instruments designed to avoid injuring the roots.' Cripples or sick old men with such crutches are often pictured in miniatures, but we never have seen one represented in actual use for digging herbs, and are not convinced of it in this case. The usual herb-collecting implement is a long-handled hatchet. To be sure, the accompanying text warns against using 'an iron tool'; this might suggest that the *wooden* crutches in the miniature were for digging. It also has been argued that the youth is Aesculapius, on the ground that in some early manuscripts he is represented as a beardless youth. However, in traditional classical representations he appears as a bearded old man, usually with a staff, and sometimes with a serpent. This suggests that one of the old men in our miniature might represent Aesculapius, the other perhaps Pseudo-Plato (Apuleius Platonicus) whose name appears in the accompanying text. The youth resembles the usual assistant or apprentice.

At any rate, the frontispiece introduces a lengthy set of instructions on the collection and uses of betony. These appear (as in most manuscripts) at the beginning of the Pseudo-Apuleius herbal, in the form of a letter entitled *De herba vettonica; Antonius Musa M. Agrippae salutem*. It ends as follows:

Collect this herb, along with its seeds and roots, without using an iron tool, in the month of August when other herbs are beginning to mature; dry it in the shade; macerate, along with the roots, in an aromatic sieve; reduce to powder when you wish to use it. [Forty-seven prescriptions follow.]

On the page following the frontispiece is another miniature, picturing the next procedure in preparing medicines: a bearded physician, seated, directs an assistant who weighs ingredients on scales, at a table of utensils, etc.

IV. PHARMACY

PHARMACY, the process of compounding materia into medicines, called for specialized handbooks not only for the collecting of simples but also for processing them into potions, pills, salves and the like. These handbooks usually were called *antidotaria*, a name derived from their supposed origin as collections of prescriptions for poison antidotes. As early as the tenth century, *antidotaria* were common in the Western world. Fulbert of Chartres, who had compounded medicines before he became Bishop of Chartres in about A.D. 1000, sent a fellow bishop several remedies, suggesting that 'the method of administering them is easily found in your *antidotaria*.'[1] Most *antidotaria* and *receptaria* (another term for such handbooks) not only described the compounding of medicines but also outlined 'the method of administering.'

Like handbooks of simples, *antidotaria* were practical compilations containing local prescriptions (sometimes named after the physician-inventor), as well as traditional prescriptions from Graeco-Roman handbooks. The oldest extant manuscripts of *antidotaria* are Western Latin works, derived largely from classical originals, especially Greek, as is evidenced by many of the names of specific antidotes, for example, *Aurea Alexandrina*, usually the first item in the alphabetical listing. Modern scholarship has tended to exaggerate the importance of 'Nicholas of Salerno' as the twelfth-century Italian founder of Western *antidotaria*. The evidence, however, is highly questionable. Henry Sigerist's *Studien und Texte zur frühmittelalterlichen Rezept-literatur* (Leipzig, 1923) presents manuscript data showing the existence before the twelfth century of an ample corpus of classical and early Western prescriptions. The appearance of the *Antidotarium Nicolai* coincided with the twelfth-century flood of translations from the Arabic. It comprised, in addition to the older prescriptions, much new material from Islamic sources. This factor, along with the fame of the South-Italian, Constantinus Africanus, as a translator, led scholars to attribute the compilation to a Salernitan named Nicholas. But in the actual manuscripts the name *Nicolaus* appears seldom and late (not until the thirteenth century). By this time there

[1] Loren MacKinney, *Early Medieval Medicine*, p. 135.

were two outstanding *antidotaria* in the West; the smaller of these, designated as *Parvum* (it contained only 500 items), was attributed to someone named Nicholas; the other (containing 2500 items), called *Magnum*, was a translation of a Greek work by a thirteenth-century Byzantine named Nicholas Myrepsus. Thus, we assume that someone named Nicholas was important enough in compiling the *antidotarium* to have his name attached to it a century or more after its origin. Whoever started the work, it was amended, revised and copied widely during the ensuing centuries. It is obvious that, regardless of authorship, our European ancestors were well supplied with drugs, just as their modern descendants are with 'patent medicines.' During the late-medieval centuries the actual compounding and dispensing of prescriptions was done by general practitioners and surgeons as well as by professional pharmacists. Often the miniatures (e.g., figs. 21 ff.) picture medical men with one or more apprentice-assistant (usually in short robes) collecting herbs, sorting and weighing them, macerating with a pestle in a mortar, stirring over a fire or rolling into pills.

21. PHARMACY IN A SURGEON'S OFFICE

(In a manuscript from the fifteenth century: Paris, BN, MS 6966, folio 154v. Guy de Chauliac, *Chirurgia*, VII, 4.)

This pharmaceutical miniature reveals the varied procedures involved in compounding medicines in a surgeon's office. At centre is an ornately garbed surgeon (or possibly a physician); he stands in an archway leading to what appears to be his reception and examination room. To exactly correspond with the text (which deals with pharmacy as an auxiliary to surgery) this should be an operating room, but there is nothing in the picture definitely to indicate it. At the left side of the room is a bed and bedside stand (perhaps for surgical or medical supplies). On the wall are implements, the one at right resembling a basket-carrier for a uroscopy flask. The foreground of the picture is entirely pharmaceutical. The surgeon directs a youth (at right) who collects herbs in an enclosed garden; he uses a knife, a violation of the prohibition in some manuscripts (see above, fig. 20) forbidding the use of 'iron' in digging herbs. To the left of the surgeon is a youth working with mortar and pestle. On the table are containers or ingredients; on the shelves behind him are jars with labels, none of which is legible.

The text below the miniature introduces chapter 4 of the book VII of Guy de Chauliac's *Chirurgia*, entitled *Antidotaria*. The passage indicates that in his day, although there were professional pharmacists, surgeons and physicians sometimes prepared their own medicines. It reads as follows:

Often it is necessary and very useful for physicians, and especially surgeons to know how to find and compound, as well as to administer, medicines to patients, since often they practise in places where there are no apothecaries, or if so they are not trustworthy, nor well supplied [with materia medica].

The text continues with citations from Galen on the practice of pharmacy, and with Chauliac's advice that surgeons carry clysters and other common remedies so as to give prompt relief to patients.

The miniature has been reproduced often in histories of pharmacy, sometimes with vague and even inaccurate captions. For example, Patrice Boussel's popular *Histoire Illustrée de la Pharmacie* (p. 61) reproduced it in colour with attribution to an unspecified French manuscript. D. A. Koning's caption in his 1951 pharmacy calendar;[1] viz., 'a fifteenth-century hospital pharmacy from a Hippocratic corpus manuscript, no. 2144 of the Bibliothèque Nationale, Paris,' should be corrected to *fourteenth*-century *pharmaceutical laboratory* in a surgeon's or physician's office; and it is from a Guy de Chauliac manuscript, no. 6966.

22. A PHYSICIAN AND ASSISTANTS PREPARE A PRESCRIPTION

(In a manuscript from fifteenth-century Flanders: Dresden, MS Db. 92–93, folio 181v. Galen, *Liber Cathagenarum, 2.*)

The scene is apparently the office of a practitioner who prepares his own medicines. He sits at the left, clad in a long ermine-trimmed robe and hat, dictating an ointment-prescription to his secretary (at right) who copies it in a book at a long desk. The physician also directs the boy assistant (centre) who compounds the *dyapalma* ointment, using a substantial pestle in a large mortar. Implements rest on a high shelf, the front side of which has the words that read 'Dyapalma with many precious ointments.'

The text at the side of the picture reads as follows: 'Here begins the first part of Galen's book on *Cathagenari*, Chapter I, on unguents. Galen said. . . .' There follows a wordy recommendation of *dyapalma* ointment, then the prescription.

The miniature is taken from a beautifully illustrated Galen manuscript at Dresden (described above, fig. 14).

[1] D. A. Koning, *Art and Pharmacy*, 2 vols. (Deventer, 1950–1958).

PHARMACY

23. A PHARMACIST DISPENSES SYRUP FOR COUGHS

(In a North-Italian manuscript of about the year 1400: Rome, Casanatense Library, MS 4182, folio 183. Elluchasem Elimithar, *Theatrum
sanitatis.*)

Here is an apothecary shop independent of a physician's or surgeon's office or
clinic. During the late Middle Ages pharmacy, like surgery, was organized and
regulated as a separate medical profession. Apothecary shops, somewhat after the
fashion of modern drug stores, sold a variety of products: spices, sugar and other
comestibles. The present miniature depicts a type of shop often pictured in late
manuscripts: an open-front structure with a street counter, and shelves stocked with
jars and flasks of various kinds. More noteworthy are the scales held by the pharmacist, and the customer about to drink his purchase, a syrup, at the counter.

Above the miniature is the caption indicating the medicine, vinegar syrup
(*siropus acetosus*). Below is a brief description that reads as follows:

By nature it is hot and frigid; it is better to cook it moderately in a clean dish. Its uses:
it cuts through, renders tenuous, cleanses and opens ailments of coitus (? *aperit nocumentum
choytu*), cough and dysentery. It eliminates ailments [if taken] with julep.

Medieval writers were confused over the term *acetosus*, which was used for the
herb *acetosa*, also for acetic substances in general. Avicenna (*Canon*, V, 1, 6), in his
De siropis acetosis, discussed a variety of acetic syrups based on sugar of honey. In a
separate treatise, *De siropo acetosa*, he distinguished these syrups from those made of
the herb *acetosa*. This miniature text concerns the herbal syrup which Avicenna
described as useful for coughs, coition (?) and ailments of the spleen and stomach.

The miniature (like fig. 21) has been popular with modern historians of pharmacy. The description for the frontispiece of Stubbs and Bligh's *Sixty Centuries of
Health and Physic* (thirteenth-century Venetian apothecary shop) should be corrected
to Lombardy (probably *Verona*) about 1400, from a manuscript entitled *Theatrum
sanitatis*. Incidentally, folio 4v of the manuscript, inscribed *Johaninus de Grassis
designavit*, suggests the authorship.

24. A PHARMACIST OR PHYSICIAN ROLLING PILLS

(In a manuscript from fourteenth-century Italy: Rome, Vatican, Urb.
Lat. MS 241, folio 400. Avicenna, *Canon*, V (antidotary), i.9.)

Among the non-liquids compounded by medieval physicians or their assistants, or (in the later centuries) by pharmacists, were the following: eye-washes (*collyria*), dusting powders (*sympasmata*), poultices (*malagma*), salves and rolls of paste (*cataplasmata*), plasters (*emplastra*), emollients (*panaces*), suppositories (*pessaria, pessula*), linaments (*illinimenta*) and various kinds and sizes of pills (*catapotia, pilluli, pillulae, trocisci*).

All of these seem to have been formed by hand, sometimes with the aid of a hand implement, such as the spatula, and a mixing tile. The early use of such implements in Roman times and the Middle Ages has been pointed out by George Griffenhagen in 'Tools of the Apothecary,' *Journal of American Pharmaceutical Association*, 1956, *17*, 810-813. Medieval miniatures, notably those of Cosmas and Damian, frequently reveal spatulas along with other pharmaceutical implements. Our miniature exemplifies the simpler method of pill-making by rolling between the hands and placing on a flat surface to dry and harden. In the text that follows the picture, 'Concerning Concoctions and Pills,' each of the twenty-eight items contains a description of the uses of the pill, the dosage, the amounts of the various ingredients and sketchy instructions concerning mixing, cooking, reducing to the proper consistency and 'shaping.' In a few cases the pills were made 'like a chick pea' or 'peppercorn' and 'dried in the shade.' Two of the prescriptions instructed 'him who makes the pills' to anoint his hands with 'odoriferous oil of balsam,' or 'sweet almond oil.' The most detailed of all the instructions reads as follows:

... vehemently macerate [the ingredients] until they can be made into little pills like peppercorns; then dry them in the shade.

V. MEDICATION: EXTERNAL AND INTERNAL

THOSE who have been accustomed to dismiss medieval medicine as merely prayer and incantations along with loathsome potions and superstitious performances by charlatan medicine-men should examine a few medical miniatures and consider the variety of prescriptions pictured in medieval handbooks. They would find that medicines were constantly used, applied either internally or externally according to principles then considered rational. External application might involve merely herbal, mineral or animal simples or compounds in the form of salves, ointments, fomentations, medicated bandages, pills, tablets and the like.

Medicines for internal ailments were usually compounds, in liquid form, taken internally. They were the ancestors of modern 'patent medicines.' Prominent among them were antidotes for general ailments or poisons, notably the famous *antidotum Mithridatum*, comprising thirty-six ingredients taken in honey and wine. It was named after a famous royal experimenter with drugs, who lived in Asia Minor in the second century B.C. Other prescriptions were named after their place of origin or their reputed inventors (e.g., 'galens'), but there also were drugs simply labelled as antidotes, confections, potions, 'holy' medicine (*hiera*), 'selectives' (*electuaria*), theriacs or treacles (*tyriaca*, a *mithridatum* improved by Nero's physician, Andromachus), cathartics, vinegar-honey and water-honey compounds (*oxymel*, *hydromel*), gargles (*gargarisma*), oils, syrups and pills or tablets. Critical modern scholars, noting that most of these prescriptions were classical in nomenclature, have sometimes suggested that the prescriptions were merely copied from ancient manuscripts and never actually used by medieval physicians. This is disproved by the writings of medieval laymen and physicians. As early as the sixth century, Bishop Gregory of Tours wrote in laudatory terms (suggestive of modern pharmaceutical 'commercials') concerning one of his favourite drugs; he called it 'an infallible theriac,' 'an ineffable pigment,' 'a praiseworthy antidote,' 'a celestial purgative,' 'a super ointment.' Three centuries later Archbishop Rabanus Maurus of Mainz warned against excessive use of *pigmenta et antidota*. Early in the eleventh century, Bishop Fulbert of Chartres wrote as follows to an ailing fellow-bishop:

I have not compounded ointment since I became bishop, but what I have from a physician's gift I give you even though I deprive myself.

To another bishop he sent 'three galen potions and an equal number of *diatesseron theriacae*' along with some 'wild nard' that the bishop had asked for. But Fulbert suggested 'oxymel and radishes . . . [or] laxative pills' as safer purgatives than the wild-nard emetic, and ended by offering 'other items almost ninety in number' if needed. Later, he had his assistant send 'hiera potion' to a friend, with detailed instructions on administering it and on convalescent diet.[1]

References such as these indicate everyday use of various drugs even during the early Middle Ages, not to mention ample evidences from the later centuries. In comparison, magical and religious ritualism is rare in medieval medical works, and even in the chronicles and biographical descriptions of physicians in action. The practitioners seem to have been trained professionals, usually clerics but not always so, clad in long formal robes with distinctively medical head-dress. Assistants, usually hatless, wore short robes. It is apparent that physicians (*medici*) and surgeons (*chirurgici*) were of relatively high rank and were treated accordingly. Charlatans and folk-healers existed and treated the common people but did not dominate the profession.

25. A PATIENT TAKING A COUGH DROP

(In a manuscript from fourteenth-century Italy: Vatican, Urb. Lat. MS 241, folio 389v. Avicenna, *Canon*, V (antidotary), i.5.)

Medieval physicians sometimes gave specific instructions as to how pills and other medicines were to be taken. Often they are pictured wagging a forefinger at the patient while emphasizing some point or other in the prescription. Our illustration of a patient taking a cough drop shows the method prescribed in the accompanying text, as follows:

Hold it in your mouth and let it trickle bit by bit as far as the lung; do not push it suddenly into the stomach, but prolong the time [of its passage] from stomach to lung (*ex stomacho ad pulmonem!*).

[1] See Loren MacKinney, *Early Medieval Medicine*, pp. 63, 135 ff., for the texts, and details concerning the passages from Gregory and Fulbert. On pp. 116 ff., are similar passages from Gerbert of Rheims and Richer concerning *antidotum philoanthropum* for the stone; also concerning the use of *antidotum* and *teriaca* by a clerical physician and a 'Salernitan' in efforts to out-poison one another.

If this text is an accurate translation of Avicenna's original Arabic text, his idea of the passage of a cough drop, to stomach and then to lung, was curiously inaccurate.

26. OINTMENT OF PIG DUNG AND HERB SCELERATA FOR SCROFULA

(In a manuscript from the thirteenth century: Vienna, NB, MS 93, folio 21v. Pseudo-Apuleius, *Herbarium*, VIII, 2.)

In this miniature the illustrator displayed a mischievous sense of humour, rather rare in medical manuscripts. Next to the patient, whose body is covered with scrofulous sores, the compounding of the pig dung and herbal ointment is shown by picturing a pig defecating while jumping over the mixing bowl. Obviously the short-cut in the process, the pig cooperating with the pharmacist, was entirely imaginary. The physician is depicted more formally, holding a jar of medicine while giving instructions to the patient. The descriptive text reads as follows:

For scrofulous tumours and boils: [use] the herb scelerata macerated and kneaded with pig dung; apply to the scrofulous tumours and boils, and within a few hours it will dissipate them and the pus will disappear.

The herb under consideration (*scelerata*) is not the one pictured in the lower half of the page (which is *botracion statice*), but appears on the preceding page. Many of the pages of this and other *Herbarium* manuscripts have the same confusing arrangement, the herb pictured on a different page from the description of its medical use. A somewhat similar illustration of a pig defecating (but not in the bowl) occurs in the *scelerata* section of another manuscript of Pseudo-Apuleius (thirteenth-century Florence, Laurentian, MS 73:16, folio 41); there is the same confusing arrangement of the pictures of the herbs. These two manuscripts indicate the popularity of the Pseudo-Apuleius handbook, and the late-medieval additions therein by Western illustrators. Originally the manuscript was copied from a Greek source, as can be seen in the classical garb of the various figures and from the Greek herbal synonyms in the descriptive texts. However, during the late Middle Ages, illustrators embellished the herbal illustrations with human-interest figures such as the pig. In the Vienna manuscript (as will be seen often *below*) marginal sketches were added to illustrate portions of the description originally unillustrated.

27. A HERBAL FOMENTATION FOR A CHILD'S INTERNAL PAIN AND A HERBAL POTION FOR NAUSEA

(In a manuscript from the thirteenth century: Vienna, NB, MS 93, folio
93v. Pseudo-Apuleius, *Herbarium*, XCIII, 2–3.)

The closing remarks concerning the preceding miniature (fig. 26) are also exemplified in another folio of the same manuscript, where two scenes represent possible uses of the herb pennyroyal (*puleium*).

The upper picture shows (at left) a mother holding her child who is struggling either from pain in the abdomen or from fear of the physician or both. The physician (at centre; shown, as always in this manuscript, without the usual medical headdress) is about to apply a bandage that has been soaked in a water solution of pennyroyal and cinnamon. Behind him, an assistant holds additional bandages. The textual description (on the preceding page) reads as follows:

For an infant's aching intestines: apply to the *umbilicus* the herb *puleium*, macerated with *ciminum* in water, and he will be well immediately.

The lower scene depicts (at left) a nauseated patient to whom the physician is giving a goblet of macerated pennyroyal in water and vinegar. Behind the physician is his assistant, holding a sprig of pennyroyal and directing an old man who is bringing a bucket of water. The text (above the picture) reads as follows:

For stomach nausea: give [the patient] a potion of the herb *puleium* macerated in water and vinegar; it will settle his nauseated stomach.

The text below the lower picture, concerning the use of the herb for an itchy skin-disease (*prurigo*), is illustrated on the succeeding page. The crude picture in the lower left-hand margin, by a later illustrator, has no direct relationship to the textual description. It seems to be a deliberate effort at pornography, as are many sketches of bathing, bloodletting, etc.

28. THE EAGLE REMEDY FOR POOR EYESIGHT

(In a manuscript from the thirteenth century: Florence, Laurentian,
MS 73:16, folio 63. Pseudo-Apuleius, *Herbarium*, XXX, 1.)

The eagle's role in medicine and the reason for its prominence in this picture are explained on the previous page of the manuscript, which has an illustration of the herb in question and an explanatory text, which reads as follows:

For dimness of vision: It is said that the eagle, when he wishes to fly high to view the nature of things, eats wild lettuce. Anoint your eyes with juice of wild lettuce and its leaves macerated with Attic honey and you will attain the maximum of clear eyesight.

The illustrator dramatized the eagle by having him hover over the patient as the physician applied the ointment with a rod. At right, showing through from the verso side, is a vulture, the flesh of which was used in eye salves.

29. OINTMENT FOR A SWORD WOUND

(In the same manuscript, folio 100v. Pseudo-Apuleius, *Herbarium*, LXXVI, 2.)

In this miniature the physician (to the right of the couch) seems to be straightening out the patient's left leg so as to make a thorough examination of the wounds in and around the badly mangled abdomen. The illustrator dramatized the scene by depicting behind the couch the cause of the wounds, a sword dripping blood.

The ointment prescription, given in the text immediately above the illustration, reads as follows:

If one has been struck down with a sword, apply to the wound the herb *senecion* [groundsell] beaten with saltfree grease until it is like liquified wax; this will heal the wound very easily.

30. AN OINTMENT FOR ARTHRITIS

(In the same manuscript, folio 55. Pseudo-Apuleius, *Herbarium*, XXI, 1.)

This miniature illustrates an ointment compounded from lily (pictured at the top of the page). Below it is the text of the prescription, reading as follows:

For aching joints: Use the herb *ieribulbum*, beaten and mixed with goat fat and oil, two pounds' worth; it will eliminate the pain wonderfully.

In the lower picture the illustrator indicated the animal and herbal ingredients of the prescription by showing a goat nibbling the herb. To the left, the physician (seated) reassures the importunate and apparently worried patient, as he strokes the aching arm.

31. A FACE-WASH FOR WOMEN'S FRECKLES

(In the same manuscript, folio 55v. Pseudo-Apuleius, *Herbarium*, XXI, 2.)

The same herb, lily, was the basic ingredient for a beauty treatment. Though not common, such prescriptions appear occasionally in pharmaceutical handbooks; and there were a few short manuscript treatises on cosmetics, usually unillustrated. Our miniature depicts a woman with freckles about to wash her face with a concoction that was supposed to clear it up. Her maid holds the wash basin while, at right, the physician with a pestle (or possibly the root or stalk of the herb) gives instructions. Below are a mortar and pestle.

Above the picture is the text of the prescription, which reads as follows:

If a woman has freckles on her face, mix together in a dish the root of lily with lupin meal; if the woman washes her face [with this] it will quickly clear her freckles.

32. A HEADACHE AND INSOMNIA REMEDY

(In the same manuscript, folio 84v. Pseudo-Apuleius, *Herbarium*, LIII, 2–3.)

Medieval medicines for headache and insomnia were more nearly like those of our grandparents than of the present tranquillizer era. Our miniature illustrates the use of wild poppy in an opium linament that was applied to the forehead. The troubled patient is shown on a couch, the physician (or possibly a servant) holds an extra bandage and wields a fan, while a maid servant binds on the aching or sleepless patient's head a bandage soaked in poppy linament. The miniature may have been intended to illustrate either or both of the uses of wild poppy as recorded in the descriptive text above the picture; it reads as follows:

For migraine or headache the herb poppy (*papaver silvaticum*), bruised with vinegar and bound on the forehead will alleviate the pain. To make a sleepless person sleep: an anointing with juice of *papaver silvaticum* will bring sound sleep.

33. VERBENA FOR BITE OF SPIDER OR MAD DOG

(In the same manuscript, folio 34v. Pseudo-Apuleius, *Herbarium*, III, 8–9.)

Among the dozen or so ailments supposedly curable by the external application of *verbena* (alias *vervain*, *verbenaca*, *verminacia*, *uminacia*), was poisoning caused by bites of animals, including spiders and mad dogs. Three curious-looking creatures at the top of the page are spiders. When bitten by them one should apply sprigs of vervain boiled in wine and then macerated; this to be followed by applications of raw vervain leaves macerated with honey. According to our manuscript, 'a dependable author affirmed the healing effects' of the following prescription when taken internally. The description, beginning on the preceding page, reads as follows:

For the bite of spiders, which the Greeks call *spalangiones*, take a small bunch of vervain cooked in wine, as a potion; then the macerated leaves applied to the wound will quickly heal it.

The chief picture on the page concerns the bite of a mad dog. At the bottom is shown the dead dog, his head having been cut off with the sword lying nearby. The nude victim of the bite, showing much concern, is being reassured by the physician. The role of the chicken (at left) is to prognosticate the man's fate, explained in the text as follows:

For bite of mad dog, and hydrophobia: put macerated vervain herb on the bite; also place from 13 to 15 whole grains of wheat on the wound; when these are soaked and swollen with mild humour [from the wound], place them in front of a hen; if she goes after them put out more grains; if she takes these, things are favourable; if not, they are serious and he will die.

The hen is pictured as if patiently waiting for the grain test. This procedure is somewhat similar to the above-mentioned prognostication by means of the *caladrius* bird (fig. 16). An eleventh-century manuscript (London, BM, Harl. MS 1585, folio 19) has a similar hen-test illustration with accompanying text.

34. PURGING WITH AN ENEMA (CLYSTER)

(In a manuscript from fifteenth-century Flanders: Dresden, MS Db. 92–93, folio 392v. Galen, *De usu farmacorum*, 1.)

People always have had trouble with their bowels. When purgative medicines failed, also sometimes as a supplement to bloodletting, medieval physicians used enemas. Here we have a typical enema scene. At left the physician (probably intended to represent Galen), in splendid ermine-trimmed robes and ermine head-dress, directs two assistants. One of them holds the enema tube in the patient's anus and supports the enema bag, into which the other assistant pours the liquid. The patient is on all fours on the bed (medieval scenes seldom show an enema patient on his back!). As bystanders there are two medical students, wearing long robes (untrimmed with ermine), and accompanied by a dog.

The scene is from the same war-damaged manuscript of Galenic works from which we have presented other miniatures. The accompanying text is less informative than another Galenic treatise, a *Commentary on Hippocrates Concerning Humours* (XII; Kuhn edition, XVI, 144 f.), which reads as follows:

Clysters are often applied in diseases for which other remedies are impossible. They can be prepared in various ways; harsh or mild; if mild they are made with warm water mixed with oil or milk ... mild clysters are applied when hard faeces press the intestines. ... Clysters are useful for ailments of the lowest intestines, for dry choler ... for flux, for constant lustful desire, etc. Sometimes we prepare a clyster of salt water, to eliminate putrid ulcers in dysentery. ...

35. REALISTIC PUBLICIZING OF A PURGATIVE-EMETIC

(In a manuscript from tenth-century Southern Italy: Munich, MS 337, folio 125. Dioscorides, *Materia medica*, IV, 157.)

We present here the first of three remarkable miniatures from the earliest surviving example of Dioscorides' *Materia medica* (in Latin, with illustrations). The manuscript, written and illustrated in Southern Italy in the tenth century, is noteworthy because it reflects a new human-interest technique in Western illustrating. Most early Western portrayals of herbs, animals and minerals seem to be crude copies of Greek originals. In contrast to these early stereotyped illustrations, here something new has been added: the illustrators have begun to depict, alongside the herbs, eye-catching examples of their curative powers. The present miniature concerns bowel trouble, which plagued medieval people. Among the many virtues that Dioscorides attributed to the herb *thapsia*, and especially the root, was its thoroughness as a purgative. The text below the picture reads as follows:

. . . . it [*thapsia*] is warm and cathartic; if taken mixed [with honey] it purges a man upward and downward. . . .[1]

At the side of a traditionally stereotyped herb, the illustrator pictured with mischievous realism a patient in the process of being purged both 'upward and downward.' Such a dramatic appeal for prospective users is comparable to the technique of the modern 'commercial' which asserts that no other remedy gets such complete and rapid action. Later manuscript miniatures occasionally portrayed pots, or squatting defecators, but none with such realistic impact as this crudely effective illustration.

36. DRAMATIZING A CURE FOR INSANITY

(In the same manuscript, folio 127. Dioscorides, *Materia medica*, IV, 151.)

Once more, in the tenth-century Latin Dioscorides (described above, fig. 35), we find dramatic action alongside uninspired copying of the Greek original of a herb. The miniature pictures a stereotyped herb (*elleborus niger*), and (at left) a light axe with which it might be cut down; in the right-hand margin is an action scene, a bare-bosomed princess stretching her hand toward the stem of the plant. The descriptive text below explains that she is a maniac who was cured by taking hellebore:

Black hellebore is also called *ectomus* or *polirizon* or *melampodion*, because Melampus cured his [and the King's] daughters who had mania. . . . It is also good for epileptics, melancholics, frenetics and arthritics. . . .

Tradition has it that Melampus was a goatherd-physician who used the herb to cure the insane daughters of King Proteus of Argos. Some Dioscorides manuscripts refer specifically to two princesses, but a Greek gem pictures three mental patients, an attendant with a tray, and Melampus.

37. DRAMATIZING A CURE FOR SNAKE BITE

(In the same manuscript, folio 86. Dioscorides, *Materia medica*, III, 58.)

Here is another example of the manner in which Latin illustrators embellished the traditional herbal pictures copied from early Greek versions of Dioscorides. The

---

[1] According to a second-century Greek medical treatise (edited by W. H. S. Jones under the title *The Medical Writings of Anonymous Londinensis*, Cambridge University, 1947. See p. 137), white and black hellebore had a similar double-action effect; '. . . the white evacuates [bilious matter] by vomiting, the black by stool.'

marginal additions, according to paleographical experts such as Elias Lowe, reflect the illustrator's uninhibited enjoyment of his task. He went out of his way to add items such as a deer nibbling a herb (folio 28), a man sleeping (99v), a bare-bosomed Venus collecting material for a love potion and a dog biting a snake (both in folio 121). All of these marginal additions illustrate some use of the herb or animal pictured.

In the present scene the herb *ligusticum* was drawn neatly but in the usual stereo-typed form characteristic of Western copies of Greek originals. But the marginal addition is far from stereotyped in its portrayal of the use of the herb; in the text there is only a brief mention of the 'virtue' of *ligusticum* in relieving 'poisonous bites.' Snake bite was a constant problem in medieval times, therefore this dramatic portrayal of a small man wrapped in the coils of a huge serpent about to bite him. Incidentally, snake bite, often mentioned in medieval medical annals, was only one of many uses for *ligusticum*. Because of its manifold virtues, Dioscorides reported that 'some call it *panacea*.'

38. A LATE DRAMATIZATION OF SNAKE BITE

(In Italian manuscript of the year 1510: London, BM, Prints & Engrav-ings, MS 197.d.2, folio 124. Kullmaurer and Meher, a medical picture-book.)

Early in the sixteenth century two German artists, Kullmaurer and Meher, did a medical picture-book with Italian captions. One of its pages contains a picture done over 500 years later than our preceding miniature (fig. 37, from the tenth-century Dioscorides manuscript), and probably 1500 years later than the many snake illustrations in ancient Greek scrolls. Such illustrations are interesting evidences of the popularity of snake-bite remedies throughout the ages. In this early sixteenth-century miniature, at right is a frantic patient covered with serpents; the physician, wearing the Hospitaller 'Cross of Malta,' and holding a medicine jar, offers him the simple herb. The caption (in Italian: *Remedio contra morsegati da serpe*) indicates 'A remedy for snake bite.'

39. CURING LUNACY WITH A SPRIG OF PEONY, AND SCIATICA WITH PEONY ROOT

(In a manuscript from the thirteenth century: Vienna, NB, MS 93, folio 72v. Pseudo-Apuleius, *Herbarium*, LXV, 1-2.)

Here are pictured two uses of peony as a simple, applied externally. The upper picture shows (at left) a 'moon-struck' man (*lunatico jacenti*) turning cartwheels; at right is the treatment of the 'lunatic.' Bound hand and foot in stocks, he has a sprig of peony around his neck which is supposed to heal him. The text (above the sketches) reads as follows:

For lunatics who suffer from the course of the moon: If peony herb is bound on the neck of one who is moonstruck, quickly he will rise up healed; and if he carries it with him he will suffer no ill.

Mental ailments were also treated with hellebore potion and surgery (figs. 36, above, and 68, below).

The lower picture (an ink sketch added by a later illustrator) portrays, at right, a seated physician holding a sprig of peony and lecturing concerning its virtues to a patient who is pointing to his sciatic leg. The text (above the illustration) reads as follows:

For sciatics: bind peony root on the [affected] member with linen [bandages]; when you have thus swathed the sufferer, things will be most healthful; and if you take it on shipboard, it will calm a tempest if used by itself.

40. AN ANTIDOTE FOR POISON

(In a manuscript from the thirteenth century: Florence, Laurentian, MS
73.16, folio 59. Pseudo-Apuleius, *Herbarium*, XXV, 2.)

Through the ages, antidotes for poisons have been one of the most popular of internal medicines. The multiple-ingredient mithridates and theriacs and the all-purpose bezoar (or 'mad') stones, etc., are well known to modern readers. Probably the locally prepared prescription represented in our miniature was used more widely by the average person in the Middle Ages.

The illustration represents a seated patient, who has imbibed some kind of poison, receiving from the physician a goblet of the antidote. The prescription reads as follows:

For poison if one has taken it: give the herb pine thistle [*camellea*], dried and reduced to powder, in a potion of wine, four *cyathos*[1]; it will counteract all of the poison.

[1] *cyetos* or *cyathos* was a liquid measure of about forty-two cubic centimetres.

The patient's swollen left leg probably indicates the poisoning. The same illustration and explanatory text appear in another thirteenth-century *Herbarium* manuscript (Vienna, NB, MS 93, folio 44).

41. POTIONS OF GLADIOLA AND GOATS' OR ASSES' MILK FOR INTERNAL PAINS

(In a manuscript from the thirteenth century: Vienna, NB, MS 93, folio 83. Pseudo-Apuleius, *Herbarium*, LXXIX, 2–3.)

This complicated illustration apparently illustrates the uses of gladiola with milk as a remedy for ailments of the spleen, colon and midriff. At top left is a naked patient showing symptoms of internal pain, which might be any of the three mentioned in the accompanying text (the position of his hands suggests the colon). At centre is the physician offering the patient a goblet containing the potion, which has been poured from a pitcher held by the physician. The potion might be either one of the two described as follows in the texts above the illustration:

ii. For aching spleen: [take] select a very mature gladiola, dried, pounded, reduced to a powder; mix with the mildest of wine, give as a potion and we say that it will wonderfully dry up the spleen.

iii. For ache of the colon or midriff: [take] gladiola berries macerated with goats' milk, or better asses' milk; drink it tepid and the pain will cease.

The latter of the two texts seems to be illustrated by the portions of the picture to the right and below. Above, to the right of the physician, is a servant holding a small bucket, perhaps of milk from the she-goat pictured with its kid. Another servant holds a sprig of gladiola, the berries of which are to be mixed with the milk. The lower picture, of an ass and its foal, seems to be an illustration of a somewhat uncertain passage of text (*melius si asinae fuerit*), which we translate 'or better, of asses' milk' (as an alternative to goats' milk). However, the woeful appearance of the ass suggests that she is sick and that the medicine was recommended for both man and beast. Another uncertainty is the marginal sketch at top right, perhaps to indicate a patient whose abdomen is swollen with the pains described. This sketch was added by a later illustrator.

42. A SOOTHING INHALANT FOR BABIES

(In the same manuscript, folio 23v. Pseudo-Apuleius, *Herbarium*, XI, 6.)

The principal illustration on this page shows a young, worried mother (left) and an equally worried attendant (right) who, following the instructions of the physician (seated, at centre, wearing a crown), holds a sprig of *artemisia tagantes* over a brazier so that the fumes will be inhaled by the baby, whom the physician holds over the brazier. The explanatory text above the illustration reads as follows:

To make an infant lively (*hilarem*), burn artemisia and suffumigate him; this will avert all harmful incursions and make him more lively.

The rather mature-looking 'infant' is shown responding readily to the treatment, stretching out his hands to the physician and to his worried mother and the attendant. This is one of the rare medieval miniatures concerning paediatrics.[1]

Artemisia is also recommended, in the text, as an ointment for nerves (illustrated by the head sketched in the upper left margin); also for feet (sketch in the upper right margin); and for fever (sketch in the lower left margin showing a bed-patient). No specific ailment described in the text fits the sketch (lower margin) showing a physician explaining to a patient the virtues of the herb, a sprig of which he holds in his hand. There is also an inexplicable stray foot in this complicated set of illustrations.

Iconographers believe that the sketches in the side and lower margins of this manuscript were added by later illustrators so as to have graphic illustrations of all of the ailments mentioned in the text.

[1] On folio 93v there is an illustration of an 'infant's intestinal pain' being treated by applying a *pulegium*-soaked bandage.

VI. HEALING BY CAUTERIZATION

CAUTERY, like bloodletting, has been widely prevalent from primitive ages well into modern times, for the purpose of re-adjusting supposed imbalances of bodily humours. Cautery, as we shall see, was well known to the Roman medical expert Celsus in the first century, as well as to the Greek authorities cited by him. About five centuries after Celsus, a Westerner named Caelius Aurelianis described different methods of cautery and certain controversies concerning it. Thereafter cautery seems to have prevailed throughout the West, especially after the twelfth-century 'Salernitans' began to employ it extensively. They cited the Moslems Avicenna and Albucasis concerning various methods: the use of hot or cold irons, the applications of corrosives, etc. This was the period of increasing Moslem influence in Western medicine, and cauterization was highly praised by them as a means of eliminating corrupt matter, of preventing the spread of infection, of staunching the flow of blood and of 'comforting the bodily members.'

Cautery was employed, sometimes along with bloodletting, corrosive ointments, setons[1] and the like, in order to remove noxious matter. For example, Celsus in the first century recommended that poison from a mad-dog bite be drawn out by cupping followed by the application of cautery irons or corrosives (*De medicina*, V, 27). The rationale of cautery seems to have been to create ulcers from which the noxious matter would drain. The ulcers were instigated by burning, scarification, setons or by application of corrosive substances such as oil of vitriol, mustard and quicklime. Burning might be lenient or harsh, shallow or deep, by a warm or hot iron, or even by burning medicinal wood on the patient's flesh (as in modern China). Celsus (*De medicina*, IV, 15) advised burning, even through an incision into a liver abscess to drain pus. Caelius Aurelianus, in his sixth-century compilation (*Tardarum passionum*, III.4.66, Drabkin edition), quoted classical authorities who

---

[1] Setons were threads or narrow linen bands, inserted under the skin by means of parallel incisions, to serve as counter irritants. They were applied locally for ailments of testes, anus, loins, navel, spleen, stomach, spine and even (under the chin) for eye trouble. See Rogerius, *Chirurgia*, III, 52; also a thirteenth-century description in *Sudhoff's Studien*, X, 79.

'prescribe puncturing the spleen in three or four places with a red-hot cautery' for a serious ailment of that organ. For localized bodily pains cautery irons often were applied externally on the opposite side of the body. For asthma, ten points on the chin, neck, chest and shoulder blades were cauterized; the resulting ulcers were kept open until coughing ceased (Celsus, *De medicina*, IV, 29). One of the strangest treatments was for rheumy eyes. The skull and/or forehead were incised and the flow of rheum stopped by cauterizing with a fine iron (Celsus, *De medicina*, VII, 7). Various types of cautery irons were employed: deep, shallow, three-pronged, coin-shaped, serrated, etc.; medieval manuscripts sometimes contain sketches of the different types inserted throughout the text.

During the burning process, care was taken to prevent harm to sinews, but (as we have noted) often the skin and even internal organs, such as the liver, were ruthlessly cauterized. Once the cautery-induced ulcers formed, they were kept active by applications of irritant corrosives. After the proper amount of drainage had taken place, dry scabs were allowed to form and the healing was considered completed. In view of the apparent brutality of much of the cautery process, it seems strange that it persisted so continuously among the highly rational Greeks, the practical Romans, the supposedly progressive 'Salernitans' and among Westerners even into the nineteenth century. It is true as Lynn Thorndike surmised (*Magic and Experimental Science*, I, 723, note 2) that by the thirteenth century 'cauterization seems to have become less common,' but it is still practised.[1]

43. CAUTERY POINTS SHOWN ON HUMAN FIGURES

(In a manuscript from thirteenth-century England: Oxford, Bodley, Ashmole, MS 1462, folio 9v. Anonymous illustrations, preceding Pseudo-Apuleius' *Herbarium*.)

As also in the case of bloodletting, physicians used charts and illustrations to assure accuracy in cauterizing for specific ailments. The illustrations in our miniature

---

[1] In 1956 the present author had his lower eyelids cauterized by an eminent London ophthalmologist for the purpose of checking excessive watering of the eyes brought on by excessive reading of medieval medical manuscripts in the British Museum; one of the manuscripts, by chance, contained a twelfth-century miniature of the same operation. See below, fig. 45, for an unusually interesting and colourful illustration of cautery of the eye in a manuscript from Italy of about the year 1300.

constitute seven out of a total of fifteen, on two pages of a general medical compendium. Reading clockwise, starting with the standing figure at left, they indicate the points at which to cauterize for elephantiasis, asthma, tertian fever (four figures) and toothache (exemplified by the seated figure). In similar fashion the preceding page of the manuscript pictures the points for shortage of breath and ailments of the liver spleen, stomach and kidneys.

44. CAUTERY POINTS AND FAMOUS HEALERS

(In a manuscript from fourteenth-century Italy: Oxford, Bodley, MS *e Museo* 19, folio 165. An illustrated page at the end of a series of surgical treatises.)

This unusually complicated series of vignettes indicates how cautery instructions expanded and became standardized in the late-medieval West. Serving as a pictorial chart, it presents for each of twenty-four specific ailments (1) the name of the ailment with brief instructions (placed to the left of the picture), (2) a figure showing the proper points at which to cauterize and (3) a famous healer presiding over the operation, in some cases actually applying the iron. We present the names of the ailments and healers by rows, beginning at the top, from left to right. 1 (top left), 'Master' holding a huge clyster; 'servant' holding a cautery iron; 2, pyorrhea and 'Esculapius'; 3, stomach trouble and 'C[h]rysippus'; 4, sciatica and 'Apollonius' (Menifites); 5, head tumour and 'Cassius' Felix; 6, short breath and 'Miles' (i.e., Milesius); 7, stomach wound and 'Erasistratus'; 8, ponderous scrotal hernia and 'Demet[riu]s'; 9, headache and 'Parm[enides]'; 10, epilenticus (?) and 'Neronis'; 11, epilenticus and 'Filominus' (i.e., Philumenus); 12, elbow tumour and 'Anciptus' (i.e., Antipater); 13, headache and 'Alexander' (Philalethes); 14, consumption (*phthisis*) and 'Prisongos' (i.e., Praxagoras?); 15, splenitis and 'Erusi' (i.e., Herophilus or Erotian); 16, podagra and 'Senofodi grassus' or 'graecus' (Senodotus of Ephesus?); 17, headache and 'Aristotle'; 18, hepatitis and 'Apollo[nius]'; 19, kidney trouble and 'Galienus'; 20, elephantiasis and 'Nestaurus'; 21, eye trouble and 'Ypocras' (i.e., Hippocrates); 22, dropsy and 'Diocles'; 23, kidney and leg trouble and 'Emiso' (i.e., Themison?); 24, throat trouble and 'Nissim.' The description (to the left of the physicians) are brief, e.g., for no. 20 'Elephantiasis is burned this way.' Each picture has several cautery points.

45. CAUTERY POINTS AND CAUTERIZING

(In a manuscript from Northern Italy of about the year 1300: Rome, Casanatense Library, MS 1382, folio 2. At the beginning of Rolandus Parmensis, *Chirurgia*.)

Here, in a series somewhat like that in the last picture, the actual procedures are shown. In the top row, at left, Hippocrates (*Ypocras*) presides, across from a patient (captioned as *languidus*), while an assistant holds aloft a uroscopy flask for inspection. To the right, in the shop (*fabrica*), Hippocrates selects a cautery iron from several in a brazier while his *discipulus* holds another iron in a glowing forge equipped with bellows and flanked by an anvil. The second row of figures illustrates cautery for demon possession (epilenticus), head tumour and catarrh of eyes, ponderous scrotal hernia, and pyorrhea. Incidentally, the first two patients in this row, and the two immediately below them in row 3, have their hands tied. The third row of pictures illustrates cautery for excessive watering of the eyes, head tumour and catarrh of eyes, headache, toothache. Similar scenes are continued on the following pages in three rows of four pictures each, concerned with trephining for melancholia and cautery for rupture, headache, dropsy; also for paralysis, hepatitis, splenitis, shortness of breath; for consumption, sciatica, kidney trouble, kidney and leg trouble. Two additional illustrations, for elbow tumour and elephantiasis, are found on folio 1 of this manuscript, which is remarkable for its colourful and vivid illustrations of operations.

46. HEATING THE CAUTERY IRON

(In a manuscript from fourteenth-century Italy: Venice, San Marco, MS Lat. 7.13, folio 22. Rogerius, Bruno, Rolandus, *Cerurgia cauteriorum*.)

This illustration of preparation for cautery shows the physician holding the iron in the fire while his assistant works the bellows. The illustration comes at the beginning of a treatise on cautery attributed to the famous 'Salernitan' surgeons Rogerius, Bruno and Rolandus. The caption above the picture reads as follows:

Here begins the Surgery of Cauteries according to Rogerius, Bruno and Rolandus.

47. THREE CAUTERY VICTIMS APPROACH THE ORDEAL

(In a manuscript from the fourteenth century: Oxford, Bodley, MS Rawl. C.328, folio 3v. Anonymous illustrations in a medical miscellany.)

Cautery in early times must have been comparable in the terrors it inflicted on patients to those suffered by dental patients before the modern era of painless dentistry. The miniature reflects vividly the anxiety of three patients, all nude or nearly so, as they approach the fire at which the physician, working the bellows, heats three cautery irons. His garb (long robe, veiled headdress, etc.) indicates that he is not a lowly barber-surgeon, but either a physician or a university-trained 'surgeon of the long robe.'

The illustration (and also the succeeding one, fig. 48) belongs to a series of twelve at the beginning of a miscellaneous collection of treatises on uroscopy, surgery, materia medica, etc. The first illustration (on the preceding folio) portrays Constantinus Africanus, in monk's garb, lecturing to a man and woman who present uroscopy flasks (see above, fig. 8). The remaining eleven concern cautery.

48. CAUTERIZING FOR ELEPHANTIASIS

(In the same manuscript, folio 9v. Anonymous illustrations in a medical miscellany.)

Here we have a close-up of the actual application of the cautery iron. The naked patient lies stretched out on a table or couch with his hands behind his back (probably tied). The physician applies the hot iron to one of the two cautery points on the patient's throat (see above, nos. 44–45 for the points for cauterizing elephantiasis). The text above the illustration describes the procedure and the location of the cautery points as follows:

For elephantiasis burn as follows: once at one of the neck veins, again at the other; at the four breast points; at the middle of each thigh and at two other [points] on the ankles.

49. A PHYSICIAN ABOUT TO CAUTERIZE AND CAUSTICIZE

(In a manuscript from the eleventh century: London, BM, MS Sloane 2839, folio 1v. At the beginning of *Liber Cirurgium Cauterium Appollonii et Galieni De Artis Medicinae*.)

According to a fifteenth-century North-African medical writer, Caelius Aurelianus (*Tardarum passionum*, III, 4), physicians disagreed on 'treatments that involve burning; some employ . . . caustic [i.e., corrosive] drugs and cauteries' for ailments of the liver and spleen. For sciatica and other ailments also, cautery and corrosives were variously applied. By the twelfth century there were manuscript descriptions giving details concerning the treatment.

Here, in one of the earliest extant manuscript illustrations of cautery, a physician holds a jar of corrosives or ointment in one hand while with the other he takes a hot iron from the fire. The naked patient anxiously awaits the application of the iron, which sometimes was dipped in the corrosive. The much-effaced text above the picture reads as follows:

Here begins Appollonius' Book of Surgery and Cautery and Galen's Art of Medicine. For aching head and flatulence of the breast and hands, and pains of the knees and feet, burn thus.

50. SURGERY AND CAUTERY

(In a manuscript from eleventh-century England: London, BM, MS Harley 1585, folio 9. Anonymous pictures preceding Pseudo-Apuleius' *Herbarium*.)

As has been indicated already (above, fig. 49) cautery was more complicated than merely burning with a hot iron. Here, in four pictures from another of the earliest extant sets of cautery miniatures, we find examples of cutting with a cold iron, burning with a hot iron, and a combination of cutting and burning (on the feet of a podagra patient).

At the top left is a seated patient who has had his feet cut for podagra; apparently the person standing at lower left is about to apply to the bleeding feet a dauber soaked in corrosives from a flask in his left hand. Above is the caption 'A podagric is cut and burned thus.' The hand at the patient's right, placing an object in his mouth, might be that of the physician applying a soporific sponge. The standing figure below to the left seems to be doing double duty, not only medicating the feet of the podagra patient but also illustrating the points at the knees and ankles at which, 'for tumour and pain of the knees, one is burned thus.'

At top right is a hernia patient showing cautery points at the groins. Below him is a brutal surgical scene: 'Haemorrhoids are cut thus.' The victim bends over, his feet on the edge of a bowl which receives the flow of blood from his cut haemorrhoids, on which the bearded surgeon works energetically, parting the buttocks with a pronged retractor while he uses a scalpel on the haemorrhoids.[1]

51. CAUTERY 'OF THE ENTIRE BODY'

(In a manuscript from the fourteenth century: Montpellier, MS 89 bis, folio 25v. Rogerius Salernitanus, *Chirurgia*, III, 45.)

Human faith in cautery as a drastic cure-all is illustrated in this portrayal of the various parts of the body at which long suffering patients might be burned for specific ailments. The instruments held by the surgeon may be intended to represent a cold iron (in his right hand) for cutting and a hot iron (in his left hand) for burning. The instructions in the accompanying text, and at intervals throughout the *Chirurgia* and other surgical treatises of the period, recommend the use of both cold and hot irons, and sometimes corrosive medicines and even setons to keep the ulcers open.[2]

The picture does not illustrate the text immediately preceding (IV, 20: *De spasmo*) nor the incomplete, misplaced caption below (from IV, 19: *Ex corruptis humoribus* . . .). Both of these are concerned with ointments, without reference to cautery. On the other hand, the picture is well-suited to a nearby text concerning cautery *ad remedium totius corporis* in cases of sciatica and arthritis (IV, 13); also a passage concerning ailments 'from shoulderblades to *genitalia*' (III, 45). Furthermore, the combination of cutting and burning irons illustrates passages throughout the four books of the *Chirurgia*, at the end of which the picture occurs.

[1] Almost identical miniatures appear in a later manuscript, London, BM, MS Sloane 1975, folios 92v–93.

[2] For example, cutting and burning, with cold knives (*rasarius*) and hot or flaming irons (*calidum* or *candens*) are recommended in the *Chirurgia*, I, 33, 36; II, 12; III, 20, 28, 30, 32; IV, 14. *Chirurgia* II, 15, recommends a hot iron and seton. For additional details, see *above*, introduction to Section VI, 'Healing by Cautery.'

VII. HEALING BY BLOODLETTING

BLOODLETTING, to reduce or to correct excessive or corrupt humours, was more widely prevalent in Western Europe than cautery, not only throughout classical and medieval times but also well into the modern era in both America and Europe. It is thought that it was excessive bloodletting rather than the ailment that killed George Washington, and a recent history of medicine in the Deep South from Colonial times through the eighteenth century reveals astonishing reliance on bloodletting and other primitive methods usually attributed to unenlightened medieval folk.[1] Like most medieval practices, bloodletting was based on methods inherited from ancient Greece and Rome. The following quoted extracts from early manuscripts (pre-1200 in date) indicate the irrational reliance on bloodletting not only for specific ailments but also as a cure-all:

In acute fevers, day or night if need be, one ought to resort to bloodletting. . . . For headache and madness open veins in the back of the neck. . . . For ailment of the mouth or toothache open two veins below the tongue. . . . For injury of the testicles open two veins above the great toe.[2]

[Bloodletting is] the beginning of health, it makes the mind sincere, it aids the memory, it purges the brain, it reforms the bladder, it warms the marrow, it opens the hearing, it checks tears, it removes nausea, it benefits the stomach, it invites digestion, it evokes the voice, it builds up the sense, it moves the bowels, it enriches sleep, it removes anxiety, it nourishes good health.[3]

Little wonder that bloodletting was a universal practice, what with such all-embracing recommendations, approval by the greats of classical antiquity, and charts showing exactly where to bleed for each ailment. Furthermore, bloodletting occupied an important place in the calendars which played the role of almanacs in early times.

---

[1] John Duffy, *The Rudolph Matas History of Medicine in Louisiana.* 2 vols., Baton Rouge: Louisiana State University Press, 1960–1962.

[2] Selected from Dr. William Sharpe's translation of Bede's *De Minutione Sanguinis sive de Phlebotomia* in *Quart. Phi Beta Pi*, 1955–1956, 52, 85–87; preceded by an excellent brief of the history of bloodletting.

[3] Quoted from Thorndike, *op. cit.*, I, 728.

Bloodletting was recommended not only for certain seasons and days of the year but also for certain times of day, usually before a meal and after clearing the bowels. As in cautery the exact place on the body for each ailment was specified. Often a spot was at a point far from the localization of the ailment. For example, blood was let between the middle and ring fingers for liver trouble. Bloodletting procedure might be as follows: with stomach and bowels empty, and no bath beforehand, the limb is bandaged so as to make the vein stand out (if not a limb, pressure might be applied); the vein (sometimes a 'pulsing vein,' i.e., an artery) is incised carefully, longitudinally, avoiding injury to nerves; blood is allowed to flow as long as it is thick and dark (unless the pulse becomes too feeble); the patient might grasp a staff or use hot or cold water to control the flow of blood; after flow ceases, wash the skin, apply a compress to the incision; watch diet carefully afterwards.

Cupping and leeching (concerning which, see below, figs. 56–59) were specialized, and less vigorous, methods, easier to control than incision of veins or arteries.

52. AN ANNOTATED BLOODLETTING FIGURE

(In a manuscript from the fifteenth century: Oxford, Bodley, MS Ashmole 789, folio 365. A lone, anonymous, annotated illustration.)

The places for bloodletting as well as cautery were carefully outlined in calendars, charts and illustrations. Often there were notations concerning 'lucky' and 'unlucky' days, seasons and even hours for this operation, as well as for uroscopy, cauterization and other miscellaneous activities. Even more prevalent were bloodletting figures showing the veins and arteries that should be incised to let blood for specific ailments. Usually such pictorial charts occupied an entire page, with the 'bleeding man' at the centre and captions or brief instructions in the margins.

In our illustration the figure of the man is anatomically crude, but the bleeding points are clearly indicated in red, with red lines leading to side captions concerning each. Noteworthy are the many bleeding points near the elbow, a favourite place because of the numerous blood vessels easily accessible there. The brevity of the captions can be seen in the following quotations of typical texts in two of the marginal circles to the left of the man's right hand:

The iliac vein is opened for ailments of the lower members.

Incise this pulsating vein for cardiac ailment; it does a great deal of [good].

Noteworthy, also, are the numerous incision points on the neck and head. Our illustrated page is from an anonymous medical miscellany of astrology, uroscopy and the like.

53. AN ANATOMICALLY REALISTIC BLOODLETTING FIGURE

(In a manuscript from the fifteenth century: Vatican, MS Pal. Lat. 1709, folios 44v–45. Anonymous double-page annotated illustration.)

Already we have seen (and shall continue to see) examples of the anatomical realism of Western illustrators. Here, however, is one of the least inhibited of many nude bloodletting figures. Depicted on two facing pages of a manuscript, with the usual bleeding points in red and marginal explanations in circles, it goes to extremes in the use of red ink. Like the nudes in miniatures portraying the attractions of the Baths of Pozzuoli, this trend in late-medieval medical illustrating is sometimes attributed to a persistence or revival of the classical appreciation of the nude human figure. It is noteworthy that the picture is found in an astrological-medical miscellany, along with classical works by Aulus Persius Flaccus and other pagan writers. It is also noteworthy that, while the supposedly pious West was following such unascetic impulses, the Byzantine East was manifesting strangely ascetic tendencies, such, for example, as a decidedly anti-Greek restraint in the depicting of the human body even in medical and anatomical works (see examples in the tenth-century Laurentian orthopaedic manuscript, below, fig. 91).

54. BLEEDING A MAN

(In a manuscript from fifteenth-century Flanders: Dresden, MS Db. 92–93, folio 320. Galen, *De flebothomia*, prologue.)

Most of the extant miniatures of actual bloodletting picture a surgeon or his assistant making an incision at or near the elbow, in the ante-cubital flexure. This miniature shows a patient whose arm has been incised by an assistant to Galen (at right), who directs the operation. The assistant is not a 'barber-surgeon' but a 'surgeon of the long robe.' He holds the scalpel in one hand and supports the patient's arm with the other. As in many illustrations, the blood is shown spurting into a vessel held by an assistant surgeon. This could be interpreted as evidence that an artery had been incised; surgeons such as Guido de Vigevano advised bleeding from veins, which were more easily controlled. The accompanying text refers to Galen's *De flebothomia*, translated from Arabic into Latin by Nicholas of Reggio and dedicated to King Robert II of Naples-Sicily.

55. BLEEDING A WOMAN

(In a manuscript from the fifteenth century: Munich, MS German 28, folio 32v. Anonymous treatise on bloodletting, in German.)

This picture shows much the same procedure as in the preceding one. Noteworthy are the following items: a woman is seated on a bench, holding a bowl into which her blood spurts from the usual elbow incision; meanwhile, she grips a staff in order to hasten or retard the flow of blood (by tightening or loosening the muscles surrounding the vein). In this case a surgeon (wearing a typical surgeon's hat) checks her pulse, with fingers properly placed on the inner side of the wrist. Early treatises on bloodletting sometimes gave explicit instructions on (1) preliminaries (e.g., no food nor bath immediately preceding; bowels clear, etc.), (2) instruments and method of incising (e.g., use of a sharp pointed scalpel, dipped in oil; longitudinal incision, avoiding nerves, etc.) and (3) on prolonging or repeating the operation; however, if the colour or consistency of the blood changed or if the pulse weakened, bleeding was stopped.

In the illustration, the old man (at left) is either washing his hand and arm preparatory to the operation, or holding the hand in warm water so as to enhance the flow of blood. The miniature illustrates a treatise on bloodletting in a collection of works concerning health; it includes a calendar, medical astrology, the four temperaments, baths, etc. The text accompanying the illustration gives the usual instructions.

56. CUPPING

(In a manuscript from thirteenth-century France: London, BM, MS Sloane 2435, folio 14. Aldobrandino da Siena, *Le régime du corps*, I, 10, in French.)

The placing of heated cups or horns on light incisions or scarifications was resorted to as a moderate form of bloodletting for the purpose of drawing off rarified blood or cleansing local infections. Hippocrates (*Ancient Medicine*, 22) recommended it, describing different types of cups. Manuscript instructions indicate that cupping could be at various points, but the illustrations usually show it on or between the shoulder blades, occasionally on the buttocks. As in other forms of bloodletting, certain times were recommended, notably when the moon was waxing, before eating or bathing, etc.

As illustrated in the miniature the cups, heated over a fire, were placed on the scarified or incised spot whence they drew off blood as the air in the cup cooled. It was recommended that the cups be left on the body for short intervals at first, increasingly longer as the patient became accustomed to the procedure. The attendant in the illustration seems to be a woman, which is not surprising since cupping often took place at bathing establishments, where women were employed as servants.

The accompanying text reads as follows:

Cupping purges the thin blood in the thin veins, also between them and the flesh. . . . One should not cup those whose blood is thick, nor before the bath. . . .

57. CUPPING IN A BATH HOUSE

> (In a manuscript from Germany in the year 1464: Edinburgh, Royal
> Observatory, MS Crawford 9.14.5, folio 78v. Anonymous treatise on
> health, in German.)

Cupping came to be generally accepted as a health measure, often resorted to while bathing. Bath attendants often performed the relatively simple operation. The miniature is an excellent illustration of three aspects of the procedure: scarification, bathing, cupping. In an enclosed bath is the patient (at right) soaking his feet in a tub of hot water to aid in the process. A male attendant seems to be scarifying at a point between the shoulder blades. The circle on the patient's back (to the right) represents either a small cup or the place from which one had been removed. The underclothing worn by the men is unusual in bath-house scenes. Nudity was the rule even where there was mixed bathing. At the top of the page is an astrological chart, and a text below it expounds the values and methods of bloodletting. The manuscript contains, among other items, a collection of treatises on astrology and health.

58. LEECHING

(In a manuscript from the fourteenth century: Paris, BN, MS French, 12323, folio 84. Aldobrandino da Siena, *Le régime du corps*, I, 11, in French.)

A third method of draining off excess or polluted blood was by means of leeches. Textual instructions indicated that this method was good for subcutaneous ulcers, haemorrhoids and even for demon possession. Leeches were carefully selected; especially recommended were green or liver-coloured ones from frog ponds covered with duckweed. They were starved for a day before applying; then, if sluggish, they were dipped in water mixed with a little wine. The point of application, usually on the legs, was washed and rubbed until red. When leeches were applied near the nose, mouth or rectum, a thread was inserted through the tail so as to keep them from straying inside. If one happened to enter the body, a salt-water drink or enema was used to expel the leech.

The illustration, like most of those in manuscripts, depicts the seated patient, his legs covered with leeches, feet in warm water to facilitate the flow of blood. The accompanying text gives details of the instructions summarized above, concerning the colour and application of the leeches.

59. AN ARABIC MEASURING INSTRUMENT USED IN BLOODLETTING

(A single folio out of an Arabic manuscript of the year 1315, from Syria (?): Washington, D.C., Freer Gallery, MS 30.76. al Jazari, 'Book of Knowledge of Ingenious Mechanical Contrivances.')

This miniature, the only medical illustration we present direct from an Islamic manuscript, pictures an extremely rare and surprisingly early medical apparatus to measure the amount of blood let by the physician. A similar illustration appears in an Egyptian manuscript of 1354 (Boston Museum of Fine Arts, single folio), but no such apparatus was known in the West.[1] Mr. Richard Ettinghausen, who was so kind as to call the al Jazari item to my attention, prepared the following description for the Freer Gallery-Book; it is quoted by his permission:

Upon a rectangular base with moulded sides which contain two empty chambers rests a shallow bronze bowl with a pipe outlet at the bottom of it. Inside the bowl this outlet is covered with a perforated dome. Rising from the bowl, but communicating with the chambers below are four hollow columns (two seen in section). These columns support a rectangular hollow podium upon the floor of which are seated the hollow figures of two scribes, in physician's dress. The figure at the left holds a pen; that at the right, a tablet with a column of figures inscribed on it.

In use, as the blood drains from the shallow bowl into the empty chamber at the right, it raises a float hanging at the end of a brazen rod which is in the hollow column at the right. The upper end of this rod is beaten flat forming the tablet and as the rod rises, a reed in the scribe's right hand indicates upon the inscribed scale, the corresponding amount of blood.

There is also a thread attached to the float, and this thread, rising alongside the rod through the column, passes out over a pulley round a spindle in the centre of the upper chamber and thence down through the left-hand column. It has attached to it a weight which drops into the left-hand chamber.

Noteworthy is the fact that all of the figures shown are automatons which perform the functions of recording. Such a complicated apparatus reminds one that Hellenistic Alexandria was famous for technological wonders in ancient times; their actual use by medical practitioners is doubtful.

[1] See E. Wiedemann and F. Hauser, 'Über Schalen, die beim Aderlass verwendet werden, und Waschgefässe nach Gazarî,' *Arch. Gesch. Medizin*, 1919, *11*, 22–43, figs. 12–15. The 1354 leaf is from Istanbul, Aya Sofya, MS 3606.

VIII. SURGERY

SURGERY, even more than other aspects of medieval medicine, can be surveyed in two distinct periods. The earlier centuries (sixth to eleventh), usually referred to as 'the Dark Ages,' can with considerable accuracy be designated as the era of 'the Decline and Fall' of classical surgery. Following the death in sixth-century Rome of Greek-trained Alexander of Tralles, and, in seventh-century Alexandria, of another Greek, Paul of Aegina, intelligent surgery was conspicuously lacking in Western Europe and was equally unprogressive among the Arabs and Byzantine Greeks. Exceptional, in Western records, are references to surgical treatment of wounds, to amputations and to Caesarean deliveries. Cautery and bloodletting dominated surgery. By about 1100 definite progress was evident, a result it seems of Arabic influences. Latin translations of the works of Rhazes, Avicenna and of a notable surgeon named Albucasis, and experimental operations by practical-minded men in the regions of Salerno, Bologna and Montpellier, mark the dawn of Western surgery. It was accompanied, probably energized, by a revival of anatomical dissection. This became evident at about the time (late eleventh century) when Constantinus Africanus of Monte Cassino translated from Arabic numerous works containing classical ideas on medicine, including some anatomy and surgery. Meanwhile, surgeons in the region of Salerno were dissecting pigs, and by 1300 Mundinus of Bologna was performing autopsies.[1]

Steady progress during the twelfth and thirteenth centuries is revealed in South-Italian regulations for the control of medical practice. In the twelfth century King Roger of Sicily insisted on state licensing of physicians. A century later, Emperor Frederick II expanded these regulations. A licence to practise was granted only after three years' preliminary study of the liberal arts, five years of medicine including some surgery, and finally a year of apprenticeship under a practising physician. One

---

[1] George Corner, 'Salernitan Surgery in the Twelfth Century' (*Brit. Journ. Surg.*, 1937, 25, 84–99), brilliantly discusses the early phases of the development (eight illustrations from MSS). See also Loren MacKinney, 'Medieval Surgery', *Journ. Internatl. Coll. Surg.*, 1957, no. 3, 393–404; and Leo Zimmerman and Ilza Veith, *Great Ideas in the History of Surgery* (Baltimore, 1961).

might also specialize in surgery by concentrating for a year and including some study of human anatomy, probably with dissection. This type of state-controlled medical-surgical education and practice was not to become general in the West for centuries, but the progressive trends involved therein are interestingly reflected in contemporary manuscript miniatures. It is noteworthy, in both miniatures and texts, that the surgeon (*chirurgicus*) was not rigidly segregated from the physician (*medicus*) until late in the Middle Ages. Frederick II's regulations indicate that some physicians studied surgery as a side line whereas, a century earlier, King Roger's regulations had not mentioned surgery. In medical treatises of this period (by Rogerius, Rolandus, Theodoricus, etc.) the operations, illustrated and described, were performed by professors (*magistri*) and physicians (*medici*), as well as by surgeons (*chirurgici*). As late as the fourteenth century John of Gaddesden, in his *Rosa Anglica seu Medicinae*, regretted the segregation of cautery and bloodletting from general medical practice. He asserted that they should not be left to 'barbers and women . . . for these are the work of chirurgiens; Galen and Rhazes performed these operations with their own hands, . . . I myself am a professional bloodletter for I let veins that the most eminent barbers cannot let.' In the twelfth and thirteenth centuries physicians were referred to not only as *medicus*, but also as *magister* and *doctor* (teacher). Medicine was becoming more academically professional and was differentiated from surgery.

One much-publicized surgical improvement, often represented as an invention of this period, appears in manuscript texts but not in miniatures. The anaesthetic sponge (*spongia soporifera*), described as early as the ninth century in a medical text, has never been found for certain in a miniature. Probably it was used, along with sedative drinks and ointments, but nothing seems to have sufficed for complete surgical anaesthesia.[1]

Constantly in miniatures patients are shown either held or tied down; and the accompanying texts sometimes recommended that the patient 'be held in chains.' Generally operations were pictured in brutal, sometimes bloody, detail (quite unlike modern pictorial drug advertisements). We now present examples in the head-to-feet sequence, usually followed in the manuscripts.

[1] John Arderne, *Treatises of Fistula in Ano, Haemorrhoids, and Clysters* (D'Arcy Power edition, Oxford University Press, 1910, pp. 100–102), mentioned several soporifics, one of which, a mandrake-opium ointment would permit 'cutting in any part of the body without feeling or pain.' Sleeping pills, he reported, were used by 'rogues in France' to enable them to rob pilgrims; also there were pills and potions 'to provoke sleep,' and prescriptions to wake the sleeper.

60. SURGICAL INSTRUMENTS

(In a manuscript from fourteenth-century Northern Italy: New Haven,
Yale Medical Library, Codex Paneth, MS 28, p. 576. Albucasis,
Chirurgia, II, 87–88.)

Various types of surgical instruments were used even in ancient Mesopotamia and
Egypt. Some of the actual instruments used by the Greeks are extant, and there are
also illustrations in relief and on vase paintings. Alexandrian and Pompeian archae-
ology has revealed similar arrays of Hellenistic and Roman implements. For the
Middle Ages, both in the Byzantine-Islamic East and the Arabic-Christian West,
there are fewer remains; manuscript miniatures are the principal sources of information. Of all the manuscripts, the Latin translations of Albucasis' *Chirurgia* are the
most valuable in both quantity and quality of illustrations. Some Albucasis manuscripts have more than 200 clearly sketched instruments, often in colour, interspersed throughout the text with captions and descriptions of usage. Only in
early-modern printed works are these manuscript illustrations matched for variety
and technical detail. There are numerous instruments sometimes in varying sizes
and shapes for cautery, bloodletting, obstetrics, probing, incising, boring, scraping,
suturing, sawing, trephining and dentistry.[1] Less common than the scalpels, lancets,
forceps, scissors, saw-edged knives and perforators, are the clysters, *specula, cannulae,*
and machines for traction and implements for fistula operations (see below, figs. 87,
91B–C). Manuscripts of the famous surgical writings of the later Middle Ages
produced no more impressive array of instrument illustrations than those of Albucasis.

As an example, we present one of a number of brightly coloured instruments
from the Albucasis section of the famous Paneth Codex, a manuscript copied and
illustrated in North Italy early in the fourteenth century, probably for the University of Prague medical library, whence it passed into the possession successively of
a church at Olmutz, the Paneth family, and finally (in 1955) the Yale Medical
Historical Library. Of the seventeen instruments shown, all but three are saw-

[1] *Sudhoff's Studien . . .* , XI–XII has detailed data on instruments, including numerous illustrations. In Mario Tabanelli's *Albucasi: un chirurgo arabo dell'alte medio evo* (Florence, 1961) there are
thirty-four plates of manuscript pages illustrating instruments in Albucasis's treatise. For a survey
of *Arabic* manuscripts of Albucasis, with twenty-one photoreproductions, see Sami Hamarneh,
'Drawings and Pharmacy in al-Zahrawi's 10th-Century Surgical Treatise,' *U.S. National Museum
(History and Technology), Bulletin 228* (1961), pp. 81–94.

edged 'irons' or knives of various sizes. Two of these are straight-edged saws with guards. Three of the knives are smooth-edged, in varying blade forms. In the left column are two bone incisors. The accompanying text explains the importance of selecting the proper instruments.

61. EXAMINING WOUNDS ON THE HEAD AND ARMS

(In a manuscript from the late fourteenth century: Vatican, MS Vat.
Lat., 4804, folio 72v. Guy de Chauliac, *Chirurgia*, III, 1, in Provençal.)

This unusually colourful picture comes from a Provençal version of the *Chirurgia* of Guy de Chauliac, one of the most famous of fourteenth-century surgeons. It appears at the beginning of Treatise III, preceding a general discussion of wounds. Probably the miniature was intended to illustrate various types of wounds: fleshy wounds such as those on the arm, and bone wounds such as those on the head and legs; both types are mentioned in the text of chapter 1.

The surgeon, clad in a tight red hat, surgeon's cape and long robe, probes a wounded cranium, while his short-robed assistant examines a bloody upper arm. This illustrates two types of surgery mentioned in the text and also the two types of surgeons prominent at this time, 'surgeons of the long robe' (the academic professionals) and 'surgeons of the short robe' (the lower-rank operators). Two other factors reflect the high artistic quality of this remarkable manuscript: the patient's face, registering pain, and the intent expressions on the faces of the two surgeons. Modern medical men find on the legs of the patient indications of specific wounds.

The text reads (in part) as follows:

Here begins Treatise III on wounds, in two doctrines [i.e., sections]: the first treats of wounds of simple members; the second, of special wounds of compound members. Doctrine I is in five chapters, Chapter 1, On Wounds in General. A wound is a lesion in a soft tissue, bloody and without pus. . . . Surgery is twofold; on flesh or on bone . . . [continues concerning wounds of the cranium and arms].

On later folios (27, 155) surgeons are shown examining chests and ulcerated legs.

62. A HEAD WOUND FROM A BRAWL

(In a manuscript from the fourteenth century: Montpellier, MS 89 bis,
folio 3v. Rogerius Salernitanus, *Chirurgia*, I, 16.)

Medieval men were no more peaceful than modern men, and in the absence of adequate police forces, heads often were broken or cut in private fights. Here we have a brawl in which the man at left, who obviously is getting the worse of it, will be a subject for the surgeons. It is not clear just what part the cat played in the quarrel, whether the cause, or a possible weapon seized by the man in order to defend himself. Suffice it to say he has suffered a sword cut that has laid open the skull. The sword wielder seems to have in his left hand another weapon, perhaps the rock mentioned in the accompanying text. A third man, at right, is either restraining the swordsman or urging him on.[1]

The accompanying text, concerned more with the cure than the cause, reads (in part) as follows:

If the skin and cranium are cut open by a blow with a sword or similar weapon, or by a blow with a rock or some such object, so that the skin hangs down or is cut, excise the hanging skin through the middle [of the wound] down to the fractured cranium. Then separate it from the projecting [parts of the] cranium with a rasp and suture from both sides . . . [continues with medication].

63. SURGICAL EXAMINATION OF A FRACTURED CRANIUM

(In a manuscript from North Italy of about the year 1300: Rome, Casanatense Library, MS 1382, folio 4v. Rolandus Parmensis, *Chirurgia*, I, 5–6; similar explanations in Rogerius Salernitanus, *Chirurgia*, I, 6 ff.)

Broken heads were handled with care. Here the physician (*magister*), with hands on each side of a bloody head wound, makes a careful examination, exploring the fracture with a finger.[2] As indicated in the accompanying text (quoted below), he probably will trephine, then cleanse the wound (note the cloth held by his assistant) and medicate (note the flask of medicine held by the assistant). A surgical ointment called *apostolicon chirurgicum* was much used in such cases.

The text, above the picture, reads as follows:

[1] The uniqueness of this representation of the actual wounding of a man justifies the use of the miniature despite its damaged condition.

[2] According to Rogerius (*Chirurgia*, I, 4), 'there is no better method of identifying a cranial fracture.' This method is still used.

Concerning cranial fracture in the shape of a fissure (*rimule*). Sometimes it chances that the cranium is fractured like a fissure and is split so that neither side seems higher than the other; also that it is uncertain whether the fracture extends inside [the cranium]. To find out, have the patient hold his mouth and nostrils shut, then blow vigorously; if any breath comes out the cleft you know that the cranium is fractured even into the cerebrum. Treat as follows. If the wound is narrow, enlarge it, and unless prevented by bleeding immediately trephine with an iron instrument, very cautiously on both sides of the fissure. Make as many holes as seems wise, then cut the cranium from one hole to another with a bistoury (*spathumina*), so that the incision extends to the edges of the fissure. Carefully remove pus oozing from above the cerebrum with a silk or fine linen cloth introduced sideways between the cerebrum and cranium by means of a feather . . . [then medicate].

64. SURGICAL EXPLORATION OF A FRACTURED CRANIUM

(In a manuscript from the fourteenth century: London, BM, MS Add. 17810, folio 41. Gulielmus de Saliceto (i.e., William of Saliceto), *Chirurgia*, I, 1.)

This picture vividly illustrates the initial cranial incision in the form of a cross.[1] This was standard procedure in head wounds, so as to determine the exact internal condition, whether the cerebrum was badly fractured. Once this was established the detailed surgical procedure could be planned (Rogerius, *Chirurgia*, 1, 2 ff.). Here, as in many of our surgical miniatures, the operator appears to be either a 'surgeon of the long robe' or, possibly, a physician. Noteworthy are the two interested bystanders, one of whom (perhaps the patient's wife) implores the aid of the surgeon. The accompanying text merely advises that 'anyone who has been struck on the head with a rock, club or stone, or who falls . . . ought to have a physician (*medicus*) find out whether the cranium is fractured.[2]

65. MEDICATING A FRACTURED CRANIUM

(In a manuscript from the thirteenth century: London, BM, MS Sloane, 1977, folio 2v. Rogerius Salernitanus, *Chirurgia*, I, 2, in French.)

Medication was an important part of surgery, as is abundantly evident not only in many sections of the texts of *Chirurgia* by Rogerius and others but also in many of

[1] The cruciform cranial incision is described in Rogerius, *Chirurgia*, I, 4, 8; also in the Bamberg surgical manuscript (*Sudhoff's Studien* . . . , XI–XII, 109, 139).

[2] Similar wounds are described in Rogerius, I, 1 ff.; Theodoricus, II, 2 ff.; and Rolandus, I, 1 ff.; similar illustrations appear in manuscripts of their treatises on *Chirurgia*.

the miniatures in this manuscript, which, incidentally, has a total of ninety-six medical illustrations. Apropos of medication, eight out of the twelve illustrations on the first two pages of the treatise picture the uses of cleansing cloths, compresses, ointments, medicated bandages and dusting powders rather than of surgical instruments. In the illustration here reproduced, a healing ointment called *apostolicon chirurgicon*[1] is being applied to the patient's partially healed cranial wound. The surgeon's garb is noteworthy: the long, sleeveless outer robe, and the coif, which is pictured more often on the heads of assistants, or even of patients, than of physicians or surgeons.

66. A CRANIAL INCISION TO DRAIN A FRACTURE

(In a manuscript from the fourteenth century: Leiden, University, MS
Voss. L.F.3, folio 37. Theodoricus de Cervia, *Chirurgia*, II, 6.)

In some cases of skull fracture there was the problem of draining the pus and blood that collected underneath. Surgeons knew that this called for an incision. In the miniature a surgeon is shown making an incision in the fore part of the cranium while his assistant holds the patient firmly. In the text immediately preceding the illustration, this is described as follows:

. . . after the bone has been reunited and bound down by the callus [scale], a large amount of bloody matter or some superfluous humor will be generated. . . . There is no escape in this instance from excision and exploration of the area, and from preventing the growth of proud flesh . . . . and the more convenient and suitable place for the incision is that which you deem most likely to permit the poison to run out and the bloody matter to be expelled, and which is more distant from the nerves, such as the forehead. . . .[2]

67. SUTURING A SUPERFICIAL HEAD WOUND

(In a manuscript from the fourteenth century: London, Wellcome
Library, MS 544(1300), page 22. *Glossulae Quatuor Magistrorum*, I, 9.)

Although our miniature is somewhat lacking in realism, it illustrates an often-overlooked element of early surgery, suturing.[3] It depicts an oversized patient with

[1] The detailed prescription is given in the accompanying text of both Latin and French versions; also in the Bamberg Surgery (*Sudhoff's Studien*, XI–XII, 109).

[2] Our translation is from Campbell and Colton, *The Surgery of Theodoric* (New York, 1955; 1961, 2 vols.) I, 123.

[3] Theodoricus (*Chirurgia*, II, 18) describes two methods of suturing abdominal wounds; viz., unitary (skin and peritoneum at the same time) and separate, as Galen recommended (first the peritoneum, then the abdominal wall). See below, fig. 72, on suturing a neck wound.

a cut on his head which is being sutured from behind by an undersized 'surgeon of the long robe' wielding a huge needle.

Of equal interest with the illustration is the accompanying text (above the picture), which describes wound-suturing and after-treatment in the following detail:

Ch. 9. Concerning a wound of the skin of the head without fracture of the cranium. If . . . the wound is lineal, without fracture . . . as in all superficial wounds the lower part is always left open and suturing begun from above; not at the wound-head, but one digit below. The needle is inserted in the two lips of the wound then a knot is made by carefully superimposing thread over thread; afterwards cut the threads. Then make another [needle] hole one digit from the other, in similar fashion; and proceed thus the entire length of the wound. Then insert a cloth plug dipped in white of egg, or a linen or feather pad and sprinkle with blackberry powder. . . . The powder is applied to check the flow of blood and to generate flesh and skin; also to prevent the dissolution of the suture holes by reason of tow adhering to the wound. If blood is not oozing from the wound on the following day, apply a cloth plug soaked in fusco or agrippa ointment so as to prevent a fistula in the wound and to corrode the dead flesh and regenerate good flesh. Proceed thus to the end.

68. MANIA CURED BY HEAD SURGERY

(In a manuscript of the fourteenth century: Montpellier, MS 89 bis,
folio 6. Rogerius Salernitanus, *Chirurgia*, I, 26.)

We have seen the treatment of mania by binding peony around the patient's neck or drinking a hellebore potion (figs. 36, 39). Here is the cure by surgery, which has been employed for ages in the form of trepanation or trephination. Prehistoric healers practised it with the aim of releasing the demons (or pressures) that were causing the mental aberration.

The text, below the miniature, vividly describes the procedure, as follows:

For mania or melancholia incise the top of the head in the shape of a cross, and perforate the cranium so as to expel the [noxious] matter. The patient is to be held in chains and the wound healed as in cures for wounds described above [Rogerius, *Chirurgia*, I, 1 ff.].[1]

[1] The same operation is described in greater detail in the twelfth-thirteenth-century Bamberg surgical manuscripts (*Sudhoff's Studien* . . . , XI–XII, 139): after shaving the head the skin was incised to the bone in cruciform shape; holes were then made with a trephine and the bone lifted out thus releasing the air from inside the cranium; extreme care was taken so as not to injure the cerebral membrane, which would be fatal.

Noteworthy is the fact that, despite the oft-mentioned soporific sponge for anaesthesia in medieval surgical texts, here (as elsewhere) the patient is shown tied or held by an assistant.[1] In this case, the operator is apparently a 'surgeon of the long robe,' wearing a skull cap and wielding a scalpel. The cruciform incision (as noted above, no. 64) was common in preliminary surgery of the head, since it permitted inspection of the skull.

69. EARLY MEDIEVAL OPERATIONS FOR CATARACT AND NASAL POLYPS

(In a manuscript from twelfth-century England: Oxford, Bodley, MS Ashmole 1462, folio 10. One of a series of illustrations preceding Pseudo-Apuleius' *Herbarium*.)

This colourful pair of surgical illustrations comes from a series on surgery and cautery that was inserted as early as the eleventh century in certain texts of Pseudo-Apuleius' *Herbarium*. The top illustration, captioned 'Cataracts of the eyes are cut out thus,' pictures a short-robed, bald-headed, bearded surgeon about to incise the eye of an agitated patient. No text accompanies these pictures, and cataract operations are seldom described in surgical treatises.

The lower illustration, captioned 'Polyps are cut from the nose thus,' depicts both surgeon and patient somewhat as in the upper picture. The surgeon holds in his left hand a tube with which to facilitate his work on the nasal passages. He has already cut the polyp, and blood is draining into a flask which is held by the patient. As described in other surgical manuscripts, notably those of Rogerius, *Chirurgia* (I, 38), this operation might proceed as follows: the polyp could be removed by cutting or scratching it out, or by cautery, or medication alone. Sometimes a hooked *tenaculum* was used to draw it out. For excision, a metal tube, somewhat like that in the surgeon's left hand, might be inserted and through this a knife introduced with which to cut out the polyp (obviously, however, the large knife in our illustration could not be introduced into the tube shown in the surgeon's hand). The same sort of tube might be used to introduce a cautery iron with which to burn out the polyp.[2]

---

[1] For other examples of forcible restraint of cautery or surgery patients, see above, figs. 45, 48, 66; and below, figs. 71, 72, 73, 75, 77, 81. Also note illustrations of doctors standing on patients' feet (BM, Sloane, 1977, *passim*). On the soporific sponge, see above, VIII (intro.). The only miniatures in which we find a possible illustration are mentioned above, fig. 50.

[2] For an example, see the quotation, below, fig. 71.

One text has the following addendum: 'if the patient fears the hot iron, insert a plug of cloth soaked in *ruptorio* ointment, then yolk of egg and oil.'

70. A LATE-MEDIEVAL OPERATION FOR CATARACT

(In an Italian manuscript of the year 1510: London, BM, Division of Prints and Engravings, MS 197.d.2, folio 15v. Henricus Kullmaurer and Albert Meher, a medical picture-book, with Italian captions.)

So as to compare cataract operations four centuries apart,[1] we present an example from a medical picture-book compiled at about the year 1510. It contains, among other illustrations, this vivid and colourful portrayal of 'The Mode of Removing a Cataract.' At left is a figure rarely seen in medieval manuscripts, a female nurse, who holds the patient in his seat. At the edge of a bandage covering the upper parts of both eyes of the patient an incision is made by a 'surgeon of the short robe.' Behind him a venerable physician (perhaps a 'surgeon of the long robe') directs the operation. Before the sixteenth century, the professions of physician and surgeon had become separate, both distinguished by long robes and formal headdress. Of lower status were the 'surgeons of the short robe'[2] (who did most of the actual cutting), and the pharmacists and midwives.

71. CUTTING AND CAUTERIZING A FACIAL FISTULA

(In a manuscript from the thirteenth century: Cambridge, St. Johns, MS 1044(o.I.20), folio 256. Rogerius Salernitanus, *Chirurgia*, I, 36, in French.)

In this pen-and-ink sketch and the accompanying French text, we have an excellent illustration of the use of cautery in a surgical operation to disinfect a wound, rather than, as was common, merely to draw off imaginary humours. The surgeon is about to lance a fistula in the lachrymal duct, after which he will apply the cautery iron held aloft in his left hand. Meanwhile, the assistant keeps the cautery fire

---

[1] Note that in the first century Celsus (*De medicina* VII, 7) described cataract operations; the Spenser edition-translation (III, 351) contains a modern diagram of four stages of this operation.

[2] John Arderne, an English master-surgeon of the early fifteenth century, was suspicious of barber-surgeons and pharmacists. He did his best to conceal his surgical methods and prescriptions from them. See his *Treatises of Fistula in Ano, op. cit.*, pp. 71, 96.

burning. The surgeon wears the pig-tail skull cap common to the profession. The French text of this section of the well-known surgical handbook of Rogerius (above the illustration) reads as follows, in a condensed translation:

When the fistula near the eye and nose becomes putrid, incise it, insert to the bottom of the incision a pad soaked in egg white, then press to the bottom an iron or chopper tube through which you insert a hot cautery iron so as to burn out the roots of the fistula. If the patient fears the iron, introduce instead a pill of ruptory ointment [lye and quicklime]. After six hours remove the pill and apply a pad soaked in egg white, leaving it until the heat fades out. Then treat as in other wounds.

72. LIGATURING A CUT VEIN IN THE NECK

(In a manuscript from the fourteenth century: Montpellier, MS 89 bis, folio 12. Rogerius Salernitanus, *Chirurgia*, II, 2.)

Wounds caused by violence might result in severing the jugular vein, as in the present case. The remedy, as indicated in the accompanying text, was ligaturing.[1] The picture shows the surgeon holding the threaded suture needle in his right hand, preparatory to tying off the vein. His left hand rests on the patient's neck where the bleeding wound shows red. (Incidentally, the red cheeks on both surgeon and patient are not indicative of wounds.) The patient's hands are either tied, or tightly clasped, in anticipation of the pain of the operation.

The text (below the picture) reads as follows:

If a wound made in the neck by a sword or similar weapon cuts the jugular vein, treat it as follows: take up the whole vein with the needle, but so that it is not perforated; from the other side draw the needle with the attached thread, binding it with the thread and tightening so that no blood flows. Do this from above and below. Apply a wet cloth to the wound.

73. MEDICATING AND OPERATING FOR SCROFULA

(In the same manuscript, folio 14. Rogerius Salernitanus, *Chirurgia*, II, 13.)

Scrofula (tuberculosis of the glands) was commonly described in medieval texts as an ailment of the throat, armpits and groins. Medication with herbs was recom-

[1] See above, fig. 67, on suturing.

mended, and this illustration shows the surgeon applying roots of radish to the patient's throat. In case medication failed, the scrofulous gland was excised; this is shown in another picture (on the same folio) in which a grim-looking surgeon (in a long black robe and skull cap) makes the incision while his assistant restrains the patient. The text describes the ailment and treatment as follows:

Scrofulas are threefold, arising in the throat, under the shoulder joint and in the groins.... There are certain small glands which are not scrofulas ... [the text identifies these]. When they [real scrofulas] come to a head, incise them according to the nature of their location so that the pus exudes. If they harden and swell for a month or half a year, or if the patient is a boy, use this oil ... [prescription follows]. At the waning of the moon ... take 11 poultices of fetid iris and wild radish; use one on the tenth day, another on the ninth, and so on to the end of the moon. On this, or some other day, bleed him once. If this medication is not sufficient surgery must be resorted to.... [the patient's throat] should be held firmly with one hand while the epidermis is cut longitudinally, then scraped and [the scrofula] caught with a hook and drawn out ... [medication and bleeding follow].[1]

74. EXTRACTION OF A BARBED ARROW FROM THE FACE

(In a manuscript poem from twelfth-century Southern Italy: Berne, Burgerbibl., MS 120, folio 110. Petrus de Ebulo, *Liber ad Honorem Augusti* (Emperor Henry VI).)

Barbed arrows created special problems for surgeons. Our miniature interestingly portrays several aspects of this common hazard of warfare. The scene illustrates the wounding of Count Richard of Acerio during the siege of Naples by Emperor Henry VI in 1191. In the lower part of the miniature are land and sea forces of Tancred and Bohemond with an archer bending his bow, at left. Medical interest centres in the caption at top left, which reads, 'When Count Richard of Acerio was wounded,' and in the other persons in the castle. The Count grasps the arrow that has pierced his face, as though about to pull it out by main force. The wounded person to the right may be one of his comrades; possibly it represents him under treatment. The physician (captioned *medicus*) likewise seems about to pull the arrow out regardless of the barb, while two women bring medicaments and towels. The

[1] Modern surgeons consider the so-called scrofula of this text to be some sort of enlarged lymph node.

handling of imbedded arrows, both here and in other surgical illustrations (such as fig. 75), does not do justice to medieval surgery. The illustrators give the impression that the arrow, barb and all, was brutally drawn from the wound. Surgical texts, as we shall see, indicate that adequate care was taken to eliminate such additional wounding by the barb.

75. EXTRACTION OF A BARBED ARROW FROM THE ARM

(In a manuscript from the fourteenth century: Montpellier, MS 89 bis, folio 4v. Rogerius Salernitanus, *Chirurgia*, I, 21.)

We have noted the difficult problem of barbed arrows and the failure of the manuscript illustrators to represent the best techniques of surgeons. This is true of the present miniature, as well as the preceding one. Here the surgeon seems about to retract the arrow-head through the arm by brute force while his assistant holds the patient. A far more intelligent procedure is evidenced in the accompanying text (below the illustration). It reads as follows:

If a wound is made by a barbed arrow we extract it as follows. If it is possible to use large forceps we carefully grasp the barbs with the forceps and, bending them back to the stem of the arrow, retract it. But if this is difficult, we work a small iron or bronze tube into one of the barbs, retracting that barb into the tube, doing the same to the other barb. Then, with much care and diligence we skilfully extract the arrow. We can do this also with two goose quills.

Similar details are given in Theodoricus, *Chirurgia* (I, 22–23), in Rolandus, *Chirurgia* (II, III, *passim*), and in the Bamberg surgical manuscript (*Sudhoff's Studien . . .*, XI–XII, 110–113).[1] The illustrator of our manuscript was unable to do justice to such a careful and diligent operation. Incidentally, in cases such as this, where the arrow-head protruded, Theodoricus (*Chirurgia*, I, 22) indicated that the arrow might be pulled on through the body.

[1] These surgical works also describe the treatment when missiles penetrate the head or vital organs. The extraction of an arrow from the stomach is described and pictured in the Leiden manuscript of Theodoricus (Leiden, University, Library Voss. L.F.3, folio 48); also the extraction of thorns (folio 27). It is noteworthy that Celsus (*De medicina*, VII, 5) centuries earlier described in detail the method of extracting missiles. The extraction of an arrow from Aeneas' leg, as described by Vergil, was pictured in a Pompeian fresco contemporary with Celsus. This has been photo-reproduced in Frederick G. Kilgour's magnificent series of colour reproductions ('Medicine in Art,' *What's New*, 1960, 3, 104).

76. EXTRACTION OF MISSILE WEAPONS FROM THE BODY

(In a manuscript from the thirteenth century: London, BM, MS
Sloane 1977, folio 4. Rogerius Salernitanus, *Chirurgia*, II, 3, in French.)

In a somewhat exaggerated wound-illustration, the patient is shown with two
weapons, a javelin and an arrow, plunged through his torso. The actual process of
extraction is not pictured, but it is described in the accompanying text of Rogerius,
Chirurgia, in French translation, beautifully illustrated in colour. Portions of the
text read as follows:

If a missile is fixed in the neck so that it perforates a vein or artery, and excess of blood
flows, remove the missile immediately, suture the wound as indicated above,[1] and dust with
red powder or dry asses' dung.

In our illustration the surgeon seems to be reassuring the troubled patient, whose
breast (not neck, as in the text caption) has been pierced by a javelin and an arrow.

77. OPERATING ON THE UPPER ARM

(In a manuscript of about the year 1375: Leiden, University Library, MS
Voss. L.F.3, folio 43. Theodoricus de Cervia, *Chirurgia*, II, 11.)

Apparently this miniature was intended to illustrate an operation in which a 'surgeon
of the long robe' probed or cleansed a gaping wound in the upper arm, using a
slender 'sound,' while his associate held the patient. The text below the picture
mentions 'wounds in whatever part of the body a cut may have occurred' and gives
general instructions concerning treatment. For example, 'above all else a wound
must be kept clean,' 'bring the lips of the wound together,' suture if necessary,
bandage, 'do not undo the dressing until the third, fourth or fifth day unless there is
pain,' and 'thereafter change dressings every third day.' A somewhat earlier manuscript (*c.* 1300) of Rolandus, *Chirurgia*, in Rome (Casanatense Library, MS 1382,
folio 20) has a similar illustration and text, concerning treatment of a severed
tendon. Illustrations of surgeons examining wounded arms are found in several
manuscripts; e.g., the Provençal version of Guy de Chauliac's *Chirurgia* (above, fig.

[1] In book I, 20–21, Rogerius deals with missile wounds in the face; and in book II, 1–4, with
those in the neck (and elsewhere). Often Rogerius refers to treatments 'as indicated above.' Only
in I, 19, is there definite mention of sutures, in a chapter on 'Wounds in the face': viz., 'leave the
extremities of all sutures open so as to insert a medicated pad' (for drainage).

61), and the often-cited manuscript of Rogerius, *Chirurgia* (above, figs. 72 ff.; see folio 19).

78. SETTING A FRACTURED ARM

(In a manuscript from Northern Italy of about the year 1300: Rome, Casanatense Library, MS 1382, folio 22. Rolandus Parmensis, *Chirurgia*, III, 17. Rogerius Salernitanus, *Chirurgia*, III, 19, has a similar description.)

This is an unusually clear representation of the procedure in setting a fracture of the lower arm. While two assistants (*discipuli*) apply traction at the patient's hand and shoulder, the surgeon (designated as *magister* in the caption and as *medicus* in the accompanying text[1]), carefully works the broken ends of the bones into place. The accompanying text reads as follows:

Concerning fractures of the arm and shoulder. If the bone of the arm or shoulder is broken to the marrow, and especially if the marrow is injured, the expectation is that the victim will die. But if it is not injured to the marrow, it can well be healed. First restore the bones to their proper places. If the flesh is not broken, one ought to take each part of the bone and lightly and easily pull them, pressing with the hands. If the fracture is in the [lower] arm, the physician has his assistant hold the patient by the hand so as to pull the fingers and the entire arm. Another [assistant] on the other side holds the patient firmly by the shoulder while the physician joins the bones and reduces them to their proper alignment. Then taking a piece of gauze four digits long, infused with egg white, he binds the arm . . . [additional medication for nine days].

79. OPERATING ON AN ABDOMINAL FISTULA

(In a manuscript from the fourteenth century: Montpellier, MS 89 bis, folio 21v. Rogerius Salernitanus, *Chirurgia*, III, 28.)

Here, a 'surgeon of the long robe' is excising a fistula in the patient's abdomen, after which he will apply a powder or ointment. As is indicated in the accompanying text, sometimes the fistula was cauterized after the operation.

[1] In many surgical treatises, *medicus* is used for surgeon. This is especially noticeable in the works of Rogerius and Rolandus. In the Casanatense manuscript of Rolandus, the term *medicus* (in the descriptive text) alternates with the term *magister* (in the captions of the miniatures). This looseness of terminology (especially in Italy) reflects the absence of that rigid segregation of surgeons from physicians which prevailed in the later Middle Ages.

Concerning fistulas, cancers and abscesses arising from them, we have spoken above[1]. . . . But when they are in fleshy places [e.g., the abdomen] and in parts of the arm, apply *ruptorium* ointment; also cut and burn.

80. PRELIMINARY TREATMENT OF INTESTINES PROTRUDING FROM A WOUNDED ABDOMEN

(In a manuscript from Northern Italy of about the year 1300: Rome, Casanatense Library, MS 1382, folio 23v. Rolandus Parmensis, *Chirurgia*, III, 26.)

This operation was more serious than some miniatures suggest by merely portraying the surgeon applying a slit fowl to the patient's abdomen.[2] As is indicated in the accompanying text, the patient's intestines have been torn as they pushed through a wound in the abdominal wall. Apparently the illustrator simplified the illustration because of the complications of the operation or lack of details in the accompanying description. The most complete description, from Rogerius, *Chirurgia*, III, 27, reads as follows:

If the intestine comes out through any sort of wound, emerging either lengthwise or slantwise but for the major part remaining sound, we treat it as follows. First, if the intestine is cold, a living animal is slit through the middle and applied to it through the break [in the abdomen]. It is left thus until the intestine is warmed, restored to its natural temperature, and softened. Meanwhile, a tube is fashioned from elderwood in the shape of the intestinal wound so that it is an inch longer than the wound on each end. The tube is very carefully inserted through the wounded intestine which is neatly sutured with a needle and silk thread. The tube is placed so that the superfluous matter from the intestine passes through without impeding healing. After this, with a sponge well soaked in warm water, the filth is gently removed. Thus cleansed, the intestine is introduced through the wound into the belly whence it came. Now the patient is placed on a [slanting] board and shaken so that the intestines are relocated in their proper position. . . . Let the wound remain open until you see that the intestine is brought together. Then sprinkle the suture daily with *rubeus* powder. . . .

---

[1] II, 14; III, 20; if the lesions are near nerves or in the neck, only medication is recommended.

[2] E.g., fourteenth-century Montpellier, MS 89 bis, folio 22. Theodoricus (*Chirurgia* II, 18), in a detailed description of the operation, recommended the application of 'a little pig or some other animal' (e.g., the cat in our example), for the preliminary warming and softening process. Incidentally, a ninth-century description of a Caesarean operation mentions the use of a pig: the newly born infant was 'wrapped in the fat of a freshly killed pig' (Loren MacKinney, *Early Medieval Medicine*, p. 41).

The illustration shows the surgeon applying a slit *catule* while his assistant holds a bowl of medicine. Eventually, the board-table will be lowered at the patient's head (the 'Trendelenberg' position). No extant manuscript has a satisfactory illustration of the actual operation. Some scholars doubt that it was ever performed.

81. A–B–C. TREATMENT OF SCROTAL HERNIA

A. *By Medication and a Truss*

(In a manuscript from the fourteenth century: Montpellier, MS 89 bis, folio 23. Rogerius Salernitanus, *Chirurgia*, III, 31.)

An experienced modern surgeon remarked that 'if one knows hernia he knows surgery.' Scrotal hernia, widely prevalent today along with hydrocele and varicocele, appears often in miniatures, usually in much enlarged form (see above, figs. 44–45). However, then and now, it does not always demand the use of the surgical knife. If the patient is a boy or if the rupture is small, medication and a bandage or truss suffice not only according to modern practice but also according to medieval authorities such as Rogerius, Rolandus and Theodoricus. Our quotations are from the works of Rogerius and Rolandus, who gave similar, if not quite identical, instructions concerning hernia, as well as other surgical problems.

Concerning rupture of the peritoneum (*siphac*). The peritoneum is the membrane that prevents the intestines from falling into the scrotum; and often it is loose or only partly ruptured. If the aperture is small, only wind will escape, inflating [the scrotum] like a nut, or if large like an egg. The intestines may descend through the inguinal canal and press the peritoneum into the testicles, thus creating a hernia. If the aperture is small and of brief duration, and if the patient is a boy, press a ligature over it and apply a poultice made of *anagallis* and yolks of 11 eggs.

The illustration, though crude in artistry, gives a clearer picture than many more beautiful and colourful miniatures of the preliminaries of bandaging a scrotal hernia.

B–C. *By Surgical Operation*

Scrotal hernia operations in medieval times were complicated and serious. We quote from the similarly detailed accounts of Rogerius (*Chirurgia*, III, 33) and Rolandus (*Chirurgia*, III, 32):

If the intestines descend into the scrotum first restore them to their proper place. If this cannot be done easily, clyster or purge, then apply mollifacients and replace the intestines as we have said.[1]

Have an assistant place a finger on the rupture while the physician (*medicus*) cuts into the thin skin above the testicle (*pelliculam supra testiculum*) at this point. Having extracted the testicle [from the peritoneum], scrape the inguinal canal even to the top with an instrument (*giova*). If there is wind in the canal decompress it internally (*remittatur interius*). Suture [the top of the inguinal canal] well with thread, and bind with thread leaving it detached at each end so that it hangs an inch outside the suture. Placing the patient on a plank, burn the inguinal canal with cauteries thrice, up to the thread. Then apply tow and egg and put the patient to bed for nine days, applying egg and oil as we have said. When the heat and the thread are gone from the wound, after nine days, foment with water in which bears' paws [*branca ursina*, a herb], vitriola, absinth, etc., has been cooked. Then treat as directed above . . . [instructions continued concerning medication, diet and general regimen for three months].

Although our two illustrations do not picture the details of the above description, they give a dramatic portrayal of the seriousness of the operation.

B

(In a manuscript from Northern Italy of about the year 1300: Rome, Casanatense Library, MS 1382, folio 24v. Rolandus Parmensis, *Chirurgia*, III, 32.)

In this, the earlier of the two manuscripts under consideration, the slant of the board is accentuated and the patient is tied hand and foot. The attendant, with towel and medicine, seems unmoved by the operation.

C

(In a manuscript from the fourteenth century: Montpellier, MS 89 bis, folio 23. Rogerius Salernitanus, *Chirurgia*, III, 33.)

This, the later of our two illustrations, also the less colourful and less artistic, is noteworthy in that it reflects the seriousness of the proceedings: the surgeon's con-

[1] Both Rogerius and Rolandus, without specific reference to the timing, recommend placing the patient 'on a board with head and shoulders depressed so that the intestines descend toward the chest,' and with 'the legs and hips elevated.' Often, miniatures show a board, slanted in the so-called 'Trendelenberg' position, named after the nineteenth-century German who popularized it.

centration, the assistant ready with instruments (either scissors, or two cutting instruments) and the worried (unanaesthetized) patient, not only tied down, but held firmly by an assistant. The board, un-slanted, in contrast to the earlier illustration (fig. 81B), suggests that there were variations in operational techniques.

82. A–B. OPERATIONS FOR BLADDER STONES
A. *The Celsan Operation*

(In a manuscript from Northern Italy of about the year 1300: Rome, Casanatense Library, MS 1382, folio 25. Rolandus Parmensis, *Chirurgia*, III, 34.)

Throughout ancient and medieval times bladder stones were removed by a method called 'Celsan' because of Celsus' detailed description in his *De medicina* (VII, 26). According to him, and also Rogerius (*Chirurgia*, III, 41–43), after the patient dieted for several days the stone was worked down into the urinary tract. Manuscripts of John Arderne's fourteenth-century *Chirurgia* contain marginal sketches showing the stone worked out into the penis whence it was excised. In the traditional procedure, however, the physician inserted a finger in the anus to work the stone downward to the outlet of the bladder while he pressed externally to assist in controlling the movement. This is described in the text which follows the miniature. Once the stone was worked to the outlet of the bladder it was removed by surgery. The operation (as today) was performed from the rear. This is shown in the miniature, with the patient in the traditional position, legs jack-knifed, held firmly by assistants while the surgeon (*magister*, i.e., a professional surgeon[1]) extracts the stone through a bloody incision. The text below the picture, along with a preceding section of text, describes the operation and also the pre- and post-operational treatment, as follows:

If there is a stone in the bladder make sure of it as follows: have a strong person sit on a bench, his feet on a stool; the patient sits on his lap, legs bound to his neck with a bandage, or steadied on the shoulders of the assistants. The physician (*medicus*) stands before the patient and inserts two fingers of his right hand into the anus, pressing with his left fist above the patient's pubes. With his fingers engaging the bladder from above, let him work over all of it. If he finds a hard, firm pellet it is a stone in the bladder, which is soft

---

[1] See above, fig. 78, for the use of *magister*, and *medicus*, to designate surgeons.

and fleshy; thus you find what impedes urination. . . . If you want to extract the stone, precede it with light diet and fasting for two days beforehand. On the third day, having done everything beforehand, as we have said, to find whether there is a stone in the bladder, locate the stone, bring it to the neck of the bladder; there, at the entrance, with two fingers above the anus incise lengthwise with an instrument and extract the stone . . . [medication, morning and night for nine days (Rogerius, *Chirurgia*, III, 36, 38, has the same text.)].

B. *An Improved Early-Modern Operation*

> (In a manuscript of about the year 1510: London, BM, Prints and Engravings MS 197.d.2, folio 18. *La via de cavar la pietra*, from Kull-maurer and Meher's medical picture-book, with Italian captions.)

Early in the sixteenth century an Italian surgeon revolutionized this operation by using a grooved catheter to locate the stone, then introducing through the groove a dilator and knife, after which the stone was removed with forceps.[1] The miniature, from the Italian picture-book already cited, shows a transitional method of operating. It improved on the Celsan procedure by using a catheter, probably to locate and fix the stone while the surgeon extracted it as in earlier times by excising from outside. In the miniature, which is captioned 'The way to cut for stone,' the patient is shown tied and held in the traditional position. A short-robed surgeon directs the operation with what may be a consulting physician in the background. The operating surgeon, having located the stone with the catheter, uses it to hold the penis and testicles out of the way while he makes the incision. A pan for blood rests on the table, with additional instruments on the bench.

83. EARLY-MODERN CATHETERIZATION FOR URINARY OBSTRUCTION

> (In a manuscript from about the year 1510: London, BM, Prints and Engravings MS 197.d.2, folio 19v. *El modo de serengar*, from Kullmaurer and Meher's medical picture-book, with Italian captions.)

In addition to catheters for locating a bladder stone (as seen in the preceding illustration) there were, according to Rogerius (*Chirurgia*, III, 37), catheters of simpler type used to introduce oil into the mouth of the bladder in which a stone was lodged,

[1] See Harry Shelley, 'Cutting for the Stone,' *Journal of the History of Medicine and Allied Sciences*, 1958, *13*, 50–67.

and to push the stone back into the bladder. Then, if necessary, it was excised (in some cases crushed). Obviously this type of catheter could also provide temporary relief for an obstructed urethra, as in cases of prostatic enlargement or post-gonorrhoeal stricture. In the miniature, which illustrates this procedure as practised centuries after Rogerius, it is impossible to determine the exact nature of the operation, whether pre-lithotomy or merely temporary catheterization. It is captioned 'The method of catheterizing,' and obviously the kneeling surgeon has catheterized the patient from whose penis urine flows freely into a receptacle. Two other patients seem to be awaiting similar treatment, which suggests that the picture was intended to illustrate non-surgical catheterization.

84. EXCISING CANCER OF THE PENIS

(In a manuscript from the fourteenth century: Montpellier, MS 89 bis, folio 22v. Rogerius Salernitanus, *Chirurgia*, III, 30.)

The surgeon (at left) bends over the patient (naked from the waist down), whose legs are spread so that the cancerous portion of 'the virile member' can be excised. Behind the patient, the surgeon's assistant holds the 'hot iron' and the medicines for application after the operation. One might consider this a case of phemosis necessitating circumcision on reading the description in the accompanying text:

If there is a cancer completely enveloping the viril member, the entire cancerous infection is excised so as to eliminate it from the living portion, and it is cauterized with a hot iron, or a gold one; then it is healed as noted above [i.e., by medication].

85. A–B. CIRCUMCISION OF CHRIST

Circumcision is an ancient surgical ritual; it was depicted in a famous Egyptian bas relief as early as the third millennium B.C. In Western Europe it was portrayed almost exclusively in non-medical treatises concerned with the life of Christ.

A. *In a Miniature*

(In a manuscript of about the year 1440: London, BM, Add. Mss. 17987, folio 114v. Anonymous treatise on bathing, bloodletting, etc., in German.)

An exception to this rule is a miniature at the end of a late-medieval manuscript (in German), which contains calendars and treatises on astrology and general health

82

regimen, such as bloodletting, exercise and bathing. Our miniature illustrates a passage (on the previous page of the manuscript) explaining that 'the eight-day old Christ child . . . was circumcised.' The scene is more pious than surgical in spirit. The Christ child stands on an altar-like table between two candles, while the operator and his assistant kneel before him. Both are in long, girdled robes, more like monastic than medical garb. The chief operator, in a tight-fitting surgical cap, holds a scalpel as if to begin the operation, and his assistant holds a napkin as if to receive the foreskin. But the entire section of the body to be operated on is a blank and apparently not erased. The text below the illustration has no bearing on circumcision.

B. *In an Altar Painting*

(An altar painting of the year 1481, in St. Wolfgang's parish church at Salzkammergut, Austria; one of a series of altar pieces on the life of Christ, by Michael Pacher.)

In marked contrast to the preceding illustration is a German altar painting about a quarter-century later in date. It pictures with surgical realism an elaborate circumcision ritual as if performed in a Gothic church. At right and left are parents and attendants. At centre, a richly robed, heavily bearded priest in jeweled mitre daintily holds between his thumb and forefinger the Christ child's foreskin, which the priest is about to cut with a long, slender knife. Two robed assistants hold the ends of a large napkin on which the child rests.[1]

86. REMOVAL OF HAEMORRHOIDS

(In a manuscript from the fourteenth century: Montpellier, MS 89 bis, folio 25. Rogerius Salernitanus, *Chirurgia*, III, 43.)

The miniature pictures the removal of external haemorrhoids by surgery. This was only one of the treatments of several types of haemorrhoids. The accompanying text (below the picture) describes not only the treatment of *external* haemorrhoids (by medication, cutting and cauterizing) but also of *internal* haemorrhoids (by fomentations, fumigation, leeching and medicines). The text reads as follows:

[1] This altar painting was brought to my attention by a friend, Mrs. Robert Wettach, who saw it in Europe and, aware of my interest in medieval surgery, obtained a colour print.

There are three kinds of haemorrhoids; internal ones that emit blood and are painful, external ones that emit pus, and external ones that do not. . . . For internal haemorrhoids that emit blood, first, to reduce the pain, foment them with root of *tassus barbassus* (black horehound and calamint); afterwards take bark of chestnut and of melon, and old sandals and put them over burning coals; have the patient stand on a stool so as to get the fumes [in his anus]. Do this two or three times a day until the bloodflow and pain are reduced, then after fomentation apply a leech . . . [clyster and more medication follow]. For external haemorrhoids not emitting pus, medicate with leaves of wormwood and abrotanum beaten with flax oil . . . [followed by detailed medication until the haemorrhoids are reduced]. Then each shrivelled haemorrhoid is tied tightly with a silk thread, and if the patient can endure it, cut; if not, loosen the thread until it falls away. Then, on one or more of the shrivelled haemorrhoids, put a small amount of *ruptorium* ointment made in a wax capsule,[1] or apply a hot iron. If pus instead of blood oozes, try a cloth plug. See whether the haemorrhoid extends toward the rump bone or buttocks-bone, or toward the colon. If toward the colon, retract it; if toward the rump bone, apply through the same opening a hot iron or *ruptorium* ointment; then heal it with egg as indicated elsewhere.

The miniature seems to represent the cutting of external haemorrhoids. See also above fig. 50.

87. A–B. JOHN ARDERNE'S OPERATION FOR ANAL FISTULA

The operation for anal fistula (*fistula in ano*) was one of the deadliest in medieval surgery. The Moslem surgeon Albucasis (d. 1013) described the operation but held that such fistulas were incurable. Similar opinions were expressed by most physicians and surgeons of the late Middle Ages. John Arderne in fifteenth-century England is thought to have lost about half of his fistula patients, but this was considered a remarkably successful record in that day. At any rate he won fame and fortune thereby. He wrote that he never charged less than 100 shillings for the operation and, if the patients were rich, forty pounds or more. Arderne was a royal and army surgeon of the English kings and may have developed his skills during service with their armies in the Hundred Years War, somewhat as the French army surgeon Paré, about a century later, learned new methods by war surgery. Incidentally, both substituted soothing oils and egg ointments for the traditionally harsh, corrosive-cautery, post-operational treatment of wounds. Inasmuch as Arderne's

---

[1] '*Ruptorium* oint ment,' mentioned often in our surgical quotations, comprised the following substances: oil of roses, iris root, beanstalks, oil of spikenard, 'saracen soap,' arsenic, lye and various kinds of lime. See Rogerius, *Chirurgia*, I, 36.

description of the fistula operation was complicated, we present it in condensed paraphrase, with references to the miniatures.

A. *Preliminary Probing*

(In a manuscript from the fourteenth century: London, BM, MS Sloane 2002, folio 24v. John Arderne, *Fistula in ano*.)

Our miniature shows the surgeon, presumably Arderne himself, about to introduce a finger into the patient's rectum to probe for the fistula.

B. *Operational Procedure*

(In a manuscript from the fourteenth century: London, BM, MS Sloane 56, folio 44. John Arderne, *Liber medicinarum*.)

Our second miniature shows four principal stages of the operation. First, the patient was placed in a leg-spread position exposing the fistulas (upper right in the miniature). This illustration shows, in addition to the rectum, six fistulas; Arderne mentioned cases involving fifteen. After the surgeon explored the rectum with his finger (upper left), a flexible probe called 'follow me' (*sequere me*) was pushed up the fistula until its end was felt by the surgeon's finger already inserted in the rectum. After the probe a four-stranded ligature called 'Caesar's bridle' (*frenum Caesaris*) was drawn through the fistula and rectum by means of a loop (lower left), so that the two ends, hanging from the openings of the fistula and rectum, could be tied together and fastened to a tightening peg on a dilator (*tendiculum*). This instrument (lower right) was pushed up the fistula to the rectum, then the peg was turned so as to tighten the ligature, as a violin string is tightened (lower right). Sometimes gradual tightening would cut the tissue between fistula wall and rectum, thus completing the operation. If not, a lance-headed director (*acus rostrata*, lower left) was pushed along the dilator, up the fistula to the rectum. There a spoon-like shield, pushed up the rectum, served to protect the rectal wall from puncture by the director and the scalpel that followed it (bottom of illustrations). Finally, scalpel and director were pulled back along the fistula wall, cutting through to the rectum, thus uniting fistula and rectum. Blood flow was staunched with sponges and styptic powder and the wound dressed with soothing oil and egg ointment.[1]

[1] For an intelligible explanation of the entire procedure see D'Arcy Power's preface (p. xvii) to *Treatises of Fistula in Ano, Haemorrhoids and Clysters by John Arderne* (Oxford, 1910). The text, in Old English, appears on pp. 8–16.

88. INCISING A THIGH: PREPARATION OF HERBAL MEDICINES

(In a manuscript from the fourteenth century: London, BM, MS Add.
15692, folio 39v. Anonymous, *Questio de septem artes mechanicis*.)

This curious double miniature illustrates the close relationship between surgery and
pharmacy. In the upper illustration a 'surgeon of the short robe' is removing a
foreign body from the patient's thigh with forceps. In the surgeon's left hand is a
box of medicines or instruments. Hanging from his belt is a purse. Behind him an
assistant holds a jar of medicines for dressing the wound.

The lower illustration depicts a woman seated at a table, selecting herbs possibly
for the preparation of medicines but perhaps for the preparation of food (the text
below the illustration refers to diet). The caption above the miniature, *Medicina*, is
amplified by the lines below which read as follows:

Medicine is the experimental operation shown here in surgery, and it is the dexterous
profession of dieting.

On the opposite page and on those following there is further explanation of the
interrelationship of medical specialists with other professions; it reads, in part, as
follows:

Medicine also includes the apothecary's profession of preparing herbs. . . . and note that
medicine is two fold; experimental and professional. . . . Professional medicine is two
fold, theoretical and practical. . . .

All of this is a part of a discussion of the Seven Mechanical Arts, which included
spinning, hunting, warfare, navigation, agriculture, medicine and weaving.

89. A–B. SURGICAL EXAMINATION OF LEGS

A. *For Cancer*

(In a manuscript from the fourteenth century: Montpellier, MS 89 bis,
folio 13v. Rogerius Salernitanus, *Chirurgia*, II, 12.)

The miniature, from a manuscript of Rogerius, *Chirurgia*, shows the surgeon (at
left) examining an apparently painful, open wound of the sort that in time might

become fistulous or cancerous. The distinction between these two, the importance of accurate diagnosis and the varying kinds of treatment are described in the accompanying text which reads, in part, as follows:

Sometimes cancer spreads in the body infecting it sometimes internally, sometimes externally. . . . All wounds of four or five months standing are called *fistulae*. Such is cancer; sometimes it is of long standing, sometimes short. . . . When it is in the throat, neck or where nerves, arteries and veins abound, it cannot be cut or burned. If of short standing we make an ointment . . . [medication with several prescriptions follows].

B. *For Ulcers*

(In a manuscript from the late fourteenth century: Vatican, MS Vat. Lat. 4804, folio 115. Guy de Chauliac, *Chirurgia*, IV, 1.1, in Provençal.)

This unusually colourful miniature is from the beginning of book IV of a Provençal version of Guy de Chauliac's *Chirurgia*, a section dealing with ulcers and ulcer operations. The miniature dramatically portrays a 'surgeon of the long robe' explaining to a worried patient the condition of his badly ulcerated legs. The heading for book IV reads as follows:

On ulcers, in two sections, the first concerning ulcers on simple members, the second on composite members especially. Section I, in 6 chapters. Chapter 1, on ulcers in general. [The miniature is in a capital letter U, beginning the chapter, as follows:] Ulcers, according to Galen's *Therapeutics* . . . [followed by descriptions of various types of ulcers, their cures, etc.; chapter 8 of section 2 deals with leg ulcers, recommending medication, caustic applications, and cautery if the bone is infected; there is no mention of an operation].

90. GRAFTING A NEW LEG IN PLACE OF AN AMPUTATED ONE

(In a manuscript from fifteenth-century Italy: London, Society of Antiquaries, The Brooke Antiphonal, folio 1.)

In this remarkably colourful miniature, by Andrea and Francesco Mantegna, in a liturgical manuscript, we have an unusual surgical scene. It depicts the surgical miracle attributed to the famous martyr-saints, Cosmas and Damian. Among the innumerable medieval and renaissance representations of the pair, this is one of the finest. In brilliance and clarity of execution, it matches any renaissance or modern portrayals of the healing saints. Furthermore, unlike most portrayals showing them merely holding pharmaceutical or medical implements, it pictures in detail a surgical scene: a negro's leg grafted on a white man whose leg (shown in the foreground) had been amputated.

According to the legend, while the patient was asleep in the Church of SS. Cosmas and Damian, they amputated his cancerous (according to some medical men) leg. From a negro, in his coffin in a nearby cemetery, a leg was taken to replace that of the patient. The bedroom scene shows Cosmas and Damian wiping the blood from their instruments. At left, a servant boy holds a towel and pitcher. On the low bench next to the bed are a bloody towel and two cases with instruments alongside. Elsewhere in the room are towels, jars and receptacles of various kinds.

At the bedside, wondering neighbours view the grafted black leg. The amputated white leg is shown twice, in the foreground near the dog, and at far right outside the negro's coffin (the extra leg troubles some modern commentators who forget that medieval miniatures often comprise a series of scenes). Others have surmised, from the patient's peaceful sleep, that he has been anaesthetized (a gratuitous assumption if one knows the conspicuous absence of anaesthesia in medical miniatures). More important is the fact that probably this is the earliest representation of an actual surgical operation by Cosmas and Damian.

IX. ORTHOPAEDICS

ORTHOPAEDICS originally was the branch of ancient Greek surgery that concerned itself with reducing or realigning bodily distortions. It is thought that it was strongly influenced by the techniques of treating athletes in the gymnasia. So far as written sources are concerned, the basic information comes indirectly from three Hippocratic works: *Joints*, *Fractures* and *Surgery*. These works are not extant but their contents were transmitted to the Western world by way of Greek manuscripts of (1) an illustrated paraphrase and commentary, entitled *Dislocations*, compiled by Apollonius in the first century B.C., and (2) a similar compilation (of about 100 A.D.), entitled *Bandages*, by Soranus. These treatises are contained in two well-illustrated Greek manuscripts. One of them, a tenth-century manuscript now at Florence in the Laurentian Library (MS 74.7) has forty unusual miniatures that probably were copied from early illustrated scrolls. These provide a comprehensive picture of the orthopaedic heritage from ancient Greece, as it was practised in the Eastern Mediterranean during the early Middle Ages. The other Greek manuscript (Bologna, University, MS 3632) is thought to have been copied, either from the Florence-Laurentian manuscript or an archetype thereof, in some late fifteenth-century Western centre.

Many of the classical orthopaedic techniques, in more or less modified form, were incorporated in the orthopaedic sections of Moslem and Western Latin manuscripts of surgical treatises by Albucasis, Rogerius, Rolandus, Theodoricus and other medical authorities of the eleventh, twelfth and thirteenth centuries. Thus, the fundamentals of orthopaedics can be traced from Hippocrates in the fifth century B.C., directly to Apollonius in the first century B.C., and Soranus in the second century A.D., and thence, less directly, to early-medieval Moslems and later to Westerners such as Rogerius and his contemporaries. Both the textual data and the illustrations in the Greek manuscripts were copied, in modified form, by Western manuscript-makers, to be reproduced in turn (the miniatures in colourless block prints) in early-modern printed editions of treatises on dislocations and bandaging.

This relatively unbroken evolution from classical Greece to the modern West is

evidenced by the unusually large number of illustrations of orthopaedics in manuscripts. These provide a unique opportunity for comparison and contrast of the
practices of the Greek East and the Latin West. On the one hand, there are the two
generously illustrated Greek manuscripts with their miniatures depicting orthopaedic operations on all parts of the body. On the other hand, there are a number of
Western manuscripts which present evidences of the blending of Greek with Moslem
and Western-Christian techniques. Although both of these post-classical civilizations took over the basic ancient science, they also contributed much from their own
pragmatic experience.

Inasmuch as exigencies of space prevent our presenting orthopaedics as completely
as we have surgery and other aspects of medicine, we limit our examples of miniatures to four examples of one operation, the reduction of spinal dislocation. The
first example is from the earliest extant Greek manuscript (tenth-century Florence,
Laurentian MS 74.7)[1]; the second is from the late-medieval copy of this Florentine
manuscript (Bologna, University, MS 3632); the third is from a Latin translation of
the late tenth-century Moslem surgery of Albucasis (fourteenth-century Vienna,
NB, MS 2641); the fourth is from the most impressive Western miniatures of orthopaedics, in Theodoricus' thirteenth-century *Chirurgia* (fourteenth-century Leiden,
University, MS Voss. L.F.3).

91. A–B–C–D. REDUCING DISLOCATED VERTEBRAE

From the age of Hippocrates to the present, the human back has given mankind
unusual trouble. Whether vertebral dislocation, slipped disk or some other displacement, the joints of the spinal column between the atlas (at the top) and the
sacro-iliac (at the bottom) tend to get out of alignment, causing pain, permanent
crippling, even death.

A fundamental factor in reducing vertebral dislocation was traction: sometimes
manually by hand-pull with foot-pressure for counter traction; sometimes mechani-
cally by ropes or straps attached to the upper and lower extremities, then tightened
by twisting or windlassing so as to stretch the spinal column. While the spine was
stretched, pressure was applied at the point of dislocation so as to realign the vertebrae. The traction mechanisms (illustrated in many miniatures) ranged from mere
twisted ropes to complicated machines.

[1] All the miniatures from this manuscript can be found photoreproduced in Herman Schöne,
Illustrierter Kommentar zu der hippokratischen Schrift Περὶ ἄρθρων (Leipzig, 1890).

ORTHOPAEDICS

A. REDUCTION BY JOLTING ON A LADDER (WITH HEAD DOWN)

(In a manuscript from tenth-century Byzantium: Florence, Laurentian
Library, MS 74.7, folio 200. Apollonius, *Dislocations*, 2, in Greek.)

In spinal reductions the merited reputation of the ancient Greeks for progressive
medical methods has an exception, the brutal method of reducing the spinal dislocation by tying the patient (or victim) to a ladder which was dropped to the ground
vertically so as to jolt the displaced vertebrae into proper alignment. This procedure was described in the fifth-century B.C. Hippocratic treatise on *Joints* (ch. 44),
copied and illustrated four centuries later by Apollonius in *Dislocations* (ch. 2), to be
copied and recopied in our two Greek manuscripts. According to the Hippocratic
tradition, 'a humped back,' considered almost incurable, might be treated by
jolting the patient while tied to a ladder. This procedure can be seen in our miniature and followed in detail in the accompanying text, of which we present a condensed translation (an almost identical illustration and description is found also in the
fifteenth-century Bologna manuscript).

Cases where the curvature is low on the spine are best treated with the head downward. . . .
Pad the ladder. . . . Lay the patient on it, on his back, using soft but strong bandages, tie
his ankles to the ladder; bind his legs together below and above the knees and bandage the
hips. Bandage him loosely at the flanks and chest; tie the arms and hands, extended along
his sides, to the body but not to the ladder. Then raise the ladder against a high tower or
house. The ground should be solid and the assistants well trained so that they will let the
ladder fall smoothly and in a vertical position. . . . It is best to drop it from a mast by a
pulley. . . . Jolting is best done with such apparatus, but it is disagreeable to discuss it in
detail. Cases where the curvature is high up on the spine . . . are better treated with the
feet downward. . . . Bind the patient firmly to the ladder at his chest, but
loosely at his neck, merely enough to keep it straight. Bind his head to the ladder
at the forehead. Bind the rest of the body loosely here and there, only to keep it
vertical. . . . Fasten the legs together, but not to the ladder, so that they hang in line with
the back.

Western manuscripts lack descriptions or illustrations of any such treatment, an
omission surely not due to any hesitancy at using rugged methods. In modern
times, until the nineteenth century, such procedures were used in medicine, and also
in corporal punishment under the name *strappado*.

B. REDUCTION BY TRACTION AND PRESSURE ON THE SPINE

(In a manuscript from the fifteenth century: Bologna, University, MS
3632, folio 428v. Apollonius, *Dislocations*, ch. 1, in Greek.)

Not all of Greek orthopaedics was as brutally primitive as the ladder treatment.
According to the illustrated descriptive text (in both Greek manuscripts) the simpler
types of spinal dislocation were treated as follows:

Give the patient a vapour bath . . . make him lie prone [on a padded plank] with extended
arms fastened to his body; wrap the middle of a long soft bandage around his chest,
passing it around twice close to the armpits, and attach the ends to a pole [at his head]; this
is used as a fulcrum for traction. Wrap a second bandage above the knees and again above
the heels, and . . . a third bandage around his loins near the hips; attach the ends to a pole
at his feet. Now make traction simultaneously toward both ends. . . . Meanwhile the
doctor (*iatros*) or a strong, trained assistant should press the palms of his hands on the curvature. . . . It will do no harm even if one sits on it . . . or *presses his feet* on it. . . . The
most powerful method is to have a thin plank inserted in an incision in the wall or in a
post, at a level below the patient's spine. . . . Putting a thickness of cloth or a pillow on the
curvature . . . have one or two assistants press down on the end of the board while traction
is applied. . . . This is done from a wheel or axle imbedded in the ground or fastened on
both ends of the plank [on which the patient lies]. . . .

Our miniature, from the fifteenth-century copy of the tenth-century Laurentian
manuscript, illustrates not only the relative crudeness of the copyist's work but also
the more intelligent methods of Greek orthopaedists: gradual traction and gentle
foot-pressure. Additional miniatures picture traction with pressure by sitting on the
patient's back or by pressing with a board (folios 427, 431). The Laurentian manuscript pictures the three methods on folios 203v, 202v, 204v.

C. REDUCTION, IN THE MOSLEM MIDDLE AGES, BY HAND-PRESSURE

(In a fourteenth-century Latin translation of Albucasis' surgery; Vienna,
NB, MS 2641, folio 76v. Albucasis, *Chirurgia*, III, 31.)

The simpler methods of reduction common in the post-classical world, both
Moslem and Christian, are illustrated in this unusually clear portrayal. Noteworthy is
the application of traction by a single windlass at the patient's head, and the gentle
hand-pressure along the spine applied by a turbaned, Semitic-featured physician

(*medicus*). The miniature is captioned in primitive style, with the explanation that 'This is the windlass, the foot-bandage and the patient.' Most of the traction machines pictured in Latin manuscripts of Albucasis are heavily roped contrivances such as that in our miniature. In many of them the patient seems to be stretched in several directions. The text below the illustration merely describes the post-operative application of a plaster. The operation itself is described in the preceding chapter of the treatise (III, 29).

D. REDUCTION BY CLASSICAL-MEDIEVAL METHODS

(In a manuscript from the fourteenth century: Leiden, University, MS L.F.3, folio 71v (left). Theodoricus de Cervia, *Chirurgia*, II, 45. Folio 64v describes and illustrates a similar operation on a standing patient.)

This final orthopaedic miniature illustrates not only post-operational bandaging of a vertebral dislocation, but also the intelligent procedures of Western surgeons. It comes from a Latin manuscript of a surgical treatise by Theodoricus de Cervia, a famous thirteenth-century Italian medical expert. As described in the accompanying text, Theodoricus, like other Westerners, followed the traditional Greek recommendations for reducing dislocated vertebrae. We present an abbreviated paraphrase of his description.

Complete dislocation is fatal [symptoms described]. Partial dislocation, if it 'tilts inward' or 'laterally,' is incurable. 'Posterior displacement' if acquired in childhood, is incurable; if recent, may be treated as follows: apply poultice of 'cow dung, good wine, salt, and sifted bran,' apply two long splints (four fingers wide) on each side of the spine, from shoulders to buttocks. Tie the patient, face downward, to a flat table top, with bands over the armpits and shoulders, and over the hips and thighs. Have all bands meet at one point on the upper and lower side. Tighten these bands, using sticks inserted where they meet. Continue tightening. Apply pressure to the displaced hump, with hands, or if necessary by sitting on it, or with a plank, one end of which is anchored to the wall. [Additional medication, bandaging, etc., follows.]

The miniature shows an interested patient, flat on his stomach, watching an assistant, directed by the head physician, pull tightly on the ends of a wide bandage around the middle of his back.

X. OBSTETRICS

MEDIEVAL manuscripts picture the process of human reproduction in broad perspective, from the begetting of the child to postnatal care of the infant.[1]

92. MIDWIVES HASTENING A SLOW DELIVERY

(In a manuscript from the thirteenth century: Vienna, NB, MS 93, folio 102. Pseudo-Apuleius, *Herbarium*, CIII, 2.)

The midwife at lower right holds a coriander seed close to the mother's vagina to help 'bring forth quickly'; the accompanying text cautions that the seed should be removed immediately lest 'the intestines follow' the foetus. Other midwives seem to be illustrating other instructions in the text: encouraging the prospective mother, perhaps jolting her up and down. Noteworthy is the absence of any physician.

[1] Once more exigencies of space limit us in this case to a single photoreproduction. Many scenes of childbirth have been reproduced in Fritz Weindler, *Geschichte der gynäkologisch-anatomischen Abbildung* (Dresden, 1908), and a few can be found also in *Sudhoff's Studien*, I. Loren MacKinney's 'Childbirth in the Middle Ages, as seen in Manuscript Illustrations' (*Ciba Symposium*, December, 1960, *8*, nos. 5–6), has fourteen photoreproductions in colour from manuscripts picturing the birth process from *coitus* through pregnancy, the foetus in the womb, normal deliveries, 'Caesarian' sections, post-parturient treatment of the mother and infant, and a final picture of a mother testing the mammary equipment of a wet-nurse.

XI. DENTISTRY

Treatment of ailing teeth in miniatures usually appears to be performed by physicians or surgeons rather than by dental specialists or charlatan 'medicine.'[1] This is exemplified in many miniatures depicting the examination of teeth by physicians, various kinds of treatment (including inhalation as well as direct medication), extractions, wiring and dentures.

93. INHALING TRANQUILLIZING FUMES FOR TOOTHACHE

(In a manuscript from the fourteenth century: Montpellier, MS 89 bis, folio 10. Rogerius Salernitanus, *Chirurgia*, I, 39.)

The accompanying text explains clearly the treatment illustrated in this unusual miniature. Translated from Rogerius' surgical treatise, it reads as follows:

Take seed of henbane and leek in equal parts; put them over burning coals and over the coals put a cover so that the patient can inhale the fumes that rise through the pipe and let them envelope his teeth. This will miraculously ease the pain.

The miniature shows the patient bending over the inhalant tube while a physician sprinkles the medicaments on the fire. Centuries earlier the Roman medical writer Celsus (*De medicina*, VI, 8), had recommended that sufferers from toothache, 'that greatest of torments,' should hold in the mouth solutions of anodynes such as henbane root, poppy seed and mandrake root.

[1] The charlatan type is more prevalent in printed works of the early-modern centuries, as seen in Curt Proskauer, *Iconographia Odontologica* (Berlin, 1926). This work is illustrated with many photoreproductions from manuscripts and printed books.

XII. BATHING FOR HEALTH AND DIVERSION

T HROUGH the ages, whether in tubs or at public 'watering places,' bathing has been resorted to for cleanliness, health and social diversion. The most elusive of the three categories so far as manuscript illustration is concerned is that of health involving specific medical treatment.

94. A. A MEDICAL BATH

(In a thirteenth-century manuscript: London, BM, MS Sloane 1977, folio 7. Rogerius Salernitanus, *Chirurgia*, III, 25, in French.)

This is one of the extremely rare examples of a bath for strictly medical purposes. The patient, according to the accompanying text, is soaking in the tub in order to heal 'a rib bent inward'; the instructions for the physician (*medicus*) are that he '. . . anoints his hands with honey, turpentine or pitch, then presses and relaxes them at the hurt place, continuing until the rib is restored to its proper place.' A similar text and illustration are to be found in a fourteenth-century Latin manuscript of Rogerius (Montpellier, MS 89 bis, folio 21). Another illustration of bath-medication, an operator rubbing a patient in a bath house, occurs in a thirteenth-century manuscript (Vienna, NB, MS 93, folio 95, Pseudo-Apuleius, *Herbarium*, XCIII, 18). Occasionally, bathers in health resorts or bath houses are shown in the process of being bled or clystered.

Tub baths appear often in miniatures but seldom if ever for cleanliness or medication. In practically all cases the social aspect is prominent, usually with a man and woman enjoying food and drink from a narrow shelf that marks the division of the tub into their respective zones. In one miniature the man is pictured in the woman's zone intent on something more than the refreshments.[1] At 'watering places,' also,

---

[1] Loren MacKinney has an unpublished survey describing and depicting 'The Tale of the Tub in the Middle Ages.' Therein are miniatures of Bathsheba, Suzanna and the Elders, bath-tub parties and a late-medieval bath house picturing activities that might justify the caption 'A House that was not a Home.'

social diversion seems to have been widely prevalent not only in ancient and early-modern times but also in the late Middle Ages. During the earlier medieval centuries the ascetic influence of monasticism forced Christians to avoid the social laxity of bathing establishments, especially those that were a part of the pagan heritage. Furthermore, the primitive conditions of life tended to reduce bathing to a minimum. Any sort of institutionalized bathing at luxury resorts, such as those in the region of Naples during Roman imperial times, was economically difficult and religiously abhorrent, a relic of pagan licentiousness.

What might be called a renaissance of bathing in the West is noticeable by the end of the twelfth century, contemporaneously with the penetration of Muslim influences and a rising tide of prosperity. Whether or not this trend is traceable to the Muslim cult of cleanliness and the Salernitan emphasis on practical medicine, the twelfth century saw a repopularization of bathing in the Neapolitan area, as a combination of health with social diversion. The most spectacular evidence of the trend is an illustrated poem concerning the Baths of Puteoli (modern Pozzuoli), written somewhere in the region of Naples during the twelfth century. Numerous manuscripts of the poem, with as many as thirty-five colourful full-page illustrations of the various baths, are to be found in European collections. Some of the illustrations show mixed nude bathing with an uninhibitedness that verges on pornography and suggest that the early-medieval Christians were justified in their condemnation of bathing resorts as instruments of the devil. Nevertheless, the late Middle Ages witnessed a marked increase in public bathing at municipal bath-houses and luxury resorts where often the activities reflect more of sex adventures than health or cleanliness. Rarely do the illustrations depict anything strictly medical; exceptions are sweating rooms, clystering and bathers drinking the health-giving waters.[1]

94. B. MIXED NUDE BATHING

(In a manuscript from the fourteenth century: Vatican, MS Rossiano 379, folio 21. Petrus de Ebulo, *De balneis Puteolanis*.)

In contrast to the preceding picture this miniature is the least medical and the most brazenly pornographic of all medieval representations of bathing. Noticeable are the

[1] Most of the extant miniatures (with the exception of the one we present) are photoreproduced in a splendidly illustrated study recently published by C. M. Kauffmann, *The Baths of Pozzuoli* (Oxford, 1959).

following: at left is a woman who is apparently excited over the enlarged genitalia of the man next to her; two other men, one of whom has oversized genitalia; a kneeling man, and a man at the extreme right who are both seemingly preoccupied with their genitalia. Some of the patients are drinking from goblets perhaps containing potions of the invigorating water. At the top of the miniature is the tent-infirmary (*tentoria infirmorum*) of the establishment.

XIII. VETERINARY MEDICINE

MEDIEVAL aristocrats valued highly their horses, dogs and falcons, evidence of which is found in the manuscript handbooks concerning their care. Frederick II's falcon book, with detailed information concerning the health of birds and with splendid illustrations, is well known.[1] Less publicized are the manuscripts concerning dogs and horses, many of which are beautifully illustrated. To be sure, the illustrations of horses are more often of equestrian rather than of veterinary interest. An exception, rare in manuscripts, is to be found in the State Library at the West Berlin Dahlem Museum (MS 78.C.15). In a generously illustrated veterinary treatise in Italian of about the year 1300 are sixty-one miniatures depicting veterinarians in action. Treatment of dogs is shown in the Leningrad manuscript from which we present a photoreproduction.[2]

95. VETERINARY TREATMENT OF DOGS

(In a manuscript of about the year 1381: Leningrad, Hermitage Museum, Department of Drawings, MS 2, folio 25v, *Livre de chasse*, in French.)

The miniature pictures nine dogs of varying breeds attended by nine veterinarians, each performing a different operation. The accompanying text is entitled 'Maladies des chiens et de leurs curacions.' A companion miniature (folio 38) shows the bathing of dogs.

[1] This work has been published in an English translation with elaborate explanatory data and splendid photoreproductions under the title *The Art of Falconry: being the De Arte Venandi cum Avibus of Frederick II of Hohenstaufen*. Casey A. Wood and F. Marjorie Fyfe (Stanford University, 1943).

[2] For details concerning the Dahlem and Leningrad manuscripts, see Loren MacKinney, 'Medieval Medical Miniatures in Central and East European Collections,' *Manuscripta*, 1961, 5, 143, 147.

XIV. A TRAGIC CASE HISTORY, ENDING IN AN AUTOPSY

(A series of eight miniatures in a manuscript from thirteenth-century
England: Oxford, Bodleian, MS Ashmole 399, folios 33–34, on an
inserted double leaf without captions or accompanying text.)

YEARS ago Karl Sudhoff and Charles Singer called attention to this unique
series of stray miniatures. Sudhoff stressed the importance of miniature
number six, the autopsy scene, but saw no special significance in the series as
a unit.[1] Singer commented on numerous details but did not consider the series as a
case history.[2] Recently Loren MacKinney has published reproductions of all eight
miniatures and interpreted them collectively as a moral in pictorial form warning
women to follow their physician's instructions or suffer dire consequences.[3] In a
four-page addenda, Harry Bober showed that the last two miniatures were added
by a later illustrator and that the entire set originated separately and was inserted in
the Oxford manuscript.

96. AN AUTOPSY

The autopsy miniature (on folio 34) is well known to medical historians and often
has been reproduced as the earliest known medieval illustration of autopsy. It pictures
the surgeon, who has dissected the body and scattered the internal organs about,
showing the physician the woman's liver, apparently the cause of her death. Singer
interpreted the scene as the dissection of a stolen corpse by a 'low surgeon' who has
been 'interrupted in his nefarious task' by the physician. Sudhoff hinted that it was a
normal autopsy for investigation of the mortal ailment. Two anatomists at the University of North Carolina question the findings of medical historians, especially with

[1] Karl Sudhoff, 'Weitere Beitrage zur Geschichte der Anatomie im Mittelalter, II,' *Sudhoff's
Archiv Gesch. Medizin*, 1914, 7, 372–374.
[2] Charles Singer, 'Thirteenth-Century Miniatures Illustrating Medical Practice,' *Proceedings of
the Royal Society of Medicine*, 1915–16, 9, part 2, History Section, 29–42.
[3] Loren MacKinney, 'A Thirteenth-Century Medical Case History in Miniatures,' *Speculum*,
1960, 35, 251–259.

respect to the identification of the liver, and propose a radically new interpretation.[1] The woman, they insist, was pregnant and had attempted an abortion by inserting a mandrake plant in her vagina; this was the cause of death and the surgeon, after cutting it from the corpse, is showing it to the physician. The two anatomists also identify other organs surrounding the corpse in a fashion that differs from the usual captioned representations in medieval manuscripts. However, this is characteristic of the reactions of many modern physicians to the assemblage of internal organs in the miniature. All in all, the absence of captions and explanatory text invites modern investigators to make their own identifications and interpretations not only for the autopsy scene but also for intriguing problems that arise from the other miniatures in the series.[2]

With the above-listed topics of obstetrics, dentistry, bathing, etc., the strictly medical aspects of our survey become somewhat non-technical, tenuous and (especially in the category of bathing) more a matter of behaviourism than of medical practice. Nevertheless, neither the subject of medical miniatures nor our collection of reproductions has been exhausted. Among the categories that must be left untouched are the following: (1) anatomy; (2) pathological cases; (3) portraits of ancient medical authorities;[3] (4) medical teaching by lecture and demonstration; (5) medical costumes;[4] (6) tranquillizers;[5] and other minor topics. A detailed listing of miniatures concerning these and the other topics illustrated in our microfilm collection appears in part II, of this volume.

We take leave of the subject and our reader-viewers with a striking example of

[1] F. R. Weedon and A. P. Heusner, 'A Clinical-Pathological Conference from the Middle Ages,' The Bulletin (University of North Carolina School of Medicine), 1960, 8, no. 2, 14–20.

[2] Dr. Walter Artelt has suggested recently that the scattered organs were sketched in later by a second illustrator.

[3] An article by Loren MacKinney, 'What did Medieval and Early Modern Illustrators Think Hippocrates Looked Like?' (News, of the University of Kansas Medical Center, Feb., 1960), presented an illustrated survey of relativity in portraiture of Hippocrates, and the author projected thirty-six reproductions of the same topic at the September, 1960, International Congress of the History of Medicine in Athens, Greece, and at the 1961 Chicago meeting of the American Association of the History of Medicine. He has similar sets of reproductions concerning Galen and Dioscorides.

[4] The data on costumes from the collection of microfilms of miniatures has been analysed by George Strong in a M.A. thesis at the University of North Carolina (1961): Medieval Medical Costumes as seen in Miniatures.

[5] An article by Loren MacKinney, 'Tranquillisers before the Modern Era,' Chemist and Druggist, (London, Special Issue, June 25, 1960, pp. 766–771) contains eighteen reproductions of miniatures, four of them in colour.

psychological healing which, so far as we know, has never been illustrated. It recounts the healing of a sick pilgrim by the ministrations of lovely Nicolette, Aucassin's lady love, as told by him in the famous twelfth-century poem.

A man of Limousin most sage Returning from a pilgrimage,
Ill and weary, sore adread; Lay in pain upon his bed,
He tossed and drew with fear his breath, Sore distressed and near to death.
But you [Nicolette] entered, pure and white; Softly to the sick man's sight
You raised the train that swept adown, You raised the ermine-bordered gown,
You raised the smock and bared to him Daintily each lovely limb [gambette].
Then a wondrous thing befell, Straight he rose up sound and well,
Left his bed took cross in hand, And sought once more his own dear land.
O Lily flower, so white, so sweet, Fair the fairing of thy feet. . . .
Sweet thy kisses, soft thy touch, All men love thee over much. . . .

Part Two

MEDICAL MINIATURES IN EXTANT MANUSCRIPTS
A checklist compiled with the assistance of Thomas Herndon

EXTANT MEDICAL MINIATURES IN TREATISES IN MANUSCRIPTS PRIOR TO *c.* 1550[1]

In the following list, capitalized letters are used for locations of manuscripts, for authors and for outstanding medical topics that are illustrated in the miniatures (we use the term 'miniatures' loosely for all illustrations whether or not in colour). Names of authors and of treatises in which there are miniatures appear in the generally accepted spellings, usually in Latin. Titles in Greek, Arabic and other unusual languages appear in the standard English spellings. In general we follow the forms used in S. A. J. Moorat, *Catalogue of the Manuscripts in the Wellcome Medical Historical Library* (London, 1962), or in Lynn Thorndike and Pearl Kibre, *A Catalogue of Incipits of Mediaeval Scientific Writings in Latin* (Cambridge, Mass., 1937) and George Sarton, *An Introduction to the History of Science* (Baltimore, 1927–1948). In rare cases the spelling in the manuscript is used, enclosed in quotation marks.

Each library and manuscript entry is preceded by a serial number; these are for use in the subject index. All listed manuscripts are in Latin unless otherwise indicated (e.g., by 'in Greek,' 'in French,' etc.). Dates of origin of manuscripts are indicated in parentheses by century (e.g., '14th c') or by the approximate year (e.g., '*c.* 1300'). Folio numbers are preceded by 'f.' or 'ff.,' with 'v' indicating the verso side of the folio. Items that are photoreproduced in this volume have in parentheses at the end of the entry the number of the figure in which the photoreproduction appears (e.g., 'Fig. 9').

[1] This list was compiled with the collaboration of Thomas Herndon as research assistant, thanks to grants from the American Philosophical Society and the National Institutes of Health, U.S. Public Health Service; Merlin Berry and Francis M. Nichols, Jr., assisted in checking and proofing. With the exception of items followed by an asterisk (*), all manuscripts were examined at first hand by Professor or Mrs. Loren MacKinney in the course of research trips to all of the great manuscript collections in Europe and the United States. Many of the items followed by asterisks (especially the Islamic miniatures) were examined in photoreproductions. The coverage of Western and Central European collections (also those in Moscow and Leningrad) is thorough. Exceptions are the many private uncatalogued collections. However, surveys of a number of these indicate that normally they contain few if any illustrated medical manuscripts. Another exception is the non-medical treatises (such as Books of Hours) in which there is a wealth of medical illustration, some of which appears in our listing. We hope to survey this tremendous reservoir of material more intensively in the near future.

1.1 ABERDEEN, Scotland, UNIVERSITY, MS 24 (12–13th c.). LEO FORTISSIMUS, *De naturis bestiarum*.[1]

ff. 1–103. MATERIA MEDICA: animals (castor, etc.). PROGNOSIS: caladrius bird looks at bed-ridden king.

.2 ——, MS 25 (13th c.). Medical miscellany.

ff. 81, 93v. AUTHOR: ISIDORUS HISPALENSIS (?) writing ('*De homine et partibus*'). ANATOMY: male and female figures ('*De homine et partibus*').

.3 ——, MS 183 (15th c.). Wonders of Nature, in Persian.*

ff. 1–450 *passim*. MATERIA MEDICA: herbs, animals, etc.

.4 ——, MS C.2.3.81 (15th c.). Astrological miscellany.

f. 84v. PROGNOSIS: ZODIAC-MAN.[2]

2.1 ABERYSTWYTH, Wales, NATIONAL LIBRARY, MS 27.I (15th c.). Medical miscellany (in Welsh).

p. 13. PROGNOSIS: ZODIAC-MAN.

.2 ——, MS 88 (1488). Medical miscellany (in Welsh).

pp. 11, 26, 28. BLOODLETTING-MAN. PROGNOSIS: ZODIAC-MAN. DIAGNOSIS: UROSCOPY flasks in circular chart.

.3 ——, MS 735.C (11th c.). Astrological miscellany.

p. 6. PROGNOSIS: circular ZODIAC chart.

3.1 BALTIMORE, Maryland, USA, WALTERS ART GALLERY, MS 136 (14th c.). AVERRHOES, *Colliget*.

ff. 1–70 *passim*. AUTHOR: Averrhoes lectures; head of Averrhoes. DISEASE: patient with hand on chest; woman in bed; woman's face. REGIMEN: family at table eating. DIAGNOSIS: doctor does UROSCOPY.

.2 ——, MS 140 (14th c.). VINCENT DE BEAUVAIS, *Speculum historiale* (in French).

f. 86v. ANATOMY: Siamese twins.

---

[1] Since bestiaries contain much less data concerning materia medica than herbals, hereafter we list only exceptional examples. Most bestiaries mention medical items only casually. For example, the medical uses of the eel, hyena, stag, wolf, dog, cock, bee (for its honey), cow (for its excreta), etc., are noted only in passing. More attention is given to the castor, for its testicles; also the caladrius bird as a means of prognosis. For specific examples see T. H. White, *The Book of Beasts* (New York, 1954) and Florence McCullough, *Medieval Latin and French Bestiaries* (Chapel Hill, N.C., 1960).

[2] Manuscripts which we describe as astrological or medical miscellanies often contain numerous charts, diagrams, etc., of devices for prognosticating the health or welfare of humans. We list only the zodiac-men, since they are not only closely associated with health, but also often show anatomical features. The varied nature of astrological miniatures is clearly shown in Harry Bober, 'The Zodiacal Miniature of the *Très Riches Heures* of the Duke of Berry—Its Sources and Meaning,' *Journal of the Warburg and Courtauld Institutes*, 1948, *11*, 1–34.

.3 ——, MS 10.668 (16th c). History (in Hindu).

detached folio. MEDICATION: doctor gives pill to prince.

.4 ——, MS 676 (15th c). Rashid ad-Din, World History (in Hindu).

detached folio. OBSTETRICS: birth of Buddha.

.5 ——, MS 750 (12th c). Dioscorides, *Materia medica* (in Arabic).

pp. 231, 240, 241. MATERIA MEDICA: herbs.

4.1 BAMBERG, West Germany, ÖFFENTLICHE BIBLIOTHEK, MS Med. 8(L.III.15) (13th c).
ALBUCASIS, *Chirurgia*.

ff. 1–27v. SURGERY: instruments in text.

.2 ——, MS Med. 15(L.III.39) (15th c). GULIELMUS DE SALICETO, *Chirurgia*.

f. 1. AUTHOR, DIAGNOSIS: Gulielmus with UROSCOPY flask.

5.1 BASEL, Switzerland, UNIVERSITY (Oeffentliche Bibliothek der Universität), MS
AN.II.3 (1491). Matriculation documents for medical faculty.

f. 84. MEDICAL SAINT: St. Luke as patron of medicine.

.2 ——, MS D.I.5 (14th c). GALENIC miscellany.

f. 1. AUTHOR: Galen expounds.[1]

.3 ——, MS D.I.11 (*c*. 1330). Medical miscellany.

f. 22v. MATERIA MEDICA: a flower (MESUE, *Antidotarium*).

.4 ——, MS D.I.22 (*c*. 1500) (in German).

detached folio. PROGNOSIS: human head with letters referring to side text.

.5 ——, MS D.II.11 (13th c). Medical miscellany.

ff. 169v–171v. ANATOMY: bone-man, vein-man, artery-man, female and male
organ figures.

.6 ——, MS D.II.18 (14th c). HALY ABBAS, *Regalis dispositio*.

ff. 111v, 139, 206v. DISEASE: naked man points to head; man with hand raised.
AUTHOR: Haly expounds.

.7 ——, MS D.III.1 (14–15th c). Medical miscellany.

f. 149v. ANATOMY: diagram of eye (ZACHARIAS SALERNITANUS, *De passionibus
oculorum*).

.8 ——, MS D.III.7 (14th c). AVICENNA, *De anima naturalium*, etc.

f. 40. ANATOMY: diagram of eye showing lines of vision.

.9 ——, MS D.III.14 (14th c). Medical miscellany.

f. 58v. PHARMACY: man in Jewish hat with pestle and mortar ('Hygia,' i.e.,
'sanitas').

[1] Throughout the volume the term "expound" indicates the professional attitude of raising
a pedagogical finger. "Lecture" is used to indicate the use of a book and the presence of
hearers.

6.1 BERLIN, East Germany, STATE LIBRARY (Deutsche Staatsbibliothek), MS Lat. F.381 (8th c). Pseudo-APULEIUS, *Herbarium*.

ff. 1182–1183. MATERIA MEDICA: herbs.

.2 ——, MS Ham. 407 (14th c). Medical miscellany (in French).

ff. 229–283v. MATERIA MEDICA: herbs, animals and minerals, in alphabetical order, with action scenes (MATTHAEUS PLATEARIUS, *Circa instans*).

.3 ——, MS Lat. 419 (now at Tübingen) (1304). Medical miscellany.

ff. 78–87. ANATOMY: marginal sketches of skeletons and various organs (HENRI DE MONDEVILLE, *Anatkomia*).

7.1 BERLIN, West Germany, DAHLEM MUSEUM (Kupferstichkabinett der Staatlichen Museen), MS 78.C.1 (14th c). Alexander romances (in French).

f. 71. PROGNOSIS: caladrius bird.

.2 ——, MS 78.C.15 (*c*. 1300). LORENZO RUSIO, *Liber mareschalciae* (in Italian).

ff. 1–46v. Veterinary Medicine: treatment of horses.

8.1 BERN, Switzerland, BURGERBIBLIOTHEK, MS 120 (12th c). PETRUS DE EBULO, *Liber ad honorem Augusti*.

ff. 97–127 *passim*. DIAGNOSIS: doctor with UROSCOPY flask at bedside of dying king. OBSTETRICS: nurse shows abortion to woman, mother in bed. SURGERY: surgeon extracts arrow from warrior's face, assistants (Fig. 74). MEDICAL MAN: 'Magister Girardus.' DISEASE: ailing emperor. MEDICATION: podagra patient dips his feet in blood of a boy.

.2 ——, MS B.524 (15th c). Astrological-medical miscellany.

f. 2. PROGNOSIS, MATERIA MEDICA: ZODIAC-MAN holds herbs, herbs in margins.

9.1 BETHESDA, Maryland, USA, NATIONAL LIBRARY OF MEDICINE, MS P.18 (15th c). MANSUR, Anatomy (in Persian).

ff. 1–39 *passim*. ANATOMY: vein-man; artery-man; bone-man; nerve-man; muscle-man; pregnant woman.

.2 ——, MS P.19 (15th c). MANSUR, Anatomy (in Persian).

ff. 1–24 *passim*. ANATOMY: vein-man; artery-man; bone-man; nerve-man; muscle-man; pregnant woman.

.3 ——, MS 509 (1476). GUY DE CHAULIAC, *Chirurgia*.

ff. 1–206 *passim*. SURGERY: instruments in text.

.4 ——, INCUNABULUM 274 (*c*. 1485). ARISTOTLE, *De anima*, with Aquinas' commentary.

f. 105v. ANATOMY: human half-figure with sense centres and related organs.

.5 ——, INCUNABULUM 379 (15th c). ARISTOTLE, *De anima* and *Physica*, with Aquinas' commentary.

f. 47v. ANATOMY: human half-figure with sense centres and related organs.

10.1 BIRMINGHAM, Alabama, USA, UNIVERSITY OF ALABAMA MEDICAL CENTER, MS Reynolds 3 (15th c). RHAZES, *Almansor*.*

    f. 67. REGIMEN: man and woman standing under canopy.

.2 ——, MS Reynolds 5 (14th c). ARNALDUS DE VILLANOVA, *Regimen sanitatis*, etc.*

    ff. 1–40 *passim*. REGIMEN, MATERIA MEDICA: people eating, drinking, etc.; herbs, etc. DISEASE: sick old man with woman attendant.

11.1 BOLOGNA, Italy, ARCHIGINNASIO (Biblioteca Comunale dell' Archiginnasio), MS A.43 (15th c). Alphabetical-herbal, mineral, alchemical (in Latin and German).

    f. 12. DISEASE: man with 'club' foot walking with a cane (cured by 'arthimisia').

.2 ——, MS A.125 (15th c). MICHAEL SAVONAROLA, *Practica*.

    f. IIv. AUTHOR: Savonarola, wearing glasses, reads book at lectern.

12.1 BOLOGNA, Italy, UNIVERSITY (Biblioteca Universitaria), MS 138(104) (15th c). Alchemical-medical miscellany.

    f. 245. AUTHOR: 'GUILLERMUS FABRI DE DYA, MEDICUS,' (*De lapide philosophorum*).

.2 ——, MS 378(620) (12th c). Herbal miscellany.

    ff. 33–99 *passim*. MATERIA MEDICA: herbs (DIOSCORIDES, *Materia medica*, alphabetized).

.3 ——, MS 1091(2222, 2224) (15th c). RHAZES, *Continens*.

    f. 1. AUTHOR: bearded Rhazes with crown; (below) young, laurel-crowned man.

.4 ——, MS 2197 (14th c). AVICENNA, *Canon* (in Hebrew).

    ff. 1–402 *passim*. AUTHOR: Avicenna lectures to six men and two women. DIAGNOSIS: doctor does UROSCOPY for nobleman, women and men await diagnoses (in margins, signs of zodiac and old man with two companions). PHARMACY: shop with doctors, customers, assistant with mortar and pestle, jars on shelves, boy with flask-carrier; marginal scenes of BATHING, BLOODLETTING, CAUTERIZING. DIAGNOSIS: (three scenes), doctor takes PULSE of bed-patient; patient's family show disapproval; doctor consults book.

.5 ——, MS 3632 (15th c). Medical miscellany (in Greek).[1]

    ff. 1–454 *passim*. MEDICAL CELEBRITIES: Aesculapius, Hippocrates, Galen, etc. AUTHOR: Hippocrates teaches five men; 'Oribasios' lectures. DIAGNOSIS: 'THEOPHILOS' does UROSCOPY, (below) twenty-one flasks (Fig. 5); student hands UROSCOPY flask to doctor; 'Paulos' with UROSCOPY flasks, two bystanders; 'Isaac' with UROSCOPY flask; chart showing PULSE beats. MATERIA MEDICA: herbs; animals. MEDICATION: doctor hands potion to patient;

---

[1] Folios 17–26v have six portraits per page. See A. Olivieri, 'Indice de' Codici Greci Bolognesi,' *Studi Ital. di Filol. Class.*, 1895, *3*, 387–495, for details on illustrations and texts, many of which are excerpts and miscellanies.

Apollo, serpent, three men hold flasks. PHARMACY: doctor, flasks on table; doctor, three patients with flasks; two doctors with mortar and pestle. SURGERY: instruments in margins. PROGNOSIS: ZODIAC-MAN. DISEASE: figures illustrating ailments of head, penis, etc. ANATOMY: diagram of eye. ORTHOPAEDIC BANDAGING: diagrams of various types of bandages (Soranus). ORTHOPAEDICS: reducing of dislocations (Apollonius).

13.1 BONN, West Germany, UNIVERSITY (Universitätsbibliothek), MS 479 (14–15th c.). Medical miscellany (in German).

ff. 52–53. DIAGNOSIS: UROSCOPY flasks and flask-carriers.

14.1 BOSTON, Massachusetts, USA, MEDICAL LIBRARY, MS 3 (15th c.). detached folio. BLOODLETTING-MAN.

.2 ——, MS 19 (15th c.). Medical-astrological miscellany (in Latin and English).

ff. 1–59v passim. DIAGNOSIS: UROSCOPY flasks. PROGNOSIS: ZODIAC-MAN.

.3 ——, MS 31 (13th c.). ISAAC JUDAEUS, De febribus.

f.1. TRANSLATOR: Constantinus Africanus, as tonsured monk.

.4 ——, MS (uncatalogued) (15th c.). Medical miscellany (in Arabic).

ff. 1–33 passim. SURGERY: instruments in text.

15.1 BOSTON, Massachusetts, USA, PUBLIC LIBRARY, MS 26 (14th c.). RHAZES, De aegritudinibus (Almansor, X).

ff. 1–132 passim. DISEASE: doctors and patients.

.2 ——, MS 100 (15th c.). Astrological miscellany (in Latin, French and English).

f. 22v. BLOODLETTING-MAN.

16.1 BRESLAU (Wroclaw), Poland, UNIVERSITY (Biblioteka Uniwersytecka), MS Acad. I.F.334 (15th c.). Medical miscellany.

f. 273. BLOODLETTING-MAN.

.2 ——, MS Acad. III.F.12/2 (15th c.). Medical miscellany.

ff. 1–47 passim. DIAGNOSIS: ROGERIUS DE BARONE does a UROSCOPY (Rogerina). AUTHOR, TEACHING: ROGERIUS DE BARONE (Rogerina) and MATTHAEUS PLATEARIUS (Circa instans) lecture.

.3 ——, MS Acad. III.Q.1 (14th c.). Medical miscellany.

f. 93v. BLOODLETTING-MAN: with side text in German.

.4 ——, MS Acad. III.Q.19 (15th c.). BENEDICTUS REGUARDATUS DE NURCIA, Regimen sanitatis.

f. 7. AUTHOR: Benedictus at desk with book.

.5 ——, MS Rhed. 458 (15th c.). Medical miscellany.

ff. 1–18 *passim*. DIAGNOSIS: UROSCOPY flasks. PROGNOSIS: ZODIAC-BLOODLETTING-MAN.[1]

17.1 BRISTOL, England, PUBLIC LIBRARY, MS 10 (15th c). Medical miscellany; illustrations from GUY DE CHAULIAC, *Chirurgia*.

ff. 1–246 *passim*. AUTHOR: GUY DE CHAULIAC presents scroll to bishop; (at right) Guy with book. ANATOMICAL DEMONSTRATION: demonstrator points to skeleton. SURGERY: operations for *apostema*; *vulnera*; *ulceres*; *fractura* of leg with splints; swollen leg with bandages and instruments; instruments in text. BLOODLETTING: blood spurts into basin held by patient.

BRNO, see BRUNN.

18.1 BRUGES (Brugge), Belgium, CITY LIBRARY (Bibliothèque de la Ville), MS 411 (*c*. 1500). THOMAS DE CANTIMPRÉ, *De rerum natura*.

ff. 1–336 *passim*. MATERIA MEDICA: herbs, animals (and monsters).

.2 ——, MS 467 (13–14th c). Medical miscellany.

f. 53. AUTHOR, PHARMACY: NICOLAUS PRAEPOSITUS holds scales (*Antidotarium*).

.3 ——, MS 593 (15th c). TROTULA, *De passionibus mulierum* (in Dutch).

ff. 3v–15v *passim*. BATHING: women in tubs, one drinks a potion. GYNAECOLOGY: instruments (syringe, pot under chair for fumigating).

19.1 BRUNN (Brno), Czechoslovakia, UNIVERSITY (Universitni Knihovna), MS Mk. 107 (15th c). AEGIDIUS CORBOLIENSIS, *De urinis*.

f. 16. DIAGNOSIS: UROSCOPY flask.

20.1 BRUSSELS (Bruxelles), Belgium, BIBLIOTHÈQUE ROYALE, MS 3701–3715 (*c*. 900). Medical miscellany.

ff. 16v, 26v–29. OBSTETRICS: diagram of uterus; diagrams of uterus showing foetal presentations (MOSCHION, *De aegritudinibus mulierum*).

.2 ——, MS 4862–4869 (14th c). Astrological-medical miscellany (in Latin and English).

ff. 66v–67. BLOODLETTING-MAN: ZODIAC-MAN.

.3 ——, MS 5874–5877 (15th c). Medical miscellany (in French).

ff. 1–154v *passim*. PROGNOSIS: ZODIAC-BLOODLETTING-MAN (*De fleubothomia*); circle of UROSCOPY flasks. MEDICAL SAINTS: Cosmas with UROSCOPY flask, Damian with PHARMACY jar. MATERIA MEDICA: herbs, animals and minerals, with action scenes (MATTHAEUS PLATEARIUS, *Circa instans*).

.4 ——, MS 9094 (1400). BARTHOLOMAEUS ANGLICUS, *De proprietatibus rerum* (in French).

[1] Additional zodiac or bloodletting figures, reported by Sudhoff and others in Breslau MSS, were not in the library in 1960.

ff. 56–111v *passim*. PHARMACY, TEACHING: doctor with apothecary jar, three patients. ANATOMY, COSMOLOGY: naked man on the ground, fire and water nearby (elements). REGIMEN: AGES OF MAN (boy, youth, doctor, adult man, old man). DISEASE, TEACHING: Bartholomaeus expounds to five concerning maladies.

.5 ——, MS 9321 (*c.* 1452). *Fleur des histoires* (in French).*

f. 76v. SURGERY: doctors castrate and cut throat of man tied hand and foot.

.6 ——, MS 10066–10077 (10–12th c). Miscellany.

ff. 142v, 143. PROGNOSIS: (1) catching caladrius bird in net; (2) 'caladrius avertit infirmo,' attendant in despair; (3) caladrius looks at bed-patient, then flies toward sun; happy attendants give thanks to Christ (*Physiologus*).

.7 ——, MS 13076–13077 (14th c). *Antiquitates Flandriae*.

f. 50v. SURGERY: eye operation, one assistant, three by-standers.

.8 ——, MS 14301–14305 (14th c). Medical miscellany; all illustrations from GALENIC commentaries on HIPPOCRATIC works.

ff. 1–150 *passim*. DISEASE: doctors or patients illustrating ailments. MEDICATION: doctor or patient with purgative for pregnant woman, *potio dulcis*; medicine for dropsy. DIAGNOSIS: doctor and two assistants attend bed-patient.

.9 ——, MS 21974 (1442). *Boeck von der Kristen Ghelove* (in Flemish).

ff. 9, 10, 13v. DIAGNOSIS: doctor does UROSCOPY. The four TEMPERAMENTS. ANATOMY: two men discuss *Physonomie*. REGIMEN: seven ages of man.

21.1 BUDAPEST, Hungary, UNIVERSITY LIBRARY (Egyetemi Konyvtar), MS 15 (13th c). ALBUCASIS, *Chirurgia*.

ff. 1–45 *passim*. AUTHOR: Albucasis with book. TEACHING: tonsured doctor expounds. SURGERY: instruments in text. OBSTETRICAL SURGERY: extraction of dead foetus. DISEASE: patient with colic, doctor. ORTHOPAEDICS: dislocated vertebra, traction. OBSTETRICS: diagrams of uterus showing foetal presentations. SURGERY: CAUTERY figures.

22.1 BURLINGTON, Vermont, USA, UNIVERSITY OF VERMONT, MS TR.F.580.M.319 (*c.* 1500). Herbal picture-book (captions in Italian).

ff. 1–141 *passim*. MATERIA MEDICA: herbs, animals and minerals, with action scenes. OBSTETRICS: woman nursing a new-born child. VETERINARY MEDICINE: dosing horse with medicine.

23.1 CAMARILLO, California, USA, ST. JOHN'S SEMINARY, MS Doheny 6809 (15th c). BARTHOLOMAEUS ANGLICUS, *De proprietatibus rerum* (in French).

ff. 1–364 *passim*. ANATOMICAL DEMONSTRATION: lecturer with naked man as subject. TEACHING: doctor lectures to three. MATERIA MEDICA: herbs and minerals.

24.1 CAMBRIDGE, England, CORPUS CHRISTI COLLEGE, MS 22 (12th c). Miscellany f.166. PROGNOSIS: Medical. CALADRIUS (Fig. 16).

.2 ——, MS 194(I.4) (14th c). Religious miscellany.

ff. 55, 66. ANATOMY: male and female Siamese twins (*Scala mundi, sive tabulae chronologicae*).

.3 ——, MS 364(19.13) (13th c). Medical miscellany.

ff. 54–54v. REGIMEN: charts of the four elements and of medicine in the liberal arts.

25.1 CAMBRIDGE, England, EMMANUEL COLLEGE, MS 69(I.3.17) (15th c). JOHN ARDERNE, *Practica chirurgiae* (in English and French).

ff. 1–190 *passim*. SURGERY, MATERIA MEDICA, MEDICATION: marginal sketches of instruments, patients, herbs, etc.

26.1 CAMBRIDGE, England, FITZWILLIAM MUSEUM, MSS 74, 118, 119, 132. Books of Hours.

MEDICAL SAINTS: Cosmas and Damian holding surgical and pharmaceutical implements.

.2 ——, MS 167 (15th c). Astrological miscellany (in French).

ff. 35v, 38, 102. PROGNOSIS: ZODIAC-MAN. ANATOMY: skeleton; planet-man, showing internal organs (the four TEMPERAMENTS in the margins).

.3 ——, MS 251 (15th c). BARTHOLOMAEUS ANGLICUS, *De proprietatibus rerum* (in French).

ff. 54v, 106. CLINIC: doctor with five patients does UROSCOPY; doctor with three patients (Fig. 10).

.4 ——, MS 288 (1280–1290). Book of Hours.

f. 6v. CLINIC: doctor does UROSCOPY, assistants prepare medicine (health calendar).

.5 ——, MS 298 (14th c). Metz Pontifical (in French).

ff. 25, 74, 81. ANIMAL DOCTORS: monkey-doctor takes PULSE and does UROSCOPY for man (Fig. 15); rabbit-doctors treat man's leg; monkey-doctor takes PULSE and does UROSCOPY for crane.

27.1 CAMBRIDGE, England, GONVILLE AND CAIUS COLLEGE, MS 147(197) (13–14th c). Medical miscellany.

f. 63. AUTHOR, SURGERY: ROGERIUS SALERNITANUS trephines patient (*Chirurgia*).

.2 ——, MS 190(223) (*c.* 1200, *c.* 1400). Medical miscellany.

ff. 1–100 *passim*. ANATOMY: artery-man; vein-man; bone-man; nerve-man; muscle-man (Pseudo-GALEN, *Figura incisionis*, *Historia arteriorum*, etc.). ANATOMY: diagrams of eye; male organs; female organs. SURGERY, DISEASE: marginal sketches of instruments, patients, etc. (JOHN ARDERNE, *Fistula in Ano*).

.3 ——, MS 336(725) (15th c). Medical-surgical miscellany (in English and Latin).

ff. 1–155 *passim*. DIAGNOSIS: UROSCOPY flasks; circular UROSCOPY chart ('A treatise of urine,' 'Expositiones urinarum'). ANATOMY: diagram of heart. BLOOD-LETTING-MAN. PROGNOSIS: ZODIAC-MAN.

.4 ——, MS 428 (11–12th c). Medical-astrological miscellany.

ff. 22–50v *passim*. REGIMEN: charts and figures of four winds; four humours; four temperaments; four seasons. PROGNOSIS: ZODIAC-MEN. ANATOMY: circular chart of liver, heart, testicles, brain.

.5 ——, MS 451(392) (15th c). Medical miscellany (in Latin and English).

pp. 58–67. DIAGNOSIS: UROSCOPY flasks (*Discretio urinarum*).

.6 ——, MS 451A(750) (14th c). Medical miscellany (in Latin, English and French).

f. 14. PROGNOSIS: ANATOMY, ZODIAC-MAN with parts of body captioned.

.7 ——, MS 480 (476) (13th c). AVICENNA, *Canon*.

ff. 1–304 *passim*. AUTHOR: Avicenna with book; expounds (several scenes). DIAGNOSIS: by UROSCOPY; by PULSE. DISEASE: human figures illustrating ailments.

28.1 CAMBRIDGE, England, KING'S COLLEGE, MS 16.I (15th c). Medical miscellany.

f. 153. PROGNOSIS: ZODIAC-MAN.

.2 ——, MS 21 (13–14th c). Medical miscellany.

pp. 149, 444v. DIAGNOSIS: doctor does UROSCOPY for bed-patient (THEOPHILUS PROTOSPATHARIUS, *De urinis*); doctor examines bed-patient (ISAAC JUDAEUS, *De dietis universalibus*).

29.1 CAMBRIDGE, England, MAGDALENE COLLEGE, MS Pepys 1916 (15th c). Sketchbook of miscellanies.

ff. 16v–17v, 24. ANATOMY: sketches of nude males and a female.

30.1 CAMBRIDGE, England, ST. JOHN'S COLLEGE, MS 19(A.19) (15th c). JAN YPERMAN, *Chirurgia*, (in Flemish).

pp. 1–106 *passim*. AUTHOR TEACHING: Jan Yperman shows skull to six. SURGERY: instruments in text. ANATOMY: men expose genitalia. MEDICATION: CLYSTER (patient seated).

.2 ——, MS 99(D.24) (13th c). Medical miscellany.

ff. 23, 59v, 103, 113. DIAGNOSIS: doctors do UROSCOPIES (JOHANNITIUS, *Isagoge in tegni Galieni*; THEOPHILUS PROTOSPATHARIUS, *De urinis*; HIPPOCRATES, *Aphorismi*). SURGERY: head operation, patient holds bowl (CONSTANTINUS AFRICANUS, *Viaticum*).

31.1 CAMBRIDGE, England, TRINITY COLLEGE, MS 645(R.4.12) (15th c). *Cronica ... scala mundi. . . .*

ff. 50, 61. ANATOMY: male and female Siamese twins.

.2 ——, MS 902.IV(R.14.29) (c. 1300). Surgical miscellany; illustrations from *Glossulae quatuor magistrorum*.

f. 139, 166v. TEACHING: two doctors argue; another expounds to student. SURGERY: operation on neck.

.3 ——, MS 922(R.14.52) (15th c.). Medical miscellany (in English). (four unnumbered folios at end). DIAGNOSIS: UROSCOPY flasks.

.4 ——, MS 941.V(R.15.18) (c. 1400). Scientific miscellany (in English).

f. 17. PROGNOSIS: ZODIAC-MAN.

.5 ——, MS 943(R.15.21) (1408). JOHANNES DE FOXTON, *Liber cosmographiae*.

ff. 12v–15v, 28v. REGIMEN: the four temperaments. PROGNOSIS: ZODIAC-BLOOD-LETTING-MAN.

.6 ——, MS 1037(0.1.13) (15th c.). Medical miscellany (in English, Italian and Latin).

ff. 23v–30 *passim*. DIAGNOSIS: UROSCOPY flasks.

.7 ——, MS 1044(0.1.20) (13th c.). Medical miscellany (in French and Latin); illustrations from ROGERIUS SALERNITANUS, *Chirurgia* (in French).

ff. 238–271v *passim*. SURGERY: operations on heads; eyes, noses (polyps); mouths, etc. PHARMACY: surgeons direct assistants in compounding medicines (some with double-pestle action). DIAGNOSIS: surgeons examine patients. MEDICA-TION: doctors and monkish patient; doctors pour medicines into patients' ears.

.8 ——, MS 1081(0.1.57) (15th c.). Scientific miscellany.

ff. 10v, 16. PROGNOSIS: ZODIAC-MAN. BLOODLETTING-MAN.

.9 ——, MS 1102(0.1.77) (15th c.). Medical miscellany (in Latin and English).

ff. 24v–27. DIAGNOSIS: UROSCOPY flasks (*Practica urinarum*).

.10 ——, MS 1144(0.2.40) (15th c.). Scientific miscellany (in Latin and English).

ff. 57v, 121. ANATOMY: human head showing sense centres and related organs. REGIMEN: diagram of the four temperaments.

.11 ——, MS 1148(0.2.44) (14th c.). HENRI DE MONDEVILLE, *Chirurgia*.

ff. 2v–16v *passim*. ANATOMICAL DEMONSTRATION: surgeon about to dissect cadaver (in vertical position). ANATOMY: bone-man; flayed-man; organ-men; male and female figures; two skulls; diagram of eye.

.12 ——, MS 1152(0.2.48) (14th c.). Pseudo-APULEIUS, *Herbarium*.

ff. 1–250v *passim*. MATERIA MEDICA, MEDICATION, PHARMACY: herbs, with action scenes. MEDICAL CELEBRITIES: Galen with students; Hippocrates with students.

.13 ——, MS 1153(0.2.49) (1450). JOHN ARDERNE, *Practica chirurgia* (in Latin and English).

ff. 1–102 *passim*. SURGERY: instruments (some for fistula); trephining. ANATOMY: sketches of hand; legs, arms; male genitalia; full figures. PHARMACY: flask on fire; mortar and pestle. MEDICATION: clysters and clystering; catheter in patient's penis. DIAGNOSIS: UROSCOPY flasks.

.14 ——, MS 1287(0.5.6) (15th c). Scientific miscellany (in Latin and English).

ff. 42v, 61v. MEDICAL CELEBRITIES: Hippocrates; Galen ('Sayings of philosophers').

.15 ——, MS 1344(0.7.16) (13th c). AUGUSTINE, *De spiritu et anima*.

f. 47v. ANATOMY: human half-body showing sense centres and related organs.

.16 ——, MS 1422(0.9.10) (15th c). Medical miscellany (in Latin, English and French).

f. 76. PROGNOSIS: ZODIAC-MAN.

32.1 CAMBRIDGE, England, UNIVERSITY LIBRARY, MS Dd.6.29 (15th c). Medical miscellany (in English).

ff. 1, 27–30. PROGNOSIS: ZODIAC-MAN. DIAGNOSIS: UROSCOPY flasks.

.2 ——, MS Ee.1.15 (15th c). Herbal-astrological miscellany (in English).

f. 11. PROGNOSIS: ZODIAC-MAN.

.3 ——, MS Ff.1.12 (14th c). Religious and astrological miscellany (in Latin and French).

f. 163v. PROGNOSIS: ZODIAC-MAN.

.4 ——, MS Ii.5.11(1846) (15th c). ALDOBRANDINO DA SIENA, *Le régime du corps* (in French).

ff. 1–85 *passim*. AUTHOR: Aldobrandino with book; seated. REGIMEN: eating and drinking; edible herbs, etc. DISEASE: doctors treat patients. BATHING: man in tub with table at side; two men bathing 'par mer.' REGIMEN: man and woman (impregnation). PAEDIATRICS: woman caring for infant. BLOOD-LETTING: by incision; by cupping; by leeching. REGIMEN: man sleeping; care of hair; of face; of liver. DENTISTRY: patient with jar medicates his teeth. DIAGNOSIS: UROSCOPY. PHARMACY: pharmacists with mortar and pestle; pharmacist with stirrer.

.5 ——, MS Kk.4.25(2040) (13th c). Scientific miscellany.

f. 45. MEDICATION: Angel Raphael with jar of salve for Tobit's eyes.

33.1 CAMBRIDGE, Massachusetts, USA, HARVARD UNIVERSITY, Printed Book 24278.116 (1512).

detached folios. ANATOMY: skeleton. BLOODLETTING-MAN.

34.1 CARPENTRAS, France, MS 322 (14th c). GUY DE CHAULIAC, *Chirurgia*.*

ff. 10–288 *passim*. SURGERY: instruments in text.

35.1 CESENA, Italy, BIBLIOTECA MALATESTIANA, MS S.XXVI.2 (15th c). LORENZO RUSIO, *Liber mareschalciae*.*

f.3. VETERINARY MEDICINE: St. Eligius miraculously shoes a hoof severed from a horse.

36.1 CHANTILLY, France, MUSÉE CONDÉ, MS *Les Très riches Heures du Duc de Berry* (1416). (in French).

f. 14v. PROGNOSIS: ZODIAC-MAN.

.2 ——, MS 328(938) (13th c). PETRUS HISPANUS, *Thesaurus pauperum*.

f. 55. DISEASE: heads of man and woman illustrate ailments.

.3 ——, MS 334(569) (14th c). Medical miscellany; illustrations in GUIDO DA VIGE-VANO, *Anathomia*.

ff. 1–287 *passim*. DISEASE: man's head (to illustrate *alopecia*). ANATOMY: cadavers showing internal organs. ANATOMICAL DISSECTION: Guido dissects cadavers. DIAGNOSIS: doctor palpates abdomen; takes PULSE (Fig. 12).

37.1 CHARTRES, France, CITY LIBRARY (Bibliothèque de Chartres), MS 1036 (14th c). Religious-medical miscellany.

f. 3. DIAGNOSIS, PHARMACY: doctor does UROSCOPY; 'Apothecarius' with scales, assistant with mortar and pestle (*Apothecarius Moralis*).

38.1 COLOGNE (Köln), West Germany, CITY HISTORICAL ARCHIVES (Historisches Archiv der Stadt Köln), MS W.144C (14th c). Astrological-medical miscellany.*

ff. 71v–72: BLOODLETTING–ZODIAC-MAN.

.2 ——, MS W.308 (14th c). Astrological-medical miscellany.*

f. IV. ANATOMY, BLOODLETTING-MAN: showing internal organs.

39.1 COPENHAGEN (København), Denmark, KONGELIGE BIBLIOTEK, MS N.K.S. 227.2° (15th c). MATTHAEUS PLATEARIUS, *Circa instans* (in French).

ff. 1–217 *passim*. MATERIA MEDICA: herbs and animals.

.2 ——, MS N.K.S.84.b.2° (15–16th c). Astrological-medical miscellany.

ff. 1–6. PROGNOSIS: ZODIAC-BLOODLETTING-MEN. OBSTETRICS: pregnant women with DISEASE names on bodies. ANATOMY: WOUND-MEN showing internal organs; human half-figure showing sense centres with lines to related organs. DIAGNOSIS: UROSCOPY flasks.

.3 ——, MS G.K.S.1633.4° (14th c). *Physiologus*.

ff. 1–63v *passim*. MATERIA MEDICA: animals. DIAGNOSIS: monkey holding UROSCOPY flask. PROGNOSIS: caladrius bird.

.4 ——, MS G.K.S.1653.4° (11th c). Medical miscellany.

ff. 17–19. OBSTETRICS: diagrams of uterus showing foetal presentations (MOSCHION, *De aegritudinibus mulierum*).

.5 ——, MS Thott. 190.2° (14–15th c). Medical miscellany (in Latin and French).

ff. 5–130 *passim*. OBSTETRICS: diagrams of uterus showing foetal presentations (MOSCHION, *De aegritudinibus mulierum*). MATERIA MEDICA: herbs and animals (Herbal in Latin and French, with occasional animal inserts).

.6 ——, MS Thott. 195.2° (1466). VINCENTIUS, *Practica*.

f. 3. DIAGNOSIS: doctor with UROSCOPY flask.

.7 ——, MS Thott. 240.2° (15th c). Astrological miscellany.

f. 12. PROGNOSIS: ZODIAC-MAN.

40.1 CRACOW (Kraków), Poland, BIBLIOTEKA JAGIELLONSKA, MS 780 (14th c). AVICENNA, *Canon*.

ff. 1–143 *passim*. AUTHOR: Avicenna lectures to two. DISEASES: human faces (in initial letters) illustrating ailments.

.2 ——, MS 794 (1440). THOMAS DE CANTIMPRÉ, *De rerum natura*.

ff. 1–235 *passim*. MATERIA MEDICA: herbs and animals (also monsters).

.3 ——, MS 815 (*c*. 1300). Medical miscellany.

ff. 1–322 *passim*. AUTHOR: JOHANNITIUS directs PHARMACIST wielding double pestles (*Isagoge in tegni Galeni*). AUTHOR, TEACHING: HALY ABBAS (*Super tegni Galeni*); CONSTANTINUS AFRICANUS and GALIENUS (*Super Hippocrates Aphorismi*). AUTHOR, DIAGNOSIS: PHILARETUS takes PULSE (*De pulsibus*). DISEASE, MEDICATION: patients with ailments (Hippocratic works); ailments illustrated by patients (in realistic marginal drolleries).

.4 ——, MS 816 (13th c). Medical miscellany.

ff. 1–155 *passim*. AUTHORS: ISAAC JUDAEUS dictates (*De definitionibus*); PETRUS HISPANUS with book and three patients (*Thesaurus pauperum*). DIAGNOSIS: by UROSCOPY (ISAAC JUDAEUS, *De febribus*; *De diversis coloribus urinae*). MATERIA MEDICA: herbs, fish (GUALTERUS AGILON, *De urinis*; ISAAC JUDAEUS, *De febribus*; *De experimentis rusticorum*). ORTHOPAEDICS: doctors bandage patient's torso (ISAAC, *De febribus*). MEDICATION: doctor brings herb to three bed-patients; doctors pour medicine into patient's mouth (ISAAC, *De febribus*). REGIMEN: people eating and drinking (ISAAC, *De febribus*; *De conferentibus*). DIAGNOSIS: doctor takes woman's PULSE (GUALTERUS AGILON, *De pulsibus*). PHARMACY: compounding *pomum ambrae* with double pestles; pharmacist with scales (PETRUS HISPANUS, *Thesaurus pauperum*) DIVINE HEALING: doctor prays to God, angels and Tobit for bed-patient's recovery. PAEDIATRICS: doctor with two babies (*De passionibus puerorum*). SURGERY: doctor operates on woman's eye (ZACHARIAS SALERNITANUS, *De morbis oculorum*).

.5 ——, MS 824 (14th c). Medical miscellany.

ff. 1, 13, 55, 90v. AUTHOR: JOHANNITIUS (*Isagoge in tegni Galeni*); HIPPOCRATES (*Aphorismi*); and HALY ABBAS (*Isagoge in tegni Galeni*) expound concerning their works. DIAGNOSIS: AEGIDIUS CORBOLIENSIS with UROSCOPY flask (*De judiciis urinarum*).

.6 ——, MS 828 (*c.* 1300). MESUE.

ff. 1, 47. DIVINE HEALING: Christ as a healer (*De consolatione medicinarum*). AUTHOR: Mesue in professorial robes (*Grabadin*).

.7 ——, Incunabulum I.R.41 (1480). AVICENNA, *Opera*.

(Inserted parchment folio): AUTHOR, DIAGNOSIS: Avicenna taking pulse, patients with UROSCOPY flasks.

.8 ——, Incunabulum 674–675 (1485). AVICENNA, *Canon*.

f. a 2. DIAGNOSIS: Two doctors (Cosmas and Damian?), one holds UROSCOPY flask.

41.1 CUES (Kues), West Germany, HOSPITAL, MS 209 (14–15th c.). Astrological-medical miscellany.*

f. 68. PROGNOSIS: ZODIAC-Microcosm figures (male and female).

42.1 DANZIG (Gdansk), Poland, CITY LIBRARY (Danziger Stadtbibliothek), MS St. Mary F.200 (1439). Medical miscellany.*

f. 270. SURGERY: instruments in margins (LANFRANCUS MEDIOLANENSIS, *Chirurgia*).

.2 ——, MS 2310 (now at Warsaw, Biblioteka Narodowa, q.v.).

43.1 DARMSTADT, West Germany, HESSISCHE LANDES- UND HOCHSCHULBIBLIOTHEK, MS 876 (1330). Religious miscellany.*

ff. 172v, 232v. DIAGNOSIS: ape-doctor does UROSCOPY for dog (marginal drollery). SURGERY: ape-surgeon cuts goat's throat, ape assistant holds bowl (marginal drollery).

44.1 DESSAU, East Germany, LANDESBIBLIOTHEK, MS Georg 271 (14th c.). ELLUCHASEM ELIMITHAR, *Tacuinum sanitatis*.

f. 1v. ANATOMY, BLOODLETTING-MAN: showing internal organs.

.2 ——, MS Georg 378 (15th c.). MACER FLORIDUS, *De viribus herbarum*.

f. 71v. PHARMACY: man with flask.

.3 ——, MS Georg L.1².Qu. (15th c.). Medical miscellany.

f. 162r–v. SURGERY: instruments (*Experimenta medicarum*).

.4 ——, MS 7 (15th c.). Old Testament (in German).

ff. 28, 150. SURGERY: three circumcision scenes.

45.1 DIJON, France, CITY LIBRARY (Bibliothèque de Dijon), MS (15th c.).*

ff. 19, 20, 21. HOSPITAL.

46.1 DRESDEN, East Germany, LIBRARY (Sächsische Landesbibliothek), MS C.310 (14th c). Medical miscellany.

f. 57v. ANATOMY: bone-man.

.2 ——, MS Db. 92–93 (15th c). GALEN, *Opera* (in two volumes).[1]

ff. 1–617 *passim*. AUTHOR, DIAGNOSIS: by PULSE and UROSCOPY (Fig. 14). PHARMACY. MEDICATION. CLYSTERING. BLOODLETTING. (Elaborately portrayed.) (Figs. 22, 34, 54.)

.3 ——, MS Oc. 62 (15th c). Miscellany (in French).

ff. 183–203. MATERIA MEDICA: herbs, full-page, on recto pages.

.4 ——, MS P.33 (15th c). Medical miscellany.

f. 268. BLOODLETTING-MAN.

.5 ——, MS P.34, no. 78 (15th c). Medical miscellany.

ff. 212v–215v. OBSTETRICS: diagrams of uterus showing foetal presentations. DISEASE: nude female. BLOODLETTING-MAN.

47.1 DUBLIN, Ireland, CHESTER BEATTY LIBRARY, MS 74 (14th c). *Histoire ancienne* (in French).★

f. 199. OBSTETRICS: Caesar's birth, Caesarian section.

.2 ——, MS 80 (15th c). *De naturis rerum.*★

f. 7r–v. REGIMEN: five ages of man. ANATOMY: skeleton.

48.1 DUBLIN, Ireland, KING'S INN LIBRARY, MS 17 (12–13th c). Medical miscellany.

pp. 1, 5. ANATOMY: male and female figures.

49.1 DUBLIN, Ireland, ROYAL COLLEGE OF SURGEONS, MS 'Lentaigne' (*c.* 1400). JOHN ARDERNE, *Practica.*

pp. 1–165 *passim*. MATERIA MEDICA, SURGERY, DISEASE, MEDICATION: marginal sketches of herbs, ailing members and organs, instruments, etc. SURGERY: instruments and operation for *fistula in ano*.

50.1 DURHAM, England, CATHEDRAL LIBRARY, MS Hunter 100 (11–12th c). Astrological-medical miscellany.

ff. 122–123v. SURGERY: CAUTERY-MEN, doctors and assistants heat and apply irons.

.2 ——, MS B.IV.38 (15th c). Scientific-religious miscellany.

f. 214. BLOODLETTING-MAN (*De flebotomia*).

51.1 DURHAM, England, UNIVERSITY LIBRARY, MS Cosin V.IV.7 (15th c). Astrological-medical miscellany (in Latin and English).

---

[1] The second of the two volumes is badly war-damaged, but all the miniatures had been photoreproduced (some in colour) by E. C. Van Leersum and W. Martin in *Codices Graeci et Latini* . . . (Leiden, 1910).

ff. 45v, 47. DIAGNOSIS: UROSCOPY flasks, in circular chart, in separate illustrations. ANATOMY: human head showing sense centres and related organs.

52.1 DURHAM, North Carolina, U.S.A. DUKE UNIVERSITY MEDICAL LIBRARY, MS Josiah Trent (15th c). Calendar (in German).

f. 1. VETERINARY MEDICINE: St. Jerome, with scalpel, removes thorn from lion's paw.

53.1 EDINBURGH, Scotland, ROYAL OBSERVATORY, MS Crawford 9.11.3 (1279). AL-HAZEN, *De aspectibus*.

f. 4. ANATOMY: diagrams of eye and optic nerve.

.2 ——, MS Crawford 9.13.2 (1497). Astrological-medical miscellany (in German and Latin).

f. 36r–v. ANATOMY: diagram and human half-figure showing sense centres and related organs.

.3 ——, MS Crawford 9.14.5 (1464). Astrological-medical miscellany (in German).

ff. 37–104v *passim*. REGIMEN: the four TEMPERAMENTS. BLOODLETTING: on woman's arm; on man's back (with cups) (Fig. 57). ZODIAC-BLOODLETTING-MAN. BATHING: couples in tubs, eating and drinking. DIAGNOSIS: doctor with UROSCOPY flask taking PULSE (Fig. 13).

54.1 EDINBURGH, Scotland, UNIVERSITY LIBRARY, MS 20 (1306). RASCHID-AD-DIN, History (in Persian).

ff. 3, 42. MEDICATION: king's shoulder smeared with human brain. OBSTETRICS: birth of Mohammed.

.2 ——, MS 161 (1307). AL-BIRUNI, World history (in Arabic).

f. 16. SURGICAL OBSTETRICS: birth of Julius Caesar by Caesarian section.

.3 ——, MS 165(D.b.II.10) (13th c). AVICENNA, *Canon*.

ff. 2v, 64, 298, 378. AUTHOR, TEACHING: Avicenna expounds to students. DIAGNOSIS: doctor takes woman's PULSE.

.4 ——, MS 169(Laing 187) (1481). Medical miscellany (in Latin and English).

f. 2v. AUTHOR, DIAGNOSIS: RHAZES does UROSCOPY (*Almansor*).

.5 ——, MS 170(D.b.VI. 1) (12–13th c). SERAPION, *Breviarium*.

ff. 1, 87v, 111v. AUTHOR, TEACHING: Serapion hands book to one of three students. DIAGNOSIS: doctor does UROSCOPY for bed-patient; takes PULSE of bed-patient.

.6 ——, MS 176(Laing 181) (15th c). PETRUS DE EBULO, *De balneis Puteolanis*.

ff. 1–8v. BATHING: patients in health baths at Puteoli.

.7 ——, MS 416 (16–18th c). MANSUR, Anatomy (in Persian).

ff. 17–97 *passim*. ANATOMY: vein-man; artery-man; bone-man; nerve-man; muscle-man; pregnant woman; separate sketches of external and internal organs.

.8 ——, MS D.b.3.24 (15th c). ANTONIUS CERMISONUS, *Consilia*.

ff. 3–35v *passim*. DISEASE: marginal figures pointing to, or displaying, ailments of head, throat, hands, etc. DENTISTRY: patient holding his extracted tooth.

.9 ——, MS D.b.3.30 (15th c). Hours of Virgin Mary (with marginal drolleries).

ff. 25v, 105v. DIAGNOSIS: ape-doctor does UROSCOPY for cat as bed-patient; ape-doctor holds UROSCOPY flask. ORTHOPAEDICS: cripple with leg in splint.

55.1 EINSIEDELN, Switzerland, STIFTSBIBLIOTHEK, MS 360 (12th c). ISIDORUS HISPALEN-SIS, *Etymologiae*, IV, 1.*

f. 48v. BLOODLETTING: doctor with bowl holds scalpel in his mouth.

56.1 ERFURT, East Germany, CITY LIBRARY (Wissenschaftliche Bibliothek der Stadt), MS Amplon. F.41 (14th c). Medical miscellany.

ff. 25, 49. MATERIA MEDICA: human half-figures point to *draguntea* and *rosa* (DIOSCORIDES, *Materia medica*, alphabetical).

.2 ——, MS Amplon. F.240 (*c*. 1300). Medical miscellany; illustrations from GULI-ELMUS DE SALICETO, *Practica*.

ff. 1–152 *passim*. AUTHOR, DIAGNOSIS: Gulielmus does UROSCOPY; hooded face of poisoner (*De venenis*). PHARMACY: doctor wields two pestles, assistants bring flasks.

.3 ——, MS Amplon. F.246 (14th c). HIPPOCRATIC works with GALENIC commentaries.

ff. 1, 53, 87. AUTHOR, TEACHING: Hippocrates lectures to student (*Aphorismi*). DIAGNOSIS: Hippocrates does UROSCOPY (*Prognostica*). DISEASE: Hippocrates attends bed-patient (*De morbis acutis*).

.4 ——, MS Amplon. F.257 (14th c). Medical miscellany; miniatures in AVICENNA, *Canon*.

ff. 2–55v *passim*. AUTHOR: Avicenna holding book (four miniatures). BLOOD-LETTING-MAN.

.5 ——, MS Amplon. F.270 (13th c). Medical miscellany.

ff. 1–35 *passim*. SURGERY: instruments in text (ALCOATIM, *De oculis*).

.6 ——, MS Amplon. F.274 (1434). GULIELMUS DE SALICETO, *Practica*.

ff. 168, 173v, 175, 324v. PHARMACY: pot on a fire. DISEASE: woman; nude man. MEDICATION: clyster.

.7 ——, MS Amplon. F.277 (14th c). MESUE. *De simplicibus medicinis*, etc.

ff. 1, 58. AUTHOR: Mesue with book. DISEASE: hatless patient (*Antidotarium*).

.8 ——, MS Amplon. F.287 (1470). Medical miscellany.

ff. 20v, 55. DIAGNOSIS: UROSCOPY flask (ISAAC JUDAEUS, *De urinis*). AUTHOR, DIAGNOSIS: HIPPOCRATES does UROSCOPY (*Aphorismi*).

.9 ——, MS Amplon. Q.173 (13th c). Medical miscellany.

ff. 13v–47 *passim*. AUTHOR: HIPPOCRATES with book (*Aphorismi*); with scroll (*Prognostica*); THEOPHILUS DIAGNOSES by UROSCOPY (*De urinis*); GALEN (*Tegni*).

.10 ——, MS Amplon. Q.178 (14th c). Medical miscellany.

f. 1. AUTHOR, DIAGNOSIS: JOHANNITIUS does UROSCOPY (*Isagoge in tegni Galeni*).

.11 ——, MS Amplon. Q.180 (13–14th c). CONSTANTINUS AFRICANUS, *Viaticum*.

f.6. DISEASE: doctor holds fainting patient, three bystanders.

.12 ——, MS Amplon. Q.184 (1147). CONSTANTINUS AFRICANUS, *Pantegni*.

f. 2. AUTHOR: Constantinus expounds.

.13 ——, MS Amplon. Q.185 (13–14th c). Medical miscellany.

ff. 1–250 *passim*. AUTHOR, TEACHING: GERARDUS CREMONENSIS and two students (*De modo medendi*). DIAGNOSIS: RICARDUS ANGLICUS (?) takes PULSE (*Prognostici Ricardi*). DIAGNOSIS, MATERIA MEDICA: NICOLAUS PRAEPOSITUS does UROSCOPY; herbs in background (*Antidotarium*). DISEASE: doctors discuss patient's condition (*Practica Rogeri*). CAUTERY-MEN (*Rogerina cyrurgia*).

.14 ——, MS Amplon. Q.210 (1304). Medical miscellany.

ff. 89–104 *passim*. ANATOMY: sketches of internal and external organs (HENRI DE MONDEVILLE, *Anathomia*).

.15 ——, MS Amplon. Q.211 (14th c). ALBUCASIS, *Chirurgia*.

ff. 19–68 *passim*. SURGERY: instruments in text.

57.1 ERLANGEN, West Germany, UNIVERSITÄTSBIBLIOTHEK, MS 431(Irm. 532) (13th c). GULIELMUS DE SALICETO, *Chirurgia*.

ff. 33, 141v. ANATOMY: diagram of diaphragm and abdominal tract. SURGERY: instrument (*canula*).

.2 ——, MS 1463 (15th c). GULIELMUS DE SALICETO, *Chirurgia* (in German).

ff. 12–80 *passim*. BATHING: two women in large square tub. ANATOMY: eye and ear diagrams; human head showing sense centres; nude woman; bone-man; squatting nude woman. DISEASE-MAN. PHARMACY: four men compound medicines. ANATOMICAL DISSECTION: cadaver ready for dissection; surgeon incises chest of cadaver. DIAGNOSIS: doctor does UROSCOPY; flasks in circular diagram; doctor takes PULSE of bed-patient. BLOODLETTING: circle of bloodletting cups; cupping-man; bloodletting-man; surgeon incises woman's lower arm. PROGNOSIS: ZODIAC-MAN; PLANET-MAN; internal organs showing.

WOUND-MAN. ORTHOPAEDICS: traction machines for legs and arms. SURGERY: amputation of leg; trephining skull; skull wounds; instruments. PROGNOSIS: circle diagram with head at centre and lines of script. OBSTETRICS: diagrams of uterus showing foetal presentations (MOSCHION, *De aegritudinibus mulierum*).

.3 ——, MS 1492 (15th c). ALBERTUS MAGNUS, *De secretis mulierum* (in Latin and German).

ff. 93v–95. OBSTETRICS: women with abdomens slit showing foetal presentations.

.4 ——, MS 1708 (1491). Medical miscellany (in German).*

ff. 34, 58. PHARMACY: woman with cup and platter inscribed 'von der artznei.' MEDICAL CELEBRITIES: Hippocrates and Galen.

58.1 ESCORIAL, Spain, BIBLIOTECA DEL ESCORIAL, MS F.I.8 (14th c). AVICENNA, *Canon*.

ff. 138v, 282–288. DISEASE: man's head illustrating ailment of ear and tongue. DIAGNOSIS: woman with UROSCOPY flask; doctor with two flasks. MEDICATION: man with two medical flasks.

.2 ——, MS H.I.15 (13th c). *Lapidario del Rey de Alfonso X* (in Spanish).

ff. 1–100 *passim*. AUTHOR, TEACHING: presents book to king; lectures to fourteen. MATERIA MEDICA: stones, men collecting (many illustrations). ANATOMY: Siamese twins.

.3 ——, MS J.16 (13th c). Alfonso X (el Sabio), *Tratado de ajedrez* (in Spanish).*

f. 31. PHARMACY: man using mortar and two pestles. DIAGNOSIS: doctor with UROSCOPY flask, servant or woman patient (?) with flask-carrier.

59.1 ETON, England, ETON COLLEGE LIBRARY, MS 204 (c. 1200). Medical miscellany.

ff. 1–80 *passim*. PHARMACY: three men collect herbs (Fig. 20); doctor and assistant compound medicine. MATERIA MEDICA: herbs (Pseudo-APULEIUS, *Herbarium*); animals (SEXTUS PLACITUS, *De medicina ex animalibus*).

60.1 EVREUX, France, CATHÉDRALE D'EVREUX, MS 114 (14th c). Medical miscellany.*

f. 57. DIAGNOSIS: BERNARDUS DE GORDONIO does UROSCOPY (*Lilium medicinae*).

61.1 EXETER, England, CATHEDRAL CHAPTER LIBRARY, MS 3506 (14th c). JOHANNES DE GADDESDEN, *Rosa Anglica (medicinae)*.

ff. 223–236v *passim*. MATERIA MEDICA: herbs (roughly sketched). DENTISTRY: man stands on his head (text concerns teeth). AUTHOR: examines book. DIAGNOSIS: doctor does UROSCOPY.

62.1 FERMO, Italy, BIBLIOTECA COMMUNALE, MS 18(4°.CA.1/18) (15th c). Medical miscellany.*

ff. 1–185 *passim*. MATERIA MEDICA: herbs and minerals.

63.1 FLORENCE, Italy, LAURENTIAN (Biblioteca Medicae Laurenziana), MS Ash. 144 (14th c). MESUE, *Grabadin*.

f. 1. AUTHOR.

.2 ——, MS Ash. 731 (15th c). Herbal (in Latin and Italian).

ff. 22–100 *passim*. MATERIA MEDICA: herbs, with action scenes. MEDICAL CELEBRITIES: 'Magister Andica medicus de Parigius' points to herb; 'Magister Aloisius erbolarius et medicus de Palermo' points to herb.

.3 ——, MS Ash. 1101 (14th–15th c). LANFRANCUS MEDIOLANENSIS, *Chirurgia*.

ff. 11–177v *passim*. MEDICAL SAINTS, AUTHOR: Lanfrancus stands between Cosmas and Damian, each with jar and spoon. SURGERY: instruments in text.

.4 ——, MS Ash. 1550 (15th c). GERARDUS DI LECIL, *Dialogus creaturarum*. . . .

ff. 20v–100v *passim*. MATERIA MEDICA: herbs, animals and minerals, with action scenes.

.5 ——, MS Conventi Soppressi 276 (14th c). MESUE, *De aegritudinibus*; *Antidotarium*.

ff. 1–121 *passim*. AUTHOR: Mesue expounds to student; holds book; receives Christ's blessing. DISEASE: man pointing to ear; nose; lips. PHARMACY: man with mortar and pestle; stirs syrup in pot on fire.

.6 ——, MS Gaddi 24 (15th c). AVICENNA, *Canon*.

ff. 1, 247v. AUTHOR: Avicenna writing (bystanders). MATERIA MEDICA: Avicenna directs assistants collecting herbs, etc. HOSPITAL: interior (Fig. 3).

.7 ——, MS Gaddi Reliq. 54 (14th c). GULIELMUS DE SALICETO, *Chirurgia*.

f. 1. AUTHOR: with book.

.8 ——, MS Pluteus 73.4 (15th c). CELSUS, *De medicina*.

f. 17. AUTHOR: standing.

.9 ——, MS Pluteus 73.12 (15th c). HIPPOCRATES, *De vagantibus et vicentibus vulgo morbis*.

f. 2v. MEDICAL SAINTS: busts of Cosmas and Damian.

.10 ——, MS Pluteus 73.16 (13th c). Pseudo-APULEIUS, *Herbarium*; SEXTUS PLACITUS, *De medicina ex animalibus*; Pseudo-DIOSCORIDES, *De herbis masculinis et femininis*.

ff. 2v–178 *passim*. AUTHOR: 'Ypocratis,' 'Plato' (i.e., Apuleius) and 'Dioscurus' (i.e., Pseudo-Dioscorides), all holding books; (below) two others holding roll and herb; 'Ypocratis' seated with open book which reads 'Ypocratis Maecenatis salutem . . .'; Pseudo-Apuleius seated with open book which reads 'Ego sum Plato medicus qui hunc libra[m scripsit?]' Pseudo-Dioscorides with book and stylus. MATERIA MEDICA: herbs alone, or in process of being collected, processed, used for MEDICATION of DISEASES, etc., (N.B. the following:) 'Precatio sancta Tellus' and 'Precatio herbarum' rituals for collecting herbs; Goddess Tellus seated at river-bank holding cornucopia with herbs and healing serpent around her, suppliant approaches, Poseidon floats in the river holding trident and paddle(?); Maecenas(?) amidst herbs; 'Escolapius ubi vettonicam ... invenit,' with bucket and hoe(?), collects vettonica; '[H]omerus auctor' with book, 'Archiater' with scroll, Mercurius with herb; men with dog uproot mandragora. Herbs used for MEDICATION, DISEASE: for bewitched person; (Fig. 32) for insomnia; (Fig. 40) for poison antidote; for snake bite; (Figs. 33, 69) for bite of mad dog; (Fig. 29) for sword wound; (Fig. 65) for head fracture; for worms; for children; for stomach ache; for scrofula; (Fig. 30) for arthritis-rheumatism; (Fig. 28) for eyes; (Fig. 31) for cosmetic ointment; PAEDIATRICS, for worms; for intestinal ailment; artemisia fumes 'to make an infant hilarious.'

.11 ——, MS Pluteus 73.21 (14th c.). Medical miscellany, miniatures in JOHANNITIUS, *Isagoge in Tegni Galeni*; HIPPOCRATES, *Aphorismi*.

ff. 2, 14. AUTHOR: Johannitius (or Galen) expounds; Hippocrates expounds.

.12 ——, MS Pluteus 73.22 (14th c.). RHAZES, *Almansor*, *Liber divisionum*, etc.

ff. 1–95 *passim*. AUTHOR: with books, blessed by Christ.

.13 ——, MS Pluteus 73.23 (13th c.). Medical miscellany; miniatures in ALBUCASIS, *Chirurgia*.

ff. 80–110 *passim*. SURGERY: doctor holds patient while assistant trephines; instruments in text. CAUTERY-MEN, and instruments.

.14 ——, MS Pluteus 73.25 (14th c.). BRUNO LONGOBURGENSIS, *Chirurgia*.

ff. 2, 39v. SURGERY: Bruno operates on head of kneeling patient. AUTHOR, TEACHING: one student.

.15 ——, MS Pluteus 73.28 (13th c.). Medical miscellany.

f. 89. ANATOMY, PROGNOSIS: ZODIAC-MAN, internal organs showing.

.16 ——, MS Pluteus 73.36 (13th c.). MESUE, *Grabadin*.

ff. 1, 25, 43. AUTHOR: Mesue.

.17 ——, MS Pluteus 73.41 (9th c.). Pseudo-APULEIUS, *Herbarium*; SEXTUS PLACITUS, *De medicina ex animalibus*; Pseudo-DIOSCORIDES, *De herbis masculinis et femininis*.

ff. 4–7 (12th-century inserts), ff. 13–117v *passim*. MATERIA MEDICA: herbs in margins. MATERIA MEDICA: herbs and animals (Centaur and Escolapius with herb, 'puer' urinates in jar). CAUTERY.

.18 ——, MS Pluteus 73.43 (14th c.). Medical miscellany; illustrations from RHAZES, *Almansor* (in Italian).

ff. 6–59 *passim*. AUTHOR, DIAGNOSIS, SURGERY: Rhazes presents book to Almansor; 'Rasis' does UROSCOPY, two assistants and bystanders; 'Rasis' operates on patient's head; 'Rasis' takes PULSE of emaciated bed-patient; Almansor (crowned) holds book. AUTHOR, TEACHING: lectures to three. MATERIA DIAETICA: animals and herbs for food (*Virtutes cibi*).

.19 ——, MS Pluteus 73.44 (15th c). RHAZES, *Almansor* (in Italian).

ff. 21v, 59v, 89v. AUTHOR: Rhazes, with book, expounds. DIAGNOSIS: doctor and kneeling woman ('De la femine'). MATERIA MEDICA: doctor with herb.

.20 ——, MS Pluteus 74.7 (10–11th c). Medical miscellany; miniatures in APOLLONIUS OF CITIUM, *Dislocations* and SORANUS OF EPHESUS, *Bandages*; (in Greek).

ff. 182–240 *passim*. ORTHOPAEDICS: reductions of dislocations (Fig. 91A). BANDAGES: various types, on patients.

.21 ——, MS Pluteus 82.16 (15th c). THEOPHRASTUS, *De historia plantarum*.

ff. 1, 7, 16v. TRANSLATOR: 'Theodorus Thessalonicensis' holds book. MATERIA MEDICA: clumps of herbs.

.22 ——, MS Strozzi 88 (13th c). Medical miscellany; miniature in CLEOPATRA, *De morbis mulierum*.★

f. 111. DIAGNOSIS: king or queen (?) holds sceptre and UROSCOPY flask.

64.1 FLORENCE, Italy, NATIONAL LIBRARY (Biblioteca Nazionale Centrale), MS 7.10.42 (14th c). Astrological-medical miscellany.★

BLOODLETTING-MAN.

.2 ——, MS Palatina 586 (*c.* 1300). Herbal miscellany (in Provençal).

ff. 4–61 *passim*. MEDICAL CELEBRITIES: Adam; Hippocrates; Avicenna; Johannitius; Averrhoes; Mesue; Serapion (all holding the ends of scrolls of texts from their works). MATERIA MEDICA: herbs (four per page) with action scenes.

GDANSK, see DANZIG.

65.1 GENOA, Italy, UNIVERSITY (Biblioteca Universitaria), MS F.VI (15th c). Herbal miscellany.

ff. 351–367 *passim*. MATERIA MEDICA: herbs.

66.1 GLASGOW, Scotland, UNIVERSITY OF GLASGOW LIBRARY, MS BE.X.6 (15th c). JACOBUS DE VORAGINE, *Legenda aurea*.

ff. 33, 179. SURGERY: circumcision of Christ child. MEDICAL SAINTS: Cosmas and Damian hold jars.

.2 ——, MS Hunter 9 (15th c). AVICENNA, *Canon*.

ff. 1–84 *passim*. AUTHOR, TEACHING: Avicenna lectures to large group of students and colleagues in medieval garb, some of whom hold books. The four TEMPERAMENTS. ANATOMICAL DISSECTION: dissectors incise abdomen; also thigh and arm of female cadaver (demonstrators, colleagues and students observe). ANATOMICAL DEMONSTRATION: demonstrators expound concerning cadavers on slabs (colleagues and students observe). DIAGNOSIS: doctor takes woman's PULSE (assistant and bystanders) (Fig. 11). DIAGNOSIS: doctors receive UROSCOPY flask from servant (other flasks on shelf).

.3 ——, MS Hunter 32 (14th c). Medical miscellany; miniatures in JOHANNITIUS, *Isagoge in tegni Galeni*; THEOPHILUS PROTOSPATHARIUS, *De urinis*; HIPPO-CRATES, *Aphorismi* with comments.

ff. 1–10 *passim*. AUTHOR: Johannitius, Theophilus, Hippocrates and Galen. DIAG-NOSIS: doctors discuss contents of UROSCOPY flask.

.4 ——, MS Hunter 35 (14th c). Medical miscellany.

f. 16. AUTHOR: holds book and herb.

.5 ——, MS Hunter 112 (14–15th c). JOHN ARDERNE, *Speculum flebotomiae, Practica*.

ff. 1v–93 *passim*. AUTHOR: in herb garden with book, desk, implements, etc. CLYSTER: patient seated. DISEASE: patient exposes penis; boy with wen on head. OBSTETRICAL SURGERY: CAESARIAN section; woman, infant, surgeon with knife in teeth.

.6 ——, MS Hunter 251 (15th c). JOHN ARDERNE, *Practica*, etc.

ff. 1–105 *passim*. (marginal sketches): DISEASED members. MATERIA MEDICA, MEDICATION, SURGERY (catheter in penis; excising stone from penis; *fistula in ano*; instruments). PHARMACY (pot on fire), etc. PROGNOSIS: ZODIAC-MAN.

.7 ——, MS Hunter 323 (1432). Medical miscellany.

ff. 2v–51v *passim*. DIAGNOSIS: UROSCOPY flasks, separate and in circular chart.

.8 ——, MS Hunter 339 (14th c). JOHN ARDERNE, *Practica*, etc.

ff. 1–232 *passim*. (marginal sketches): DISEASED MEMBERS. MATERIA MEDICA. MEDICATION. SURGERY. PROGNOSIS: ZODIAC-MAN.

.9 ——, MS Hunter 414 (14–15th c). Medical miscellany.

ff. 48, 121. AUTHOR: bearded, wavey-haired author of *Liber minucionis*. ANATOMY: nude, male figure to illustrate four humours (*Liber medicinalis*).

.10 ——, MS Hunter Or. 40 (1532), Ibn Jazla, *Tacuinum aegritudinum* (in Arabic).

f. 3v. MEDICAL CELEBRITIES: portrait sketches of Aristotle, Galen, Plato, al-Hakim.

.11 ——, MS Hunter Or. 477 (15th c). ISAAC JUDAEUS, *De urinis* (in Hebrew).

ff. 1–66 *passim*. DIAGNOSIS: UROSCOPY flasks in margins.

67.1 GLENCOE, Illinois, JOEL SPITZ, MS 514 (15th c). Book of Hours. MEDICAL SAINTS: Cosmas and Damian with medicine jars.

68.1 HEIDELBERG, West Germany, UNIVERSITY (Universitätsbibliothek), MS Pal. Germ. 5 (15th c). Astrological-medical miscellany (in German).*

BLOODLETTING-MAN.

.2 ——, MS Pal. Germ. 90 (1477). Saints' lives (in German).★
f. 80. DISEASE: Saint heals woman bed-patient; doctor and bystander.

.3 ——, MS Pal. Germ. 144 (1419). Saints' lives (in German).★
ff. 131–410 *passim*. MEDICAL SAINTS: Cosmas and Damian; Pantaleon martyred.

.4 ——, MS Pal. Germ. 164 (1320). *Sächsisches Lehnrecht* (in German).★
f. 8. BATHING: bath house.

.5 ——, MS Pal. Germ. 215 (1488). Medical miscellany (in German).★
ff. 2v–9 *passim*. MATERIA MEDICA: herbs.

.6 ——, MS Pal. Germ. 291 (1471). Astrological-medical miscellany (in German).★
ff. 28v–55v *passim*. REGIMEN: four TEMPERAMENTS. BLOODLETTING: woman patient. BLOODLETTING-MEN. BATHING: couple in a tub. MEDICAL MEN: two doctors.

.7 ——, MS Pal. Germ. 300 (*c.* 1450). CONRAD VON MEGENBURG, *Buch der Natur* (in German).★
ff. 3v–339 *passim*. BLOODLETTING-MAN. MATERIA MEDICA: herbs and animals.

.8 ——, MS Pal. Germ. 320 (*c.* 1470). THOMASIN VON ZIRKLAERE, *Der Wälscher Gast* (in German).★
f. 43v. SURGERY: doctor about to operate on patient tied to post; another doctor and bed-patient.

.9 ——, MS Pal. Germ. 463 (1463). JAKOB VON CESSOLIS, *Schachzabel* (in German).★
f. 50v. MEDICATION: doctor, seated with book and salve box.

.10 ——, MS Pal. Germ. 558 (*c.* 1500). Astrological-medical miscellany (in German).★
f. 129v. BLOODLETTING-MAN.

.11 ——, MS Pal. Germ. 644 (*c.* 1450). Medical miscellany (in German).★
ff. 1v–108 *passim*. DISEASE: sick patient. ZODIAC-BLOODLETTING-MAN. DISEASE-MAN. WOUND-MAN. DIAGNOSIS: UROSCOPY.

.12 ——, MS Pal. Germ. 832 (*c.* 1490). Astrological miscellany (in German).★
ff. 104–105v. REGIMEN: Four TEMPERAMENTS.

69.1 HERTEN CASTLE, West Germany, LIBRARY OF GRAF NESSELRODE-REICHENSTEIN, MS 192.I (9th c). Pseudo-APULEIUS, *Herbarius* and SEXTUS PLACITUS, *De medicina ex animalibus*.★
ff. 1–20 *passim*. MATERIA MEDICA: herbs and animals.

70.1 INNSBRUCK, Austria, UNIVERSITY (Universitätsbibliothek), MS (*c.* 1500). Herbal.★
ff. 1–67 *passim*. MATERIA MEDICA: herbs.

71.1 ISTANBUL, Turkey,[1] BIBLIOTHÈQUE DE FATIH, MS 79 (15th c). CHARAF ED-DIN, *Chirurgia* (in Turkish).*

passim. SURGERY. OBSTETRICS. MEDICATION. DENTISTRY. ORTHOPAEDICS. (illustrations similar to those in Paris, BN, MS Suppl. Turc. 693, q.v.)

72.1 ISTANBUL, Turkey, TOP KAPI SARAY, MS Ahmed III, 3472 (1254). AL-JAZARI, *Automata* (in Arabic).*

BLOODLETTING: Automatic device for measuring amount of blood extracted (Fig. 59).

73.1 ISTANBUL, Turkey, SANCTA SOPHIA LIBRARY, MS 3606 (1354). AL-JAZARI, *Automata* (in Arabic).*

BLOODLETTING: Automatic device for measuring amount of blood extracted.

.2 ——, MS 3703 (formerly 2147–2148) (13th c). DIOSCORIDES, *Materia medica* (in Arabic).*

passim. AUTHOR. MATERIA MEDICA (chiefly herbal). PHARMACY. MEDICATION. DISEASE.

74.1 JENA, East Germany, UNIVERSITY (Universitätsbibliothek), MS EL.F.80 (1372). BARTHOLOMAEUS ANGLICUS, *De proprietatibus rerum* (in French).

ff. 50, 261v, 310. CLINIC: doctor and six patients. MATERIA MEDICA: trees, herbs and animals.

75.1 JERUSALEM, Israel, ARMENIAN PATRIARCHAL LIBRARY, MS 370 (1294). Medical miscellany (in Greek).*

ff. iv, 383. MEDICAL MEN: four doctors; two doctors and patients.

KALININGRAD, see KÖNIGSBERG.

76.1 KARLSRUHE, West Germany, BADISCHE LANDESBIBLIOTHEK, MS Reich. 145 (1460). *Quaestiones super Aristotelis Physicae.*

---

[1] The uncertain shelf numbers of manuscripts in these Istanbul libraries, and the fact that many of them have detached folios in Western collections, both public and private, makes it impossible to present specific data concerning their wealth of miniatures. We cite recent works by experts on Islamic illustrated manuscripts in general and note briefly the types of medical miniatures found in Islamic manuscripts. For surgery, see below, our MS 133.63 (Paris, BN, MS Suppl. Turc. 693). For automata used in bloodletting, see below, our MS 168.1 (Washington, D.C., Freer Gallery of Art, MS 30.76). For veterinary medicine, see Hugo Büchthal, 'Early Islamic Miniatures from Baghdad', *Journal of the Walters Art Gallery*, 1942, 5, 18–39, and Richard Ettinghausen, *Arab Painting*, Cleveland, Ohio, 1962. Dr. Ettinghausen, in response to my requests, has given invaluable information on various types of medical miniatures not only in Istanbul but also on detached folios dispersed throughout the Western World. For materia medica, and especially a widely dispersed Dioscorides manuscript, see both Büchthal and Ettinghausen (cited above) and, for oriental MSS in general, Ibrahim S̲h̲abbūḥ *Catalogue of Arabic Medical MSS in Cairo*, (Cairo, 1959).

f. 1 ANATOMY: human half-figure showing sense centres and related organs; diagram of eye focusing on an object.

77.1 KASSEL, West Germany, LANDESBIBLIOTHEK, MS 2°. Astron. 1 (15th c). Astrological miscellany.

ff. 33, 34. PROGNOSIS: ZODIAC-MAN; ZODIAC-WOMAN.

.2 ——, MS 2°. Phys. Hist. Nat. 10 (9th c). Pseudo-APULEIUS, *Herbarium*.[1]

ff. 1–39v *passim*. MEDICAL CELEBRITIES: 'Aescolapius Medicus Mag[ister]' enthroned; 'Constantinus Magister' (in 12th-century hand); enthroned anonymous author with book; 'Ypocras' (i.e., Hippocrates); 'Apollo'; 'Galienus medicus.' MATERIA MEDICA: herbs (e.g., 'Centaurus medicus' holding herb 'centaurus.').

KÖLN, see COLOGNE.

78.1 KÖNIGSBERG (Kaliningrad), USSR, UNIVERSITY (Staats- und Universitätsbibliothek), MS (15th c). MATTHAEUS PLATEARIUS, *Circa instans* (in French).[2]*

KRAKÓW, see CRACOW.

KUES, see CUES.

79.1 LEIDEN, Holland, UNIVERSITY (Bibliotheek der Rijksuniversiteit), MS B.P.L.1283 (15th c). Pseudo-APULEIUS, *Herbarium*; SEXTUS PLACITUS, *De medicina ex animalibus*.

ff. 1–57 *passim*. MATERIA MEDICA: herbs and animals.

.2 ——, MS Voss. Lat. 3.2° (c. 1375). THEODORICUS DE CERVIA, *Chirurgia*.

ff. 2–173v *passim*. MEDICAL MEN (some in monastic garb, some with books). DIAGNOSIS: doctor and assistant diagnose diseased parts. SURGERY: many scenes of doctors and assistants operating, extracting arrows. CAUTERY. MEDICATION: doctors with jars of medicine attending patients. DISEASE: doctor's assistant catches fainting patient. PHARMACY: doctor with mortar and pestle; doctor and assistant mixing unguent. ORTHOPAEDICS: doctors reducing dislocations and fractures (Figs. 66, 77). BANDAGING: patients. DENTISTRY: doctor feels in patient's mouth (*passio dentium*).

.3 ——, MS Voss. Lat.9.II.4° (c. 700). Medical miscellany; miniatures in Pseudo-APULEIUS, *Herbarium*.

ff. 35v–61 *passim*. MATERIA MEDICA: herbs.

.4 ——, MS Voss. Lat. 13.4° (11th c). Pseudo-APULEIUS, *Herbarium*.

ff. 4v–13 *passim*. MATERIA MEDICA: herbs.

[1] This manuscript was destroyed in World War II, but the author has duplicates of extant colour microfilms.

[2] This manuscript, not available for examination, is similar to Berlin, East Germany, Deutsche Staatsbibliothek, MS Ham. 407 (q.v.).

.5 ——, MS Voss. Gr. Q.50.4° (c. 1470). Anonymous, *Hippiatrica*.

ff. 10–118 *passim*. VETERINARY MEDICINE: diseased horses being treated.

.6 ——, MS Voss. G.G.3.A.2° (1340). VINCENT DE BEAUVAIS, *Speculum historiale* (in French).

ff. 269, 336. SURGERY: circumcision of Christ. MATERIA MEDICA, MEDICATION: queen picks herb, offers medicine to sick man.

80.1 LEIPZIG, East Germany, UNIVERSITY (Universitätsbibliothek), MS 1114 (15th c). Medical miscellany (in German).

ff. 153v–154v. CAUTERY.

.2 ——, MS 1117 (15th c). GALEN, *Tegni*, etc.

ff. 1, 3v. AUTHOR, TEACHING: Galen lectures to four students. DISEASE: patients and friends await treatment.

.3 ——, MS 1118 (13th c). GALEN, *De elementis*, *De interioribus*, etc.

ff. 1–162 *passim*. AUTHOR: Galen with book (at beginnings of sections). DIAGNOSIS: Galen does UROSCOPY.

.4 ——, MS 1119 (13th c). GALENIC miscellany.

ff. 1–74 *passim*. MISCELLANEOUS: monk with book (Haly Abbas, *In tegni Galeni*); monk copies book (Galen on Hippocrates, *Aphorismi*); old man reads book (Galen on Hippocrates, *Prognostica*).

.5 ——, MS 1122 (1400). Medical miscellany.

f. 348. OBSTETRICS, ANATOMY: pregnant woman (internal organs showing).

.6 ——, MS 1125 (14th c). Medical miscellany.

ff. 1–315 *passim*. AUTHOR, DIAGNOSIS: RHAZES does UROSCOPY. MISCELLANEOUS: men with books (at beginnings of sections of Rhazes, *Almansor* and *Liber divisionum*). SURGERY: instruments (CONSTANTINUS AFRICANUS, *De chirurgia*). AUTHOR, SURGERY: JOHANNES DE PARMA expounds; operates on patient's head (*Practica*). CAUTERY scenes.

.7 ——, MS 1138 (c. 1400). AVICENNA, *Canon*.

f. 2v. AUTHOR: with book.

.8 ——, MS 1145 (15th c). CONSTANTINUS AFRICANUS, *Pantegni*. f. 81v. AUTHOR: expounds.

.9 ——, MS 1154 (14th c). Medical miscellany.

ff. 1, 94v, 204v. AUTHOR: CONSTANTINUS AFRICANUS seated (*Viaticum*); DIAGNOSIS: Constantinus Africanus (translator) or ISAAC JUDAEUS (author) takes PULSE and feels head of bed-patient (*De febribus*); ISAAC JUDAEUS does UROSCOPY, flask-carrier nearby (*De urinis*).

.10 ——, MS 1175 (1418). Medical–alchemical miscellany.

ff. 32v, 225v. DIAGNOSIS: UROSCOPY flasks in circular diagram. MEDICATION: by pessary (*pessarium*).

.11 ——, MS 1177 (1400). Medical miscellany.

f. 28. DIAGNOSIS: UROSCOPY flasks in circular diagram.

.12 ——, MS 1189 (14th c). BERNARDUS DE GORDONIO, *Lilium medicinae*.

ff. 1–108 *passim*. AUTHOR: Bernardus lectures to two. DIAGNOSIS: Bernardus points to patient's throat (*De difficultate transgluciendi*); Bernardus points to patient's penis (*De paucitate coitus*); Bernardus examines head of patient (*Alopecia*).

.13 ——, MS 1190 (14th c). BERNARDUS DE GORDONIO, *Lilium medicinae*.

ff. 1–135 *passim*. MATERIA MEDICA: monk holds lily (*Lilium*). DIAGNOSIS: doctors hold UROSCOPY flasks. DISEASE: patient with hand over mouth (*De difficultate transgluciendi*). MEDICATION: patient drinks medicine (*De mala complexione*).

.14 ——, MS 1192 (15th c). Medical miscellany (in Latin and German).

ff. 263v–264v, 277. OBSTETRICS: diagram of uterus showing foetal presentations (German text). DIAGNOSIS: UROSCOPY flasks in circular diagram.

.15 ——, MS 1194 (15th c). NICOLAUS PRAEPOSITUS, *Antidotarium*.

f. 1. AUTHOR: head of Nicolaus (crudely drawn).

.16 ——, MS 1210 (15th c). GUY DE CHAULIAC, *Chirurgia*.

f. 107r–v. SURGERY: instruments in text.

.17 ——, Incunabulum (1490). GALENIC miscellany.

f. 1. DIAGNOSIS: Galen holding UROSCOPY flask.

81.1 LENINGRAD, USSR, ACADEMY OF SCIENCE (Biblioteka Akademii Nauk SSSR), MS F.N.121 (15th c). GUY DE CHAULIAC, *Chirurgia*.

ff. 38–49, 81. SURGERY: instruments in text.

.2 ——, MS (14th c). Chronicle (in Russian).★

f. 55v. DISEASE: Plague-stricken city.[1]

82.1 LENINGRAD, USSR, HERMITAGE MUSEUM (Gosudarstvennyj Ermitazh), Department of Drawings, MS 2 (1381). *Livre de chasse* (in French).

ff. 25v, 38. VETERINARY MEDICINE: veterinarians care for dogs (*Maladies des chiens*) (Fig. 95); veterinarians bathe dogs (*Mener les chiens e abatre*).

83.1 LENINGRAD, USSR, PUBLIC LIBRARY (Publichnaja Biblioteka), MS F.v.III.4 (15th c). BRUNETTO LATINO, *Tresor* (in French).

---

[1] See N. A. Bogoiavlenskii, *Old Russian Medical Practice, XI–XVII Centuries* (Moscow, 1960, in Russian), fig. 25, for photoreproductions of this (also other miniatures). Mrs. Angele Aviconis translated the captions and texts of this and MS 82.2.

ff. 28v, 38–110 *passim*. DIAGNOSIS: doctor does UROSCOPY for bed-patient. MATERIA MEDICA: animals.

.2 ——, MS F.v.IV.12 (15th c.). *Monde universel* (in French).

ff. 3v, 4v. PHARMACY: Noah's ark with *apoteckarie* house on the deck.

.3 ——, MS F.v.VI.1 (16th c.). DIOSCORIDES, *Materia medica* (in French).

ff. 3v–168. AUTHOR: Dioscorides writes (splendid full-page colour portrayal). MATERIA MEDICA: herbs, animals and minerals.

.4 ——, MS Q.v.VI.1 (15th c.). GUY PARAT, *Pour garder . . . la sante* (in French).

f. 1. AUTHOR: Guy Parat at the court of the Duke of Burgundy.

84.1 LENINGRAD, USSR, RUSSIAN MUSEUM, Icon (15–16th c.). MEDICAL SAINTS: Cosmas and Damian hold medicine case and medical implements.

85.1 LISBON, Portugal, BIBLIOTECA DE AJUDA, MS 1006–1019 (52.VI.35) (14th c.). ALDOBRANDINO DA SIENA, *Le régime du corps* (in French).*

ff. 2, 19v. DISEASE: doctor and patient in consultation. BLOODLETTING: doctor pierces elbow of patient who holds bowl for spurting blood.

86.1 LONDON, England, BRITISH MUSEUM, MS Add. 8928 (15th c.). Medical miscellany.

ff. 28–62. MATERIA MEDICA: herbs (Pseudo-APULEIUS, *Herbarium*) and animals (SEXTUS PLACITUS, *De medicina ex animalibus*).

.2 ——, MS Add. 11866 (15th c.). Book of Hours.

ff. 120, 145, 170v. ANATOMY: three skeletons. MEDICAL SAINTS: Cosmas and Damian (with other saints); Cosmas and Damian holding medicine jars.

.3 ——, MS Add. 15097 (15th c.). BONIFACIO DA CALABRIA, *Libro de la menescalcia* (in Italian).

ff. 1–109v *passim*. VETERINARY MEDICINE: treatment of ailing horses. AUTHOR: at table of books and flasks, scribe writes. VETERINARY PROGNOSIS: ZODIAC-HORSE (rare; cf. New York, Pierpont Morgan Library, MS 735).

.4 ——, MS Add. 15582 (14th c.). Medical miscellany (in Irish).

f. 166. BLOODLETTING–MAN.

.5 ——, MS Add. 15692 (15th c.). Picture-book of miscellanies.

f. 39v. SURGERY, MATERIA MEDICA: doctor operates on patient's thigh, assistant with jar; (below) hooded figure at table covered with herbs (Fig. 88).

.6 ——, MS Add. 15697 (1443–1444). Astrological miscellany (in German).

ff. 30–50v *passim*. MEDICAL CELEBRITIES: (illustrating monthly horoscopes) Hippocrates (February); Galen (March); Avicenna (May); Constantinus Africanus (November).

.7 ——, MS Add. 15813 (1525). Calendar of Saints' Days.

ff. 260v, 318v. MEDICAL SAINTS: Cosmas and Damian, Cosmas expounds. ANATOMY: skeleton (unusually detailed).

.8 ——, MS Add. 17063 (15th c). Pseudo-APULEIUS, *Herbarium*.

ff. 1–54 *passim*. MATERIA MEDICA: herbs.

.9 ——, MS Add. 17810 (14th c). GULIELMUS DE SALICETO, *Chirurgia*.

ff. 1, 41, 75, 111. SURGERY: operations on boy's arm; on man's head; doctor bandages lower arm; surgeon cauterizes patient's lower leg (ten bystanders).

.10 ——, MS Add. 17987 (1446). Astrological-medical miscellany (in German).

ff. 91–116v *passim*. BLOODLETTING-MAN: front and back views. PROGNOSIS: ZODIAC-MAN. AUTHOR: dictates to scribe. BLOODLETTING: surgeon attends seated woman who grips staff and catches her blood in a cup. DIAGNOSIS: surgeon (wearing pointed Jewish hat) expounds concerning bowls of blood on table. BATHING: man and woman in tub, food on cross-board. SURGERY: surgeon with scalpel about to circumcise the Christ child, assistant with napkin (Fig. 85A).

.11 ——, MS Add. 18192 (15th c). Book of Hours.

f. 215v. MEDICAL SAINTS: Cosmas and Damian, each holding jar and stirrer.

.12 ——, MS Add. 18851 (15th c). Breviary.

ff. 462, 481. MEDICAL SAINTS, DIAGNOSIS, PHARMACY: Cosmas with UROSCOPY flask, Damian with mortar and pestle. ANATOMY: skulls (in margin).

.13 ——, MS Add. 18854 (1525). Book of Hours.

ff. 144, 146v. MEDICAL SAINTS, DIAGNOSIS, PHARMACY: Cosmas with UROSCOPY flask, Damian with vase and spoon; angel touches bloody spot on thigh of St. Roche.

.14 ——, MS Add. 20698 (1475). *City of Women* (in Dutch).

f. 231v. MEDICATION: 'dochters van Salerne' at bedside of woman (two women attendants).

.15 ——, MS Add. 21115 (15th c). Pseudo-APULEIUS, *Herbarium*.★

passim. MATERIA MEDICA: herbs and animals.

.16 ——, MS Add. 22553 (15th c). Miscellany.

f. 1v. ANATOMY: human head showing sense centres with lines to related organs.

.17 ——, MS Add. 24068 (13th c). Medical miscellany.

f. 26r–v. BLOODLETTING: bloodletting instruments in margins and text.

.18 ——, MS Add. 28725 (15th c). Folded medical calendar. PROGNOSIS: ZODIAC-MAN. BLOODLETTING-MAN.

.19 ——, MS Add. 29301 (15th c). Medical miscellany (in Latin and English); miniatures in JOHN ARDERNE, *Practica chirurgia, Diversitates herbarum*.

ff. 3–54v *passim*. SURGERY: operations for *fistula in ano*, etc., (surgical instruments). BLOODLETTING. DISEASED members. PHARMACY: implements. MEDICATION. PROGNOSIS: ZODIAC-MAN. MATERIA MEDICA: herbs.

.20 ——, MS Add. 34111 (15th c). Medical miscellany (in English).

f. 36v. PROGNOSIS: ZODIAC-MAN.

.21 ——, MS Add. 36617 (*c.* 1300). Medical miscellany; miniatures in ALBUCASIS, *Chirurgia.*

ff. 2–51 *passim.* SURGERY: instruments in text.

.22 ——, MS Add. 41623 (1410-1430). Pseudo-DIOSCORIDES, *Materia Medica.*

ff. 1–148 *passim.* MATERIA MEDICA: herbs and animals (unusually realistic). ANATOMY: cadaver with internal organs showing (on blank folio).

.23 ——, MS Add. 41996V (15th c). Herbal.

Two detached folios. MATERIA MEDICA: herbs (similar to MS Add. 41623).

.24 ——, MS Add. 47680 (formerly Holkham 458) (1326–1327). Pseudo-ARISTOTLE, *Secreta secretorum.*

ff. 1–76 *passim.* AUTHOR: Pseudo-Aristotle expounds; lectures; listens; argues with king. DIAGNOSIS: king, adviser, and doctors with UROSCOPY flasks. DISEASE: king and doctors discuss ailments. PROGNOSIS: king, astrologer with globe, and doctors. REGIMEN: king and companions dine, examine foods and drinks. MEDICATION: king and two bystanders, doctor with laxative herb, doctor with medicine jar.

.25 ——, MS Arund. 251 (14th c). Medical miscellany (in Latin and German).

ff. 36v, 37, 46. BLOODLETTING-MAN. ANATOMICAL DISEASE-MAN: disease captions on body, sense centres captioned. PROGNOSIS: ZODIAC-MAN.

.26 ——, MS Arund. 295 (14th c). Medical miscellany (in Latin and German).

ff. 16, 256. SURGERY: instruments (GOTFRIDUS, *Flores medicinae*). DIAGNOSIS: doctor takes PULSE of woman.

.27 ——, MS Arund. 306 (15th c). Astrological-medical miscellany.

f. 29v. BLOODLETTING-MAN.

.28 ——, MS Burney 3 (13th c). *Biblia ROBERTI abbatis de libraria Sanctae Augustini Cantuariensis.*

ff. 1, 177. PHARMACY: plan of monastic dormitory in three stories, with an *apotecaria* on each. SURGERY: kneeling doctor circumcizes (?) one of three nude males (*Incipit Liber Josue*; cf. ch. 5:2–5, and MS Egerton 1894 for similar biblical circumcisions).

.29 ——, MS Cotton, Nero D.II (14th c). Miscellany of chronicles (in Latin and French).

f. 36. MEDICAL CELEBRITY: Galen holds UROSCOPY flask ('Galenus insignis medicus').

.30 ——, MS Cotton, Vitellius C.III (11th c). Miscellany (in Latin and English); miniatures in Pseudo-APULEIUS, *Herbarium.*

ff. 11v–74v *passim.* AUTHOR: Aesculapius, Centaurus, 'Plato,' with herbs, books, etc. MATERIA MEDICA: herbs, with action scenes.

.31 ——, MS Cotton, Vitellius D.IX (14th c). Miscellany.

f. 4. BLOODLETTING-MAN.

.32 ——, MS Egerton 747 (*c.* 1300). MATTHAEUS PLATEARIUS, *Circa instans.**
passim. MATERIA MEDICA: herbs.

.33 ——, MS Egerton 1065 (15th c). JULIUS CAESAR, *Commentarii* (in French).

f. 9. OBSTETRIC SURGERY: Caesar's birth by surgery, stitches visible on mother.

.34 ——, MS Egerton 1070 (15th c). Book of hours of René of Anjou.

ff. 53, 102v. ANATOMY: cadaver with abdomen slit open (liturgy for the dead). MEDICAL SAINTS: Cosmas and Damian holding tall medicine jars.

.35 ——, MS Egerton 1624 (15th c). Astrological-medical miscellany (in Latin, French and English).

ff. 118, 120v, 216v. PROGNOSIS: ZODIAC-MAN. BLOODLETTING-MEN.

.36 ——, MS Egerton 1894 (14th c). Pictorial Bible (with descriptions in French).

ff. 9v–19 *passim.* SURGERY: circumcision scenes to illustrate *Genesis* 17:10.23 and 34:24. OBSTETRICS: midwife marks one of twins to illustrate *Genesis* 38:28 (cf. MS Burney 3 for similar biblical circumcisions).

.37 ——, MS Egerton 2020 (*c.* 1400). SERAPION, *De medicamentis* (in Italian).

ff. 1–170 *passim.* AUTHOR: Serapion with book. MATERIA MEDICA: herbs (very naturalistic).[1]

.38 ——, MS Egerton 2188 (1353). Miscellany (in Dutch).

f. 10. PROGNOSIS: ZODIAC-MAN.

.39 ——, MS Egerton 2572 (15th c). Miscellany (in Latin and English).

ff. 50–51. BLOODLETTING-MAN. PROGNOSIS: ZODIAC-MAN. MEDICAL SAINTS: Cosmas with UROSCOPY flask, Damian with spatula and medicine case.

.40 ——, MS Egerton 2724 (15th c). Folding almanac (in English). PROGNOSIS: ZODIAC-MAN.

.41 ——, MS Harley 1585 (11–12th c). Pseudo-APULEIUS, *Herbarium*; SEXTUS PLACITUS, *De medicina ex animalibus*; Pseudo-DIOSCORIDES, *De herbis femininis*.

ff. 1–92 *passim.* PHARMACY: doctor with scroll directs assistant using mortar and pestle. CAUTERY: surgeon cauterizes patient. CAUTERY-MEN with disease captions. SURGERY: surgeons excise haemorrhoids; cataract; nasal polyps (Fig. 50). MATERIA MEDICA: suppliant and minister bless herbs (*Precatio omnium herbarium*). MATERIA MEDICA: herbs and animals, with action figures (through-

[1] For the importance of this manuscript and its relationship to Egerton, MS 747 and Venice, MS Lat.VI.59, see Otto Pacht, "Early Italian Nature Studies . . . ," *J. Warburg and Courtauld Institutes,* 1950, *13,* 29 ff.

out the MS). PROGNOSIS: chicken eats grain, indicating favourable prognosis (f. 19). MEDICAL CELEBRITY: 'Omerus Auctor, Archiater Mercurius' with a herb (f. 33v).

.42 ——, MS Harley 2332 (15th c.). Astrological miscellany.

f. 18. PROGNOSIS: ZODIAC-MAN.

.43 ——, MS Harley 3140 (13th c.). Medical miscellany.

ff. 1–278 passim. AUTHOR: JOHANNITIUS expounds (Isagoge ad tegni Galeni); GALEN lectures to two (Liber tegni); HIPPOCRATES and GALEN argue (Aphorismi); ISAAC JUDAEUS lectures to three (De febribus). DIAGNOSIS: HIPPOCRATES takes PULSE (Prognostica); THEOPHILUS PROTOSPATHARIUS does UROSCOPY (De urinis); CONSTANTINUS AFRICANUS takes PULSE (Viaticum). MEDICATION: HIPPOCRATES medicates bed-patient (De regimine acutorum). REGIMEN: ISAAC JUDAEUS with fish, birds, herb; and with a man at table (De dietis universalibus). PHARMACY: NICOLAUS PRAEPOSITUS directs assistant using mortar and two pestles (Antidotarium).

.44 ——, MS Harley 3487 (14th c.). ARISTOTELEAN Miscellany.

f. 105. REGIMEN: man and woman in bed, baby in cradle (De generatione).

.45 ——, MS Harley 3719.IX (14th c.). Medical miscellany (in Latin and English).

ff. 154, 158–159. PROGNOSIS: ZODIAC-BLOODLETTING-MAN; BLOODLETTING-MAN (double-page illustration).

.46 ——, MS Harley 3812 (15th c.). Calendar.

f. 5v. BLOODLETTING-MAN.

.47 ——, MS Harley 4375 (15th c.). VALERIUS MAXIMUS, Memorabilia (in French).

f. 38. DIAGNOSIS: doctor takes PULSE of female patient.

.48 ——, MS Harley 4379 (15th c.). JEAN FROISSART, Chroniques (in French).

p. 245. DIAGNOSIS: doctor does UROSCOPY for dying count.

.49 ——, MS Harley 4986 (12th c.). Medical miscellany; miniatures in Pseudo-APULEIUS, Herbarium.

ff. 1–49 passim. MATERIA MEDICA: herbs.

.50 ——, MS Harley 5294 (12th c.). Medical miscellany; miniatures in Pseudo-APULEIUS, Herbarium and Pseudo-DIOSCORIDES, De herbis femininis.

ff. 1–58. MATERIA MEDICA: herbs, with action scenes.

.51 ——, MS Harley 5311 (15th c.). Astrological-medical calendar.

ff. 1, 6, 8. BLOODLETTING-MAN. PROGNOSIS: ZODIAC-MAN. DIAGNOSIS: circular UROSCOPY chart.

.52 ——, MS Prints and Engravings 197.d.2 (c. 1510). HENRICUS KULLMAURER and ALBERT MEHER, medical picture-book (full-page illustrations with captions in Italian).

ff. 1–205. ANATOMY: pregnant woman with slit abdomen, two diagrams of uterus; sketches of skeletons and nude men. OBSTETRICS: diagrams of uterus showing foetal presentations. PHARMACY: men hold herbs, implements, etc. MATERIA MEDICA: herbs and animals. MEDICATION: Knight of Malta treats bloody leg; Chiron treats body wounds; turbaned doctors give pills to patients drinking from bottles; herbs and potion for snake bite; herb for leg wound (Fig. 38); 'Diavolo,' 'Angelo' and 'Medico' attend patients. SURGERY: removal of cataract (Fig. 70); hernia operation; caesarian section; operation for stone (Fig. 82b); removal of foetus (by Knight of Malta); operation for leg wound; catheterization of urinary tract (Fig. 83). DENTISTRY: doctors probe teeth of patients. MEDICAL CELEBRITIES (ff. 93–116v passim): Avicenna; Haly Abbas; Celsus; Bartholomew; Mesue; Rhazes; Dioscorides; Serapion; Pliny; Albucasis; Hippocrates, etc. PROGNOSIS: ZODIAC-MAN. PAEDIATRICS: children, in bed, defecating, nurse. REGIMEN: man broken on wheel; man kills serpent; Adam; seven ages of man; tomb of Aesculapius, etc.

.53 ——, MS Royal 6.E.VI (14th c). JACOBUS, Omne bonum (vol. I).

ff. 3, 269, 122v, 258v, 179, 503. SURGERY: circumcision scenes. MEDICATION, DISEASE: 'apostema'; 'cerebrum.' BATHING: man with woman attendant. DENTISTRY: doctor extracts tooth.

.54 ——, MS Royal 10.E.IV (14th c). GREGORY IX, Decretales.*

ff. 52, 53v. ANIMAL DOCTORS: fox and monkey as doctors (marginal drolleries).

.55 ——, MS Royal 15.E.II (1482). BARTHOLOMAEUS ANGLICUS, De proprietatibus rerum (in French).

ff. 60, 77v, 139v, 165. The four TEMPERAMENTS. MEDICATION: two doctors treat patient. CLINIC: doctors MEDICATE elbow, UROSCOPY (four patients) (Fig. 2).

.56 ——, MS Royal 15.E.VI (c. 1445). Literary miscellany (in French).

ff. 21v, 273. PROGNOSIS: caladrius bird (Hystoire du bon roy Alixandre). PAEDIATRICS: mother in bed, nurse with seven babies in nearby cradle (Hystoire du chevalier au Signe).

.57 ——, MS Royal 16.F.VIII (15th c). ALDOBRANDINO DA SIENA, Le régime du corps (in French).

f. 1. PROGNOSIS: astrological clinic.

.58 ——, MS Royal 16.G.VII (1473). Commentaires de Caesar (in French).

f. 32. OBSTETRICAL SURGERY: Caesar's birth by caesarian section.

.59 ——, MS Royal 17.F.II (1479). Hystoire Caesar (in French).

f. 9. OBSTETRICAL SURGERY: Caesar's birth by caesarian section.

.60 ——, MS Royal 18.A.VI (15th c). Medical miscellany (in English).

ff. 27–28, 32–34v. DIAGNOSIS: UROSCOPY flasks in circular diagrams (Anon., *On colour of urines*). ANATOMY: blood-vessel-man (front and rear views); nerve-man (front, rear); internal organs; bone-man (anonymous, without text; see London, Wellcome MS 290 for miniatures with text).

.61 ——, MS Royal 19.B.X.1 (15th c.). ALDOBRANDINO DA SIENA, *Le régime du corps* (in French).

f. 2. PROGNOSIS: astrological clinic.

.62 ——, MS Royal 19.B.XVII (1382). *Legende dorée* (in French).

f. 36v, 266. SURGERY: circumcision of Christ child (realistic). MEDICAL SAINTS: Cosmas and Damian holding medicine jars.

.63 ——, MS Royal 19.C.VI (*c.* 1500). XENOPHON, *Anabasis* (in French).

f. 20. MEDICATION: doctor with flask administers to dying King Darius.

.64 ——, MS Royal 19.D.I (14th c.). *Hystoire du bon roy Alixandre* (in French).

f. 39v. PROGNOSIS: caladrius (?) bird.

.65 ——, MS Royal 20.A.V (14th c.). *Hystoire du bon roy Alixandre* (in French).

f. 75v. PROGNOSIS: caladrius (?) bird.

.66 ——, MS Royal 20.B.IX (15th c.). ALDOBRANDINO DA SIENA, *Le régime du corps* (in French).

f. 1. PROGNOSIS: astrological clinic.

.67 ——, MS Royal 20.B.XX (15th c.). *Hystoire du bon roy Alixandre* (in French).

ff. 83, 86v. PROGNOSIS: caladrius (?) bird. OBSTETRICS: mother, new-born child, nurse, bath-basin.

.68 ——, MS Royal 20.C.IX (15th c.). JEAN CHARTIER, *Cronique du temps de très chrestien roy Charles* (in French).

f. 311. DIAGNOSIS: death-bed of Charles VII, doctor holds flask.

.69 ——, MS Sloane 6 (*c.* 1400). Medical miscellany; miniatures in JOHN ARDERNE, *Practica de fistula in ano* (in English).

ff. 141–182 *passim.* SURGERY: fistula operation and instruments. MEDICAL CELE-BRITIES, CLINICS: Apollo lectures to three; Aesculapius instructs patient; Aesculapius teaches two to collect herbs; Aesculapius instructs assistants concerning scales and mortar and pestle; Hippocrates and Galen discuss materia medica (f. 175r–v). CAUTERY-MEN. BLOODLETTING: woman places bloodletting cups on back of patient. SURGERY: instruments.

.70 ——, MS Sloane 56 (14th c.). JOHN ARDERNE, *Liber chirurgiae.*

ff. 1–100 *passim.* SURGERY: operations and instruments (in margins); *fistula in ano* (Fig. 87b). MATERIA MEDICA: herbs. MEDICATION: with clysters; and medicines. DIAGNOSIS: UROSCOPY flasks. PHARMACY. DISEASE: woman with spot on breast; man with crutches; man with sores on penis, etc. (ailing members, *passim*). GYNAECOLOGY: breast cupping. AUTHOR: John Arderne expounds (f. 84v).

.71 ——, MS Sloane 134 (14th c). Medical miscellany.

f. 25. BLOODLETTING-MAN.

.72 ——, MS Sloane 249 (15th c). Medical miscellany (in English).

ff. 196v–197v. OBSTETRICS: diagrams of uterus showing foetal presentations.

.73 ——, MS Sloane 277 (15th c). Medical miscellany (in English).

ff. 49v, 50v, 64. SURGERY: instruments in text (GULIELMUS DE SALICETO, *Chirurgia*); instruments and operation for *fistula in ano* (JOHN ARDERNE, *Fistula in Ano*).

.74 ——, MS Sloane 282 (14th c). Astrological-medical miscellany.

ff. 21v–30, 47v–48. DIAGNOSIS: UROSCOPY flasks.

.75 ——, MS Sloane 335 (14th c). JOHN ARDERNE, *Liber medicinarum*.

ff. 1–87 *passim*. SURGERY: instruments and operations, *fistula in ano*, etc. DIAGNOSIS: UROSCOPY flasks. CLYSTERS. PHARMACY: implements. MATERIA MEDICA: herbs (full-page). MEDICATION, DISEASED MEMBERS, etc., (rough marginal sketches throughout).

.76 ——, MS Sloane 420 (14th c). Medical miscellany.

f. 84v. ANATOMY: diagram of eye (concentric circles) focussing on object.

.77 ——, MS Sloane 433 (15th c). Medical miscellany (in Latin and English).

ff. 60–64, 99r–v. DIAGNOSIS: UROSCOPY flasks (captions in English). PROGNOSIS: ZODIAC-MAN. BLOODLETTING-MAN (rear view with cupping points).

.78 ——, MS Sloane 563 (15th c). Surgical miscellany; miniatures in JOHN ARDERNE, *Fistula in Ano* (in English).

ff. 62v–121v *passim*. PROGNOSIS: ZODIAC-MAN. SURGERY: instruments and operation for *fistula in ano*, etc. MEDICATION. DISEASED MEMBERS. PHARMACY: implements. MATERIA MEDICA: herbs (marginal sketches throughout).

.79 ——, MS Sloane 635 (15th c). Medical miscellany.

ff. 88–98. DIAGNOSIS: UROSCOPY flasks.

.80 ——, MS Sloane 783 (15th c). Medical miscellany.

ff. 221–225 *passim*. DIAGNOSIS: UROSCOPY flasks.

.81 ——, MS Sloane 795 (15th c). JOHN ARDERNE, *Practica chirurgiae* and *Liber medicinarum*.

ff. 20v–163 *passim*. SURGERY: instruments and operations for *fistula in ano*, etc. DISEASED MEMBERS. MATERIA MEDICA: herbs. MEDICATION. PHARMACY: implements, etc. (marginal sketches throughout).

.82 ——, MS Sloane 963 (15th c). Miscellany (in Latin and English).★

f. 5. PROGNOSIS: ZODIAC-BLOODLETTING-MAN with side captions on zodiac, constellations, etc.

.83 ——, MS Sloane 981 (14–15th c). Medical miscellany.

f. 68. ANATOMY: diagram of eye (concentric circles).

.84 ——, MS Sloane 1975 (12–13th c). Medical miscellany.

ff. 10v–93v *passim*. MATERIA MEDICA; herbs, with action scenes, animals (Pseudo-APULEIUS, *Herbarium*; Pseudo-DIOSCORIDES, *De herbis femininis*; SEXTUS PLACITUS, *De medicina ex animalibus*). PHARMACY: doctor directs assistant with mortar and pestle. CAUTERY and SURGERY: operations on haemorrhoids, nasal polyps, cataract (at end of MS).

.85 ——, MS Sloane 1977 (13th c). Medical miscellany (in French).

ff. 1–9v, 47v, 49v–51v, 136r–v. AUTHOR: with book (*Christ as Creator*). SURGERY: cases (six to a page) illustrating DIAGNOSIS, OPERATIONS, ORTHOPAEDICS, MEDICATION, BANDAGING (Fig. 25) (ROGERIUS SALERNITANUS, *Chirurgia*). AUTHOR: lectures to three; directs assistant in PHARMACY; examines DISEASED patients displaying their ailments (MATTHAEUS PLATEARIUS, *Circa instans*). MEDICAL CELEBRITIES, CLINIC: Galen and Hippocrates consult over URO-SCOPY flask and bed-patients (*Livre de Cyrurgie . . . Les ordonements des Galen et Ypocras*). BATHING (Fig. 94A).

.86 ——, MS Sloane 2002 (15th c). JOHN ARDERNE, *Fistula in Ano*.

ff. 24r–v, 42, 52v–181 *passim*. SURGERY: instruments and operation for *fistula in ano* (AUTHOR probing anus) (Fig. 87a). PROGNOSIS: ZODIAC-MAN. DIAGNOSIS by UROSCOPY. CLYSTERS. DISEASED MEMBERS. MEDICATION.

.87 ——, MS Sloane 2156 (15th c). Scientific miscellany.★

f. 11. ANATOMY: sense centres (ROGER BACON, *De perspectiva*).

.88 ——, MS Sloane 2250 (15th c). Folding calendar.

PROGNOSIS: ZODIAC-MAN.

.89 ——, MS Sloane 2320 (14th c). Astrological-medical miscellany.★

f. 20. PROGNOSIS: ZODIAC-MAN.

.90 ——, MS Sloane 2435 (15th c). Scientific miscellany; miniatures in ALDOBRAN-DINO DA SIENA, *Le régime du corps* (in French).

ff. 1–73v *passim*. AUTHOR: Aldobrandino writes. BATHS: man and woman in separate tubs. REGIMEN: man and woman in bed. BLOODLETTING: doctor incising arm of patient; patient with leeches on legs; cupping (Fig. 56). MEDICATION: potion for purging; ointment for head; medicine for ear. DISEASE: patient vomiting. OBSTETRICS: doctor instructing pregnant woman; mother and wet-nurse. DENTISTRY: doctor with patient who points to aching tooth. REGIMEN: food and drink.

.91 ——, MS Sloane 2463 (15th c). Medical miscellany (in English).
   ff. 217–218v. OBSTETRICS: diagrams of uterus showing foetal presentations.

.92 ——, MS Sloane 2839 (c. 1100). Medical miscellany.
   ff. 1v–3. SURGERY: surgeons CAUTERIZE (Fig. 49).

.93 ——, MS Sloane 2947 (14th c). Medical miscellany.
   f. 67. AUTHOR: RHAZES with book (*Liber divisionum*).

.94 ——, MS Sloane 3983 (15th c). ALBUMASAR, *Flores astrologiae*.
   f. 8v. ANATOMY: Siamese twins (one torso, two arms) represent *gemini*.

.95 ——, MS Yates Thompson 19 (14th c). BRUNETTO LATINO, *Tresor* (in French).
   f. 28. MEDICATION: doctor with flask, patient with head bandaged.

87.1 LONDON, England, INDIA OFFICE, MS 2296 (17th-century copy of arabic treatise of
   c. 1400). MANSUR, Anatomy (Pseudo-GALEN, *Figura incisionis, Historia arteriorum*).
   ff. 6v–11. ANATOMY: bone-man; nerve-man; muscle-man; vein-man; artery-
   man; pregnant-woman.

88.1 LONDON, England, ROYAL COLLEGE OF PHYSICIANS, MS 09.61(36) (14th c).
   Scientific miscellany.
   f. 132. ANATOMY: diagram of eye (AL-HAZEN, *Optica*).

.2 ——, MS 09.61(124) (15th c). Astrological-medical miscellany (in English).
   f. 67v. BLOODLETTING-MAN, ribs and veins of arms showing.

.3 ——, MS 09.61(227a) (15th c). Surgical-anatomical miscellany; sketches in HENRI
   DE MONDEVILLE, *Anathomia*.
   ff. 184v, 226–229v, 193. ANATOMY: sketches of stomach; breasts and heart; blood-
   vessels; lungs; liver; omentum; kidneys and uterus. SURGERY: instruments in
   text.

89.1 LONDON, England, ROYAL COLLEGE OF SURGEONS, MS 129a.1.5 (15th c). TROTULA,
   De passionibus mulierum (in English).
   ff. 28v–31. OBSTETRICS: diagrams of uterus showing foetal presentations.

90.1 LONDON (KEW), England, SIR SYDNEY COCKERELL MS (15th c). Folded calendar.
   PROGNOSIS: ZODIAC–MAN: BLOODLETTING–MAN.

91.1 LONDON, England, ST. PAUL'S CATHEDRAL, MS 40.B (13th c). AVICENNA, *Canon*.
   ff. 2v, 66, 394. AUTHOR: Avicenna with book; Avicenna expounds. DIAGNOSIS:
   doctor takes woman's PULSE.

92.1 LONDON, England, VICTORIA AND ALBERT MUSEUM, MS 718 (c. 1300).
   detached folio. REGIMEN: man holds woman's hand (catalogued as 'Doctor taking
   pulse'; more likely an illustration of adjacent text, *De paucitate coytus*).

93.1 LONDON, England, E. WEIL, BOOKSELLER, Catalogue 30, no. 11 (15th c). detached folio. BLOODLETTING-MAN (text in German).*

.2 ——, Catalogue 30, no. 60 (15th c). Surgical miscellany; miniatures in GULIELMUS DE SALICETO, *Chirurgia*.*

ff. 1–44v *passim*. DIAGNOSIS: doctor examines hydrocephalic child; doctor examines man's penis. SURGERY: Gulielmus directs surgeon's operation for fistula on man's arm; on fractured skull; extraction of arrow from man's neck.

94.1 LONDON, England, WELLCOME HISTORICAL MEDICAL LIBRARY, MS 7 (15th c). AEGIDIUS CORBOLIENSIS, *Carmina de judiciis urinarum* (in Latin and English).*

ff. 2–3. DIAGNOSIS: UROSCOPY flasks.

.2 ——, MS 31(1317)[1] (1390). ALDOBRANDINO DA SIENA, *Le régime du corps* (in French). f. 1. AUTHOR: Aldobrandino lectures to six.

.3 ——, MS 39 (14th c). Folded calendar.* BLOODLETTING-MAN.

.4 ——, MS 40(953) (1463). Folded calendar. BLOODLETTING-MAN. PROGNOSIS: ZODIAC-MAN.

.5 ——, MS 49(5000) (*c*. 1420). Medical miscellany of brief texts (in Latin and German) in Apocalypse manuscript.[2]

ff. 35–45v *passim*. ANATOMY: vein-man; bone-man; muscle-man; nerve-man; pregnant disease-woman; four regions of the body; disease-man, sense centres; alimentary canal; wound-man; internal organs, sketched separately (Pseudo-GALEN, *Figura incisionis, Historia arteriorum* . . .). OBSTETRICS: diagrams of uterus showing foetal presentations; Caesarian section. GYNAECOLOGY: women confer; woman suffumigated. CAUTERY-MAN. PROGNOSIS: ZODIAC-MAN. BLOODLETTING-MAN. DIAGNOSIS: circle of UROSCOPY flasks.

.6 ——, MS 55(630) (15th c). Scientific miscellany. f. 93. ANATOMY: human half-figure showing sense centres and related organs (ALBERTUS MAGNUS, *Parvus philosophiae naturalis*).

.7 ——, MS 82 (14th c). Medical miscellany. f. 42v. DIAGNOSIS: doctor does UROSCOPY (HIPPOCRATES, *Aphorismi*).

.8 ——, MS 93 (early 16th c). Medical miscellany (in German).*

----

[1] The numbers in parentheses are those of the original card catalogue. These have been superseded by those in the printed *Catalogue of Western Manuscripts on Medicine and Science in the Wellcome Historical Medical Library*. Compiled by S. A. J. Moorat (London, 1962).

[2] For details, see *Catalogue of Western Manuscripts* . . . , cited in preceding note; also unpublished dissertation at the University of North Carolina, *Fünfbilderserie in Medieval Anatomy*, by Boyd Hill. (Chapel Hill, 1963)

ff. 41–87v *passim.* ANATOMY: nude female; veins of head, arm, hand, foot. BLOOD-LETTING-MAN. DIAGNOSIS: UROSCOPY flasks.

.9 ——, MS 230(999) (15th c). LEONARDO DI STAGIO (DATI), *Sfera mundi* (in Italian).

ff. 4, 12v–13v. DIAGNOSIS: doctor does UROSCOPY, three bystanders; doctor does UROSCOPY. REGIMEN: the four TEMPERAMENTS.

.10 ——, MS 270 (1500–1525). Medical miscellany (in Latin and Italian).*

ff. 9v–250 *passim.* MATERIA MEDICA: herbs (FERANDUS; JOHANNIS DE GADDESDEN, *Rosa medicinae*). DIAGNOSIS: UROSCOPY flasks (various urine treatises).

.11 ——, MS 285(635) (14th c). GALENIC miscellany.

ff. 1–99 *passim.* AUTHOR: Galen in doctor's garb with student; Galen expounds (*Methodus medendi*); Galen lectures (*De diebus criticis*). DISEASE: swollen face (*phlegmones*); facial tumours (*Methodus medendi*); emaciated patient (*De mala complexione*); bed-patient with nose-bleed (*De crisibus*). DIAGNOSIS: doctor and bed-patient, bystanders with UROSCOPY flasks (*De differentiis febrium*).

.12 ——, MS 286(1512) (14th c). GALENIC miscellany.

ff. 133v, 142v. AUTHOR: Galen with book expounds (*De accidenti et morbo*). ANATOMY: diagram of eye (*De accidenti et morbo*).

.13 ——, MS 287(998) (14th c). GALEN, *Methodus medendi* (books III–VII).

f. 1. SURGERY: doctor operates on patient's head, assistants with instruments.

.14 ——, MS 290(2348) (15th c). Pseudo-GALEN, *Anathomia* (in English).

ff. 49v–53v. ANATOMY: nude man, front and rear views; bone-man, front and rear views; muscle-man, front and rear views; pregnant woman (organs captioned); wound-man.

.15 ——, MS 334 (15th c). Herbal picture-book.*

ff. 1–78 *passim.* MATERIA MEDICA: herbs (captioned, with brief prescriptions).

.16 ——, MS 335(1596) (c. 1490). Miscellany.

pp. 75–371 *passim.* MATERIA MEDICA: herbs.

.17 ——, MS 336(1030) (15th c). Herbal picture-book (captions and brief descriptions in Italian).

ff. 1–103 *passim.* MATERIA MEDICA: herbs. REGIMEN: woman brings bowl of barley broth to bed-patient.

.18 ——, MS 346 (c. 1490). JOHANN REUCHLIN, *Herbarius Latinus.**

ff. 1–27. MATERIA MEDICA: herbs (with Reuchlin's descriptive notes).

.19 ——, MS 349(744) (1488). HEYMANDUS DE VETERI BUSCO, Astrological miscellany.

f. 22. PROGNOSIS: ZODIAC-MAN.

.20 ——, MS 353 (15th c). HIPPOCRATES, *Aphorismi.**

f. 2v. AUTHOR: Hippocrates seated on grass reading, two bystanders argue.

.21 ——, MS 376(2048) (*c.* 1475). JACOBUS DE SANATIS DE PADUA, Commentary on AVICENNA, *Canon.*

f. 1. AUTHOR: Avicenna expounds.

.22 ——, MS 404 (15th c). Medical miscellany (in English).*

ff. 32, 33v. DIAGNOSIS: circular diagram of UROSCOPY flasks. BLOODLETTING-PROGNOSIS: circular ZODIAC diagram for BLOODLETTING.

.23 ——, MS 437 (1516). DOMENICO DI LODI, *Libro del modo de governar cavalli et medicar* (in Italian).*

ff. 1–120 *passim.* VETERINARY MEDICINE: treatment of horses for various ailments

.24 ——, MS 500 (early 16th c). Miscellany (in Italian).*

ff. 61–98. MATERIA MEDICA: herbs, with action scenes.

.25 ——, MS 507 (*c.* 1375). Scientific miscellany; miniatures in MICHAEL SCOTUS, *Phisionomia.*

ff. 49, 57v, 64v. AUTHOR: presents book to Emperor. ANATOMY: author and nude man; author demonstrates anatomy of nude man.

.26 ——, MS 508(3012) (1451). Astrological-medical miscellany (in Latin and German).

f. 57v. BLOODLETTING-MAN with ZODIAC signs.

.27 ——, MS 529 (1470). Alchemical-medical miscellany.

ff. 55–62 *passim.* DISEASE: penis and bandaged head; fingernail; female heads.

.28 ——, MS 536(625) (13th c). Salernitan medical miscellany.

f. 2. BLOODLETTING-MAN.

.29 ——, MS 544(1300) (14th c). Medical-surgical miscellany.

pp. 19v–193v *passim.* DISEASE: bed-patient with facial wounds; cheek wound; arrow in cheek; nose and jaw wounds; spotted neck; woman with eye trouble; bed-patient with nasal polyp; bed-patient with wounds on head (*Glossulae quatuor magistrorum*). SURGERY: doctor sutures head wound (Fig. 67). AUTHOR: TROTULA holds orb(?) (*De passionibus mulierum*). DIAGNOSIS: UROSCOPY flask (Anon., *De urinis*). PHARMACY: small medicine jars (ROGERIUS SALERNITANUS, *Chirurgia*).

.30 ——, MS 550(4250) (15th c). Medical miscellany; miniatures in anonymous, *De fistula in ano.*

ff. 187, 193v CAUTERY iron. MEDICATION: doctor clysters a *fistula in ano* patient who is on hands and knees (miniature pasted over illustration of clystering a pig[?]).

.31 ——, MS 564 (1475). HENRI DE MONDEVILLE, *Chirurgia* (in English).*

ff. 128v–130v. DIAGNOSIS: UROSCOPY flasks (with notes in English).

.32 ——, MS 573(3150) (13th c). Pseudo-APULEIUS, *Herbarium*; SEXTUS PLACITUS, *De medicina ex animalibus.*

ff. 1, 4–147 *passim*. MISCELLANEOUS: Christ with book gives blessing (*Precatio omnium herbarum*).[1] MATERIA MEDICA: herbs and animals.[2]

.33 ——, MS 574(2287) (15th c.). Pseudo-APULEIUS, *Herbarium* preceded by *De herba vettonica*.

ff. 1–52 *passim*. Two doctors (Musa? and Agrippa?) argue concerning *herba vettonica*. MATERIA MEDICA: herbs (104 miniatures).

.34 ——, MS 626 (*c.* 1480–1500). MATTHAEUS PLATEARIUS, *Circa instans* (in French).

ff. 1–261. DIAGNOSIS: doctor does UROSCOPY. MATERIA MEDICA: herbs, animals and minerals, with action scenes (over 400 miniatures).

.35 ——, MS 712 (*c.* 1475). Alchemical-medical miscellany; miniatures in anonymous, *Trattato delle urine* and AEGIDIUS CORBOLIENSIS, *Delle urine* (in Italian).*

ff. 109–123v *passim*. DIAGNOSIS: UROSCOPY flasks.

.36 ——, MS 749(301) (14th c.). SERAPION, *Breviarium*.

ff. 3, 53v, 75, 119 *passim*. AUTHOR: Serapion expounds (three miniatures). TEACHING: monk with book and one pupil.

95.1 LUCCA, Italy, BIBLIOTECA GOVERNATIVA, MS 196(B.150) (15th c.). Herbal (in Italian).*

ff. 1–216. MATERIA MEDICA: herbs.

.2 ——, MS 295 (14th c.). Medical miscellany.

f. 1–38 *passim*. AUTHOR: Christ-like figure with book (at beginning of *Antidotarium*). MATERIA MEDICA: herbs, occasionally with men or animals (*Tractatus praeceptorum medicinalium*, i.e., alphabetical *Antidotarium*).

.3 ——, MS 296(B.196) (9th c.). Medical miscellany; miniatures in Pseudo-APULEIUS, *Herbarium*; SEXTUS PLACITUS, *De medicina ex animalibus*; Pseudo-DIOSCORIDES, *De herbis femininis*.

ff. 2–81v. MATERIA MEDICA: herbs and animals, with action scenes.

96.1 LUCERNE (Luzern), Switzerland, GILHOFER AND RANSCHBURG, MS 512 (1933 catalogue) (1477). MUNDINUS, *Anathomia* (MS sold).*

f. 164. ANATOMY: sketches of uterus and bladder.

[1] The figure with quadrated halo, giving the sign of benediction, is Christ, not 'Hippocrates? or Aesculapius?' as suggested in the Wellcome Catalogue. It closely resembles figures at the beginning of Mesue's *Grabadin* in Florence, Laurentian, MS Conventi Soppressi 276, f. 70v, and Vatican MS Borgese 353, f. I. In the Wellcome MS the haloed Christ is a suitable illustration of the *Precatio omnium herbarum*.

[2] The Wellcome Catalogue cites Dr. Charles Singer's opinion that the two haloed figures awed by a nude youth (f. 75v) represent 'probably a Christian version of the presentation to Apuleius of the 'Herbarius' by Aesculapius and Chiron.' We suggest that the youth (penis prominent) is about to urinate: the next page discusses *urina puerorum*, which was used as a medicine and often illustrated in manuscripts by a boy urinating.

97.1 LUCERNE (Luzern), Switzerland, ZENTRALBIBLIOTHEK, MS K.B.Msc.20.4° (15th c). MESUE, *Grabadin*.*

ff. 1, 75. DIAGNOSIS, AUTHOR: with UROSCOPY flask. PHARMACY: author reads, assistant with mortar and pestle and scales.

98.1 MADRID, Spain, BIBLIOTECA DEL PALACIO, MS 3207(44) (14th c). DIOSCORIDES, *Materia medica* (in Greek).

ff. 1–120 *passim*. MATERIA MEDICA: herbs and animals.

99.1 MADRID, Spain, BIBLIOTECA NACIONAL, MS 928 (14th c). AVICENNA, *Canon*.[1]

ff. 42–141 *passim*. MATERIA MEDICA: herbs and animals. TEACHING: Galen expounds to group of students. DISEASED MEMBERS. SURGERY: doctors prepare to operate on patient's head. DENTISTRY: doctor pulls tooth.

1st duplicate numbering, 73–131 *passim*. DISEASED MEMBERS. GYNAECOLOGY: *abortio*.

2nd duplicate numbering. ff. 1, 18–78v *passim*. DIAGNOSIS: doctor takes PULSE, assistant with utensils. DISEASED MEMBERS.

3rd duplicate numbering, f. 1. MEDICATION: patient receives CLYSTER.

.2 ——, MS 1408(L.61), (14th c). Medical miscellany.

f. 55. DIAGNOSIS: doctor does UROSCOPY, another doctor stands by (AVICENNA, *Canon*).

.3 ——, MS 1410 (L.65), (14th c). Medical miscellany.

ff. 9v–193 *passim*. AUTHORS: RHAZES (*Almansor*; *Liber divisionum*; *De passionibus*); MESUE (*De consolatione medicarum*); GALEN (*Liber experimentorum*). PAEDIATRICS: woman with ailing baby (RHAZES, *De egritudinibus puerorum*). DIAGNOSIS: MESUE with UROSCOPY flask (*Grabadin*).

.4 ——, MS 1424(L.67), (12–13th c). CONSTANTINUS AFRICANUS, *Pantegni*.

f. 1. AUTHOR: Constantinus with book.

.5 ——, MS Vitr. 26.1, (14th c). Medical miscellany (in Greek).

f. 1v. AUTHOR: BANZAPHAR (top) with translator and copyist (below).

100.1 MANCHESTER, England, CHETHAM LIBRARY, MS A.4.91, (14th c). Medical miscellany.

f. 1. DIAGNOSIS: doctor takes PULSE of woman (HIPPOCRATES, *De aere et aqua*).

.2 ——, MS A.4.99, (c. 1460). Astrological miscellany, calendar, etc. (in English).

f. 21v. PROGNOSIS: ZODIAC-MAN.

---

[1] This manuscript is not numbered consecutively throughout but has four separate numbering systems; we cite the duplicate folio numbers separately.

101.1 MANCHESTER, England, JOHN RYLANDS LIBRARY, MS 52, (1501). Book of Hours.
f. 230v. MEDICAL SAINTS: Cosmas and Damian hold medicine jar and UROSCOPY flask.

.2 ——, MS 69, (15th c). *Speculum salutatis.*
ff. 3–42 *passim.* MATERIA MEDICA: herbs and animals, with occasional action scenes. PROGNOSIS: caladrius bird looks at patient.

102.1 MANCHESTER, England, UNIVERSITY LIBRARY, MS from Medical Society Library, (1497). Medical miscellany.*
ff. 4–13v. ANATOMY: full-figure showing organs *in situ*; separate sketches of stomach, spleen, liver, kidneys, heart, lungs, skull, brain, *cerebri lacuna.*

103.1 MARBURG, West Germany, UNIVERSITY (Universitätsbibliothek), MS 9 (15th c). Astrological-medical miscellany.
f. 137v. BLOODLETTING-MAN.

.2 ——, MS 19(B.3) (15th c). Astrological-medical miscellany.
f. 37. BLOODLETTING-MAN.

104.1 METZ, France, BIBLIOTHÈQUE DE METZ, MS 176 (15th c). Medical miscellany; miniatures in GUY DE CHAULIAC, *Chirurgia* (in German).*
ff. 124–216 *passim.* SURGERY: instruments in text.

.2 ——, MS 1228(i.e., M.15 or Salis. 78) (*c.* 1300). Surgical miscellany (in French).[1]*
ff. 97–185 *passim.* SURGERY: instruments in text (ALBUCASIS, *Chirurgia*). CAUTERY-MEN; CAUTERY with setons. BLOODLETTING: by cupping.

105.1 MILAN, Italy, BIBLIOTECA AMBROSIANA, MS A.125 inf. (13th c). AVICENNA, *Canon* (in Arabic).*
ff. 5–29v *passim.* AUTHOR: Avicenna in various activities.

.2 ——, MS C.59 sup. (13th c). Medical miscellany; miniatures in BRUNO LONGO-BURGENSIS, *Chirurgia.*
ff. 85–92. SURGERY: instruments.

.3 ——, MS C.102 sup. (198) (15th c). Herbal-astrological miscellany (in Greek).
ff. 30–120, 125v–126. MATERIA MEDICA: herbs (a miscellany of DIOSCORIDES, etc.). ANATOMY: front and rear views of man with parts of body captioned.

.4 ——, MS D.2 inf. (12th c). Medical miscellany.
ff. 2–3v. SURGERY: CAUTERY-MEN. MEDICAL CELEBRITY: 'Ypocras' seated alongside one of the cautery-men.

.5 ——, MS D.120 inf. (14th c). ALBUCASIS, *Chirurgia.*[2]

[1] This manuscript was reported lost during World War II.
[2] Although the manuscript has 'liber cirurgie Rasis' in both incipit and explicit, this is the *Chirurgia* of Albucasis.

ff. 1, 2v–42 *passim*. SURGERY: Rhazes (?) operates on patient's head; instrument in text.

.6 ——, MS E.35 sup. (14th c). Astrological miscellany.*

f. 155. PROGNOSIS: ZODIAC-MAN.

.7 ——, MS E.78 inf. (14th c). CONSTANTINUS AFRICANUS, *Opera*.

f. 5. AUTHOR: Constantinus Africanus (commentary on HIPPOCRATES, *Aphorismi*).

.8 ——, MS G.108 inf (9th c). HIPPOCRATIC-GALENIC miscellany.

f. 114. DIAGNOSIS: circular captioned diagrams of pulse beat (*diastolin*); signed above and below, 'Ex voce Agnello yatrosofisto ego Simplicius audivi, legi, contuli, deo iuvante, et scripsi feliciter' (GALEN, *De pulsibus ad Tirones*).

.9 ——, MS I.6 inf. (15th c). PETRUS DE EBULO, *De balneis Puteolanis*.

ff. 2–25. BATHING: baths at Puteoli.

.10 ——, MS I.130 inf. (14th c). RHAZES, *Almansor*; *Liber divisionum*.

ff. 1, 71v. AUTHOR: Rhazes (or GERARDUS CREMONENSIS) writing. DISEASE: man with polyps.

.11 ——, MS N.55 sup. (14th c). Astrological miscellany.

f. 12. PROGNOSIS: ZODIAC-MAN.

.12 ——, MS. R.76 sup. (14th c). ALBUCASIS, *Chirurgia*; CONSTANTINUS AFRICANUS, *Anathomia*.

ff. 3–92 *passim*. AUTHOR: Albucasis and students. SURGERY: instruments in text; cauterizing patient's skull; operation on head. BLOODLETTING: by cupping. DISEASE: doctor and patients (all illustrations in Albucasis).

f. 93. Constantinus and students (*Anathomia*).

.13 ——, MS S.15 sup. (15th c). NICOLAUS PRAEPOSITUS, *Antidotarium*.

ff. 15–151 *passim*. DISEASE: parts of bodies illustrating ailments and 'antidotes' for their cure.

.14 ——, MS Y.179 sup. (15th c). LANFRANCUS MEDIOLANENSIS, *Chirurgia* (in Italian).

ff. 7–88v *passim*. SURGERY: instruments in text.

106.1 MODENA, Italy, BIBLIOTECA ESTENSE, MS II.101(993 al.9.28) (1458). MATTHAEUS PLATEARIUS, *Circa instans* (in French).*

ff. 25–142. MATERIA MEDICA: herbs and animals, with action scenes.

107.1 MONTE CASSINO, Italy, BIBLIOTHECA CASINENSIS, MS 97 (10th c). Medical-herbal miscellany; miniatures in Pseudo-APULEIUS, *Herbarium*; Pseudo-DIOSCORIDES, *De herbis femininis*; SEXTUS PLACITUS, *De medicina ex animalibus*.

pp. 476–544 *passim*. MATERIA MEDICA: herbs and animals, with action scenes.

.2 ——, MS 203 (14th c). Medical miscellany; miniatures in Gulielmus de Saliceto, *Chirurgia*.

pp. 1, 89. Surgery: operations on skull; on nose.

108.1 Montpellier, France, Bibliothèque de l'école de Médicin, MS 89 bister (14th c). Surgical miscellany; miniatures in Rogerius Salernitanus, *Chirurgia*; Bruno Longoburgensis, *Chirurgia*; Albucasis, *Chirurgia*.

ff. 1–36 *passim*. (Rogerius). Author: Rogerius lectures. Medication: doctors apply salves, ointments, potions. Disease: patients with ailments; e.g., sword wound in head (Fig. 62). Orthopaedics: reducing and bandaging dislocated jaw; back; shoulder. Dentistry: doctor extracts tooth; patient inhales for toothache (Fig. 94). Surgery: operations on head, neck, torso, genitals; e.g., nose (Fig. 71); head suture (Fig. 72); scrofula (Fig. 73); fistula (Fig. 79); head, for mania (Fig. 68); arrow extracted from arm (Fig. 75); neck (Fig. 73); hernia (Fig. 81A); cancer of penis (Fig. 84); cancer of leg (Fig. 89A); haemorrhoids (Fig. 86). Cautery patient tied to post (Fig. 51). Bathing. Gynaecology: doctor examines woman's breast.

ff. 37, 43v. Author: Bruno lectures; demonstrates wounds on patient.

ff. 95–179 *passim*. Author, Clinic: Albucasis treats patients, medicine jars on shelf. Surgery: instruments throughout text.

.2 ——, MS 95 (14th c). Albucasis, *Chirurgia* (in French).*

passim. Surgery: instruments in text.

.3 ——, MS 161 (13th c). Medical miscellany. (15–16th-century miniature).

f. 1. Diagnosis: doctor takes Pulse of bed-patient, two women and two boys attend with candles, one holds Uroscopy-flask carrier, medicines and instruments on table (frontispiece to Gerardus Cremonensis, gloss on Constantinus Africanus, *Viaticum*).

.4 ——, MS 184 (1363). Guy de Chauliac, *Chirurgia* (in French).

ff. 13v, 124, 134, 256. Anatomical Dissection or Autopsy: doctor opens female corpse, another removes omentum(?), three women observers, assistant holds tub for excised organs, instruments on stool, doctor with book explains procedure to students. Surgery: instruments in text.

.5 ——, MS 277 (14th–15th c). Medical miscellany.

ff. 162–163v. Obstetrics: diagrams of uterus showing foetal presentations.

109.1 Montreal, Quebec, Canada, McGill University, Osler Library, MS 7508 (1256). Al-Ghafiki, *Materia medica* (Alphabetical, A–K) (in Arabic).

ff. 1–284 *passim*. Materia Medica: herbs, animals and minerals.

.2 ——, MS 7579 (15th c). Medical miscellany; miniatures in *Liber medicalis qui dicitur Copiosa*.

ff. 1, 42–152 *passim*. SURGERY: trephining operation; instruments throughout text.

.3 ——, MS 7590 (14th c). Medical miscellany; miniatures in *De morbis*.

ff. 44–98 *passim*. DIAGNOSIS: UROSCOPY flasks in margins.

.4 ——, MS 7628 (14th c). Medical miscellany (in Latin and Italian).

f. 1. AUTHOR: NICOLAUS PRAEPOSITUS expounding (*Antidotarium*).

110.1 MOSCOW, USSR, LENIN LIBRARY (Biblioteka SSSR imeni V.I.Lenina), MS 173, Pysig.8.MDA.N.102 (16th c). Religious-astrological miscellany (in Russian).

ff. 165–168v. MATERIA MEDICA: herbs and animals.

111.1 MOUNT ATHOS, Greece, GRAND LAURA MONASTERY, MS M75 (12th c). DIOSCORIDES, *Materia medica* (in Greek).*

f. 45v. MATERIA MEDICA: herbs, woman plucks blossom.

112.1 MOUNT SINAI, Egypt, ST. CATHERINE'S MONASTERY, MS 500 (11th c). *Menologion* (in Greek).*

f. 5. MEDICAL SAINTS: Cosmas and Damian.

113.1 MUNICH (Munchen), West Germany, STATE LIBRARY (Bayrische Staatsbibliothek), MS Germ. 28 (15th c). Astrological-medical miscellany (in German).

ff. 26–34 *passim*. PROGNOSIS: men with astrolabe, quadrant, book. FOUR TEMPERAMENTS. PROGNOSIS: ZODIAC-MAN. BLOODLETTING: woman catches blood in bowl; man prepares for bloodletting. BATHING: man and woman in tub with food and drink. BLOODLETTING-MAN. DIAGNOSIS: doctor does UROSCOPY.

.2 ——, MS Germ. 32 (*c.* 1370). Astrological-medical miscellany (in German).

ff. 1,2, 21v. PROGNOSIS: ZODIAC-MAN. BLOODLETTING-MAN. PHARMACY: stirring rods(?).

.3 ——, MS Germ. 317 (15th c). Astrological-medical miscellany (in German).*

f. 130. BLOODLETTING-MAN.

.4 ——, MS Germ. 349 (1458). Astrological-medical miscellany (in German).*

f. 71v. BLOODLETTING-MAN. PROGNOSIS: ZODIAC-MAN.

.5 ——, MS Germ. 398 (1435). Astrological-medical miscellany (in German).*

f. 10. PROGNOSIS: ZODIAC circles.

.6 ——, MS Germ. 430 (15th c). Astrological-medical miscellany (in German).*

f. 12. PROGNOSIS: ZODIAC circles.

.7 ——, MS Germ. 597 (*c.* 1485). Astrological-medical miscellany (in Latin and German).

ff. 240–263v *passim*. SURGERY: CAUTERY-MEN. BLOODLETTING-MEN. WOUND-MAN. OBSTETRICS, ANATOMY: pregnant woman; diagrams of uterus showing foetal presentations.

.8 ——, MS Germ. 728 (15–16th c). Medical miscellany (in Latin and German); miniatures in MACER FLORIDUS, *De viribus herbarum*.

ff. 71–115 *passim*. MATERIA MEDICA: herbs.

.9 ——, MS Lat. 12 (1464). MICHAEL SAVONAROLA, *Practica*.

f. 3. MEDICAL SAINTS: Cosmas and Damian, Luke (head of a bull).

.10 ——, MS Lat. 25 (15th c). BARTHOLOMAEUS DE MONTAGNANA, *Consilia medica*.

ff. 1v, 11. AUTHOR: Bartholomaeus does UROSCOPY, consults book (Fig. 9). MEDICAL SAINTS: Pandolfus and Pantaleon (with UROSCOPY flask), between them is a lady (personsifying 'Medicina') holding glass and stirrer.

.11 ——, MS Lat. 30 (15th c). MATTHAEUS SILVATICUS, *Pandectae*.

f. 11v. MEDICAL CELEBRITY: Dr. Hartman Schedel, owner of the manuscript.

.12 ——, MS Lat. 38 (14th c). AVENZOAR, *Practica*; *Antidotarium*.

f. 51v. AUTHOR: Avenzoar holding scales (*Antidotarium*).

.13 ——, MS Lat. 73 (1413). NICOLAUS BERTRUCIUS, *Collectorium*.
(front guard folio). ANATOMY: human head showing sense centres.

.14 ——, MS Lat. 161 (13th c). Medical miscellany; miniatures in ALBUCASIS, *Chirurgia*, and anonymous treatises.

ff. 1–40 *passim*, 75v, 76. AUTHOR: Albucasis expounds. SURGERY: instruments throughout Albucasis text, and ff. 75v, 76. CAUTERY-MEN. OBSTETRICS: diagrams of uterus showing foetal presentations.

.15 ——, MS Lat. 182 (15th c). CHRISTOPHORUS DE BARZIZIIS, Miscellaneous works.

f. 3v. AUTHOR: with book.

.16 ——, MS Lat. 206 (15th c). GULIELMUS DE SALICETO, *Practica*, preceded by anonymous works.

ff. 25, 37, 41v. BLOODLETTING-MAN. AUTHOR: Gulielmus does UROSCOPY. OBSTETRICS: pregnant woman.

.17 ——, MS Lat. 207 (*c*. 1440). Medical miscellany.

f. 3. AUTHOR: 'Antonius Cermisonus medicorum monarchia.' (ANTONIO CERMISONE, *Consilia*).

.18 ——, MS Lat. 259 (14th c). GULIELMUS DE SALICETO, *Chirurgia*.

f. 94v. SURGERY: instruments in margin.

.19 ——, MS Lat. 262 (15th c). GUY DE CHAULIAC, *Chirurgia*.

ff. 67–95v *passim*. SURGERY: instruments.

.20 ——, MS Lat. 337 (10th c). DIOSCORIDES, *Materia medica*.

ff. 4–156v. AUTHOR: writing. MATERIA MEDICA: herbs, animals and minerals, with realistic action scenes (occasionally with implements for PHARMACY, CLYSTER, etc.) (Figs. 35–7).

.21 ——, MS Lat. 355 (14th c). ALBUCASIS, *Chirurgia*.

ff. 1v–37v *passim*. SURGERY: instruments throughout text.

.22 ——, MS Lat. 376 (12th c). Medical miscellany; miniatures in ROGERIUS SALERNITANUS, *Chirurgia*.

ff. 1–16. SURGERY: instruments in text and margins.

.23 ——, MS Lat. 'Msc. 418' (1466). Medical miscellany.*

ff. 1 *passim*. PHARMACIST with mortar and pestle. MEDICAL SAINTS: Cosmas with jars, Damian, 'Medicina' with book and crown, (in background) Avicenna and Johannitius. DISEASE: girl holding fan and cup for bed-patient. DIAGNOSIS: doctor does UROSCOPY and takes woman's PULSE.

.24 ——, MS Lat. 527 (13–14th c). Scientific-medical miscellany.

f. 64v. ANATOMY: human head showing sense centres (*Anathomia capitis*).

.25 ——, MS Lat. 733 (15th c). MESUE, *Grabadin*; JOHANNES DE SANCTO AMANDO, *Additiones Mesue*.

f. 32. AUTHOR: Mesue with book.

.26 ——, MS Lat. 2777 (15th c). Astrological-medical miscellany.*

f. 17. BLOODLETTING-MAN.

.27 ——, MS Lat. 3521 (14th c). ISAAC JUDAEUS, *De dietis*; *De urinis*.

ff. 149, 188v. AUTHOR: Isaac (*De dietis*). DIAGNOSIS: Isaac does UROSCOPY (*De urinis*).

.28 ——, MS Lat. 4394 (14–15th c). Astrological-medical miscellany.

f. 115r–v. BLOODLETTING-MAN. DISEASE-WOMAN.

.29 ——, MS Lat. 5595 (15th c). Astrological-medical miscellany.

ff. 51v, 56, 53. PROGNOSIS: ZODIAC-MAN, PLANET-MAN. BLOODLETTING-MAN.

.30 ——, MS Lat. 5905 (15th c). Medical miscellany (in Latin and German).

ff. 1–198 *passim*. MATERIA MEDICA: herbs ('Herbarius iste depictus est per fratrem Vitum Auslasser . . .') and animals (SEXTUS PLACITUS, *De medicina ex animalibus*).

.31 ——, MS Lat. 5961 (1441). Medical miscellany.*

f. 1v. ANATOMY: human head showing sense centres.

.32 ——, MS Lat. 13002 (1165). Miscellany with medical treatises (identical with MS Lat. 17403).

ff. 1v–3. CAUTERY-MEN. ANATOMY: artery-man, vein-man, bone-man, muscle-man, nerve-man (Pseudo-GALEN, *Figura incisionis, Historia arteriorum . . .*).

.33 ——, MS Lat. 13042 (14th c). Scientific miscellany.

f. 109v. ANATOMY: bone-man.

.34 ——, MS Lat. 13057 (*c.* 1300). Surgical miscellany.

f. 65. AUTHOR: ROGERIUS SALERNITANUS examines head wound (*Chirurgia*).

.35 ——, MS Lat. 17403 (13th c). Miscellany with medical treatises (ff. 2v–4, identical with MS Lat. 13002, q.v.).

ff. 239–242v. MATERIA MEDICA: herbs ('Herbae pictae cum explicatione').

.36 ——, MS Lat. 18294 (1471), Medical miscellany.

f. 282v. BLOODLETTING-MAN.

114.1 NAPLES, Italy, BIBLIOTECA GOVERNATIVA DEI GIROLAMINI, BIBLIOTECA ORATORI-ANA, MS CF.4.10 (15th c). BONIFACIO DA CALABRIO, *De la menescalcia.**

f. 32v. VETERINARY MEDICINE: doctor forces medicine into horse's mouth, massages horse's shoulder.

115.1 NAPLES, Italy, BIBLIOTECA NAZIONALE, MS 1 (formerly VIENNA, BN, Sup. Gr. 28) (7th c). DIOSCORIDES, *Materia medica* (in Greek).

ff. 1–172. MATERIA MEDICA: herbs.

.2 ——, MS VIII.D.25 (14th c). HIPPOCRATES, *Aphorismi*; *Prognostica*.

ff. 12–112 *passim*. AUTHOR: Hippocrates dictates to scribe; lectures; writes; talks with patient and bystanders. TEACHING: doctors expound. OBSTETRICS: maid supports pregnant woman in bed, doctor stands by. DISEASE: attendant holds spastic patient in bed, doctor and assistant stand by; similar scene for woman with dropsy. DIAGNOSIS: doctors do UROSCOPIES for bed-patients (assistants and other bystanders). PROGNOSIS: six doctors, one points to star.

.3 ——, MS VIII.D.26 (14th c). HIPPOCRATIC miscellany; miniatures in CONSTAN-TINUS AFRICANUS, commentary on Hippocrates, *Aphorismi*; HIPPOCRATES, *Prognostica*.

ff. 1, 36. DIAGNOSIS: Hippocrates (or Constantinus) does UROSCOPY. AUTHOR: HIPPOCRATES holds book (*Prognostica*).

.4 ——, MS VIII.D.27 (15th c). Anonymous, commentary on HIPPOCRATES. *Aphorismi*.

f. 1. TEACHING: professor-commentator lectures to thirteen doctors each with a book.

.5 ——, MS VIII.D.32 (15th c). Medical miscellany.

ff. 300r–v, 333. CAUTERY instruments. BLOODLETTING-ZODIAC-MAN.

.6 ——, MS VIII.D.33 (14th c). MESUE, *Grabadin*.

f. 1. AUTHOR, DIAGNOSIS: Mesue does UROSCOPY, boy with flask-carrier.

.7 ——, MS VIII.D.38 (13th c). Medical miscellany.

f. 58. AUTHOR: BERNARDUS DE GORDONIO with book (*De phlebotomia*).

.8 ——, MS VIII.D.39 (13th c). CONSTANTINUS AFRICANUS, *Pantegni*.

f. 1. AUTHOR, DIAGNOSIS: Constantinus does UROSCOPY.

.9 ——, MS VIII.G.67 (15th c). Medical miscellany (in Italian).

ff. 7v–8, 11, 67. BLOODLETTING-MAN. AUTHOR: BRUNO LONGOBURGENSIS stands with legs wide-spread (*Chirurgia minor*). PROGNOSIS: ZODIAC-MAN (mutilated folio).

.10 ——, MS VIII.G.100 (15th c). Medical miscellany.

f. 98. SURGERY: instruments for eye operations (DAVID of Armenia, commentary on ACCANAMOSALI, *De oculis*).

.11 ——, MS XIII.C.37 (14th c). Anonymous, *Regimen sanitatis.**

ff. 51v, 55. REGIMEN: preparing and eating food and drink.

116.1 NAPLES, Italy, SOCIATA NAPOLETANA DI STORIA PATRIA, MS XX.C.5 (early 16th c). Miscellany (in Italian); miniatures in PETRUS DE EBULO, *De balneis Puteolanis*.

ff. 192–211. BATHING: bathing scenes.

117.1 NEW HAVEN, Connecticut, USA, YALE MEDICAL LIBRARY, MS 2,[1] (14th c). Medical miscellany; miniatures in RHAZES, *Almansor*; *Liber divisionum*; *Antidotarium*.

ff. 1–49 *passim*, 131. MEDICAL CELEBRITY: Almansor and the AUTHOR; AUTHOR with book; in Almansor's presence (in each of the treatises). DIAGNOSIS: Rhazes holding UROSCOPY flask.

.2 ——, MS 3 (1448). Medical miscellany; miniatures in MESUE, *Grabadin*; NICOLAUS PRAEPOSITUS, *Antidotarium*.

ff. 24–177v *passim*, 265. TEACHING: doctors expound concerning remedies for diseases. AUTHOR: Nicolaus.

.3 ——, MS 12 (13th c). ARISTOTELEAN miscellany.

ff. 189–206 *passim*. AUTHOR: Aristotle (*Physica*). REGIMEN: man asleep (*De somno*). ANATOMY: a corpse (*De morte et vita*). MATERIA MEDICA: man picks a herb (*De plantis*).

.4 ——, MS 18 (*c.* 1400). Pseudo-APULEIUS, *Herbarium*; Pseudo-DIOSCORIDES, *De herbis femininis*; SEXTUS PLACITUS, *De medicina ex animalibus*.

ff. 1–174. AUTHOR: in consultation. MATERIA MEDICA: herbs and animals, with action scenes (miniatures throughout the manuscript, similar to those in Florence, Laurentian, MS Plut. 73.16, q.v.).

.5 ——, MS 26 (*c.* 1530). Medical-astrological miscellany (in English).

ff. 2v–4v. ANATOMY: bone-man; man with internal organs captioned. BLOODLETTING-MAN. PROGNOSIS: ZODIAC-MAN, internal organs showing.

---

[1] Manuscripts are designated by the numbers in the *Census of Medieval and Renaissance Manuscripts in the United States and Canada*, in both the De Ricci edition (1935–1940) and the W. H. Bond *Supplement* (1962).

.6 ——, MS 28, 'Codex Fritz Paneth' (1326). Medical miscellany; various works by the AUTHORS cited below.

pp. 1–1378 (ff. 1–685) *passim*. AUTHOR. DIAGNOSIS. REGIMEN. DISEASE. MATERIA MEDICA. MEDICATION. PHARMACY. SURGERY. VETERINARY MEDICINE. Among the authors are MESUE, ISAAC JUDAEUS, GERARDUS, RHAZES, ALBUCASIS, ELLUCHASEM ELIMITHAR, BRUNO LONGOBURGENSIS, ROLANDUS PARMENSIS, ROGERIUS SALERNITANUS, CONSTANTINUS AFRICANUS, MACER FLORIDUS, MATTHAEUS PLATEARIUS, DAUCUS, GALEN, HIPPOCRATES, THEOPHILUS PROTOSPATHARIUS, PHILARETUS and AEGIDIUS CORBOLIENSIS, holding their books or practising medicine; also illustrations of instruments (Fig. 60), operations, etc. (qualitatively and quantitatively, a remarkable manuscript).

.7 ——, MS 44 (15th c). (In French).
detached folio. ANATOMY: man, internal organs showing ('les parties interieures').

.8 ——, MS 49 (14–15th c). Medical miscellany; miniatures in anonymous herbal (in Italian).

ff. 1–50 *passim*. MATERIA MEDICA: herbs.

.9 ——, Islamic MSS (17–19th c), several MSS (in Persian and Arabic).
ANATOMY: bone-men, etc. MATERIA MEDICA.[1]

118.1 NEW YORK, New York, USA, HANS P. KRAUS, 'The Cipher MS' (*c.* 1500). Medical-astrological miscellany (in Latin cipher).

ff. 1–102v *passim*. MATERIA MEDICA, PHARMACY: herbs, occasionally with pharmaceutical implements. PROGNOSIS: ZODIAC and planetary diagrams. ANATOMY, BATHING: nude females in pools or tubs.

119.1 NEW YORK, New York, USA, NEW YORK ACADEMY OF MEDICINE, MS 4[2] (14–15th c). Medical miscellany (in Latin and Italian).

f. 1. AUTHOR: GULIELMUS DE SALICETO with book (*Chirurgia*).

.2 ——, MS 12 (15th c). GUY DE CHAULIAC, *Chirurgia* (in English).

ff. 73v–164v *passim*. SURGERY: instruments in text.

.3 ——, (no shelf number) (13th c). Medical miscellany; miniatures in ALBUCASIS, *Chirurgia*.

ff. 1–43 *passim*. CAUTERY. SURGERY: instruments throughout text.

.4 ——, (no shelf number) (14th c). BERNARDUS DE GORDONIO, *De conservatione vitae humanae*.

[1] For details see Loren MacKinney and Thomas Herndon, 'American Manuscript Collections of Medieval Medical Miniatures and Texts,' *J. History of Medicine and Allied Sciences*, 1962, 17, 291.

[2] Manuscripts are designated by the numbers used in the De Ricci *Census*, with the exception of the last two manuscripts, which were not listed therein and which have no shelf numbers.

Two detached folios. AUTHOR lectures. DIAGNOSIS: doctor taking patient's PULSE.

120.1 NEW YORK, New York, USA, PIERPONT MORGAN LIBRARY, MS 165 (15th c). Medical miscellany; miniatures in ALDOBRANDINO DA SIENA, *Le régime du corps* and *Le livre ypocras* (in French).

ff. 7v–123v *passim.* PROGNOSIS: doctor consults stars. REGIMEN: people eating and drinking, grain, fruit and other foods; sleeping; bathing; *coitus.* BLOOD-LETTING: by cupping; by leeching. DISEASES: scenes illustrating ailments. OBSTETRICS: pregnant woman; birth scene. MEDICATION: man drinks potion for stomach ailment; man with three medicine jars. AUTHOR: Hippocrates with book (*Le livre ypocras*).

.2 ——, MS 355 (1386). Calendar.*

f. 9v. PROGNOSIS: ZODIAC-MAN.

.3 ——, MS 358 (*c.* 1450). Book of Hours.

f. 20v. ANIMAL DOCTOR, DIAGNOSIS: rabbit-doctor does UROSCOPY for two crippled dogs.

.4 ——, MS 537 (15th c). BARTHOLOMAEUS ANGLICUS, *De proprietatibus rerum* (in French).

ff. 280, 297v, 353. MATERIA MEDICA: king examines stones; two men discuss herbs; four animals.

.5 ——, MS 652 (10th c). Medical miscellany; miniatures in DIOSCORIDES, *Materia medica;* NICANDER, *Theriaca* and *Alexipharmaca* (in Greek).

ff. 1v–381 *passim.* MATERIA MEDICA: herbs, animals and minerals, with action scenes and implements, receptacles, etc.

.6 ——, MS 735 (*c.* 1400). Medical miscellany; miniatures in BONAFACIO DE CALAB-RIA, *De la menescalcia* (in Italian).

ff. 1–48 *passim.* VETERINARY MEDICINE: ailments and treatment of horses; including ZODIAC-HORSE (very rare).

.7 ——, MS 873 (14th c). Picture-book of Dioscorides' *Materia medica* (no text, captions in Latin), arranged in alphabetical order.[1]

ff. 1–94. MATERIA MEDICA: herbs, animals and minerals, with action scenes.

121.1 NEW YORK, New York, USA, WILLIAM SCHAB, Sales catalogue 30, item 117 (15th c). Medical miscellany.*

[1] Catalogued as 'Johannes Platearius: Compendium Salernitanum,' its contents, arrangement ('aloes' to 'zuchara') and miniatures resemble Vatican, MS Chigi F.158; and others mentioned in Otto Pacht, 'Early Italian Nature Studies . . .' (*op. cit.*) and Loren MacKinney and Thomas Herndon, 'American Manuscript Collections . . .' (*op. cit.*, p. 288). It is closely related to MATTHAEUS PLATEARIUS, *Circa instans.*

ff. 43, 133, 139. Four TEMPERAMENTS. PROGNOSIS: ZODIAC-BLOODLETTING-MAN with ANATOMICAL captions. BATHING: man and woman in tub.

122.1 OXFORD, England, ALL SOULS COLLEGE, MS 71 (14th c). Medical miscellany; miniatures in JOHANNITIUS, *Isagoge in tegni Galieni*; THEOPHILUS PROTOSPA-THARIUS, *De urinis*; HIPPOCRATES, *Aphorismi*, GALEN, *Tegni*.

ff. 1–113v *passim*. AUTHOR: GALEN or JOHANNITIUS lectures to two. DIAGNOSIS: doctor does UROSCOPY. MISCELLANEOUS: two monks argue concerning the *Aphorismi*. PROGNOSIS: doctor explains to bed-patient, two monks stand by. PHARMACY: doctor directs assistant compounding medicines.

.2 ——, MS 72 (14th c). Medical miscellany; miniatures in NICOLAUS PRAEPOSITUS, *Antidotarium*; JOHANNES DAMASCENUS, *Aphorismi*.

ff. 1, 67. DIAGNOSIS, PHARMACY: Nicolaus with UROSCOPY flask, assistants with utensils; doctor with UROSCOPY flask.

.3 ——, MS 79 (14th c). GILBERTUS ANGLICUS, *Compendium medicinae*.

ff. 33v–131 *passim*. DISEASES: doctors with patients pointing to ailing members (head, eye, mouth, throat, liver). DIAGNOSIS: doctor takes woman's PULSE.

123.1 OXFORD, England, BALLIOL COLLEGE, MS 101 (15th c). ALBERTUS MAGNUS, *De vegetalibus et plantis*.

f. 2. AUTHOR: Albertus reads book in garden.

.2 ——, MS 238 (1448). DOMENICO BANDINI DE ARECIO, *Fontes memorabiles*.

ff. 18, 82v. ANATOMY: female Siamese twins. PROGNOSIS: ZODIAC-MAN.

.3 ——, MS 367 (11th c). Anonymous, *Antidotarium*.

ff. 8, 12v. MEDICATION: doctor with flask treats patient's arm for snake bite (serpent below). PHARMACY: barefooted man holds two receptacles (*Antidotarium Teodoricon*).

124.1 OXFORD, England, BODLEIAN LIBRARY, MS Ashmole 5 (14th c). NICHOLAS DE LYNN, *Tabula kalendarii*.

f. 34. PROGNOSIS: ZODIAC-MAN.

.2 ——, MS Ashmole 8 (14th c). Folded calendar (in English). PROGNOSIS: ZODIAC-MAN.

.3 ——, MS Ashmole 210.I (14th c). RICARDUS ANGLICUS (THORPPE), *Kalendarium*.

ff. 9, 11. PROGNOSIS: ZODIAC-MAN. BLOODLETTING-MAN.

.4 ——, MS Ashmole 370 (15th c). Calendar (in English).

f. 27v. PROGNOSIS: ZODIAC-MAN with side notes on BLOODLETTING.

.5 ——, MS Ashmole 391.V (14th c). Astrological-medical miscellany.

ff. 3–10 *passim*. PROGNOSIS: ZODIAC-MAN. BLOODLETTING-MAN. DIAGNOSIS: circular chart of UROSCOPY flasks.

.6 ——, MS Ashmole 399 (13th c). Medical miscellany.

ff. 1–34v *passim*. TEACHING: two doctors expound (*De physiognomia*). ANATOMY: internal organs in text. (CONSTANTINUS AFRICANUS, *De coitu*). OBSTETRICS: diagrams of uterus showing foetal presentations (MOSCHION, *De aegritudinbus mulierum*). ANATOMY: vein-man, artery-man, muscle-man, bone-man, nerve-man, wound-man (Pseudo-GALEN, *Figure incisionis, Historia arteriorum*); diagram of sense centres and ocular-nasal connections. A CASE HISTORY in eight scenes; an ailing woman; MEDICATION (four scenes); UROSCOPY; AUTOPSY (Fig. 96); doctor departs.

.7 ——, MS Ashmole 424 (14th c). WITELO, *De perspectiva*.

f. 1. AUTHOR: with book, expounds.

.8 ——, MS Ashmole 789.VIII (15th c). Astronomical-medical miscellany.

ff. 363–365. PROGNOSIS: ZODIAC-MAN. DIAGNOSIS: circular chart of UROSCOPY flasks (Fig. 62). BLOODLETTING-MAN (Fig. 52).

.9 ——, MS Ashmole 1431 (11th c). Pseudo-APULEIUS, *Herbarium*; Pseudo-DIOSCORIDES, *De herbis femininis*.

ff. 3v–36v *passim*. MATERIA MEDICA: herbs.

.10 ——, MS Ashmole 1434.I (15th c). Medical miscellany; miniatures in JOHN ARDERNE, *Practica chirurgiae*; *Liber medicinarum*.

pp. 1–328 (ff. 1–136) *passim*. SURGERY: instruments in text and margins; operation for *fistula in ano*. MATERIA MEDICA. MEDICATION, etc.

.11 ——, MS Ashmole 1438.I (15th c). Miscellany.

p. 77. BLOODLETTING-MAN (vellum folio bound in MS of paper folios).

.12 ——, MS Ashmole 1462 (12th c). Medical miscellany.

ff. 9–10, 13v–77 *passim*. SURGERY: CAUTERY-MEN (Fig. 43); operations for cataract and nasal polyps (Fig. 69). MATERIA MEDICA: herbs, with action scenes (Pseudo-APULEIUS, *Herbarium*; SEXTUS PLACITUS, *De medicina ex animalibus*; Pseudo-DIOSCORIDES, *De herbis femininis*).

.13 ——, MS Ashmole 1477.III (15th c). Medical miscellany (in English).

ff. 11–12v. DIAGNOSIS: UROSCOPY flasks.

.14 ——, MS Ashmole 1511 (13th c). Miscellany.

f. 95v. AUTHOR: ISIDORUS HISPALENSIS writes (*De natura hominis*).

.15 ——, MS Auct. F.5.31(3637) (13th c). Medical miscellany; miniatures in Pseudo-APULEIUS, *Herbarium*; Pseudo-DIOSCORIDES, *De herbis femininis*.

ff. 1–31v *passim*. MATERIA MEDICA: herbs.

.16 ——, MS Bodley 130 (c. 1100). Pseudo-APULEIUS, *Herbarium*; Pseudo-DIOSCORIDES, *De herbis femininis*; SEXTUS PLACITUS, *De medicina ex animalibus*.

ff. 1–95 *passim*. MATERIA MEDICA: herbs and animals.

.17 ——, MS Bodley d.138(Arch. O.d.9) (1239). DIOSCORIDES, *Materia medica* (in Arabic).

ff. 1–200 *passim*. AUTHOR: with book (head surmounted with halo-turban). MATERIA MEDICA: herbs.

.18 ——, MS Bodley 211(2927) (15th c). Miscellany; miniatures in ROGER BACON, *De retardatione senectutis.*

pp. 1, 5. AUTHOR: and son present book to nobleman; AUTHOR with book. DIAGNOSIS: doctor with large UROSCOPY flask.

.19 ——, MS Bodley 264 (*c.* 1400). Miscellany; miniatures in Alexander romance (in French).

ff. 220, 249v. DIAGNOSIS: doctor does UROSCOPY. DISEASE: doctor, nurse and two assistants attend bed-patient.

.20 ——, MS Bodley 360 (Misc. 2461) (14th c). Medical miscellany; miniatures in ALBUCASIS, *Chirurgia*; SERAPION, *Breviarium.*

ff. 1v–39, 47. SURGERY: instruments in text. AUTHOR, DIAGNOSIS: Serapion with UROSCOPY flask.

.21 ——, MS Bodley 489(Misc. 2069) (12th c). CONSTANTINUS AFRICANUS, *Viaticum.*

f. 2v. AUTHOR: with book.

.22 ——, MS Bodley Add. A.23(24721) (15th c). MACER FLORIDUS, *De viribus herbarum* (in Italian).

ff. 1–90 *passim*. MATERIA MEDICA: herbs, with action scenes showing uses.

.23 ——, MS Canonici Lat. Misc. 248 (14th c). Astrological miscellany.

f. 42. PROGNOSIS: ZODIAC-MAN.

.24 ——, MS Canonici Lat. Misc. 427 (14th c). Astrological miscellany.*

f. 3. BLOODLETTING-MAN.

.25 ——, MS Canonici Lat. Misc. 559 (14th c). Astrological miscellany.

f. 2. PROGNOSIS: ZODIAC-MAN bent backwards with feet touching back of head; at centre of concentric circles of zodiac signs and planets.[1]

.26 ——, MS Corpus Christi 123 (14th c). Astrological miscellany.

f. 29. PROGNOSIS: ZODIAC-MAN.

.27 ——, MS Digby 29 (15th c). Medical miscellany (in Latin and English).

ff. 78v–130 *passim*. PROGNOSIS: UROSCOPY flasks; circular charts of UROSCOPY flasks.

[1] This miniature and many of the usual type of zodiac- and bloodletting-man are reproduced in Harry Bober, 'The Zodiacal Miniature of the *Très Riches Heures* of the Duke of Berry,' *Journ. Warburg and Courtauld Inst.* 1948, *11*, 1–34.

.28 ——, MS Digby 88 (15th c). Astrological-medical miscellany (in Latin and English).

    f. 30. BLOODLETTING-MAN.

.29 ——, MS Douce 2 (14th c). Medical miscellany.

    ff. 13, 113. GYNAECOLOGY: 'Coitus mulierum' (Pseudo-ARISTOTLE, *Secreta secretorum*). AUTHOR, DIAGNOSIS: ARNALDUS DE VILLANOVA does UROSCOPY (*Regimen sanitatis*).

.30 ——, MS Hatton 29 (14th c). Medical miscellany (in English).

    ff. 68v–72. DIAGNOSIS: UROSCOPY flasks.

.31 ——, MS Huntington 156 (1465). ALBUCASIS, *Chirurgia* (in Arabic).

    ff. 3–163 *passim*. SURGERY: instruments throughout text. DENTISTRY: DENTURE (f. 45v).

.32 ——, MS Laud Misc. 724 (14th c). Surgical miscellany.

    ff. 94–97v *passim*. SURGERY: six head operations (ALBUCASIS, *Chirurgia*). CAUTERY-MEN. BLOODLETTING: cupping glasses. OBSTETRICS: diagrams of uterus showing foetal presentations (MOSCHION, *De aegritudinibus mulierum*).

.33 ——, MS e Museo 19 (14th c). Surgical miscellany.

    ff. 1, 60, 138–165 *passim*. SURGERY: instruments in margins (GULIELMUS DE SALICETO, *Chirurgia*); instruments throughout text (ALBUCASIS, *Chirurgia*). ORTHOPAEDICS: patient on traction machine (ALBUCASIS, *Chirurgia*). Twenty-four scenes of famous doctors directing CAUTERY (Fig. 44). DIAGNOSIS: doctor takes woman's PULSE (ROGERIUS SALERNITANUS, *Chirurgia*).

.34 ——, MS Rawlinson C.328 (15th c). Medical miscellany.

    f. 3–154 *passim*. AUTHOR, DIAGNOSIS: CONSTANTINUS AFRICANUS does UROSCOPY for women patients (Fig. 8) (*De urinis*). SURGERY: CAUTERY and CAUTERY-MEN (Figs. 47, 48); instruments throughout text (ALBUCASIS, *Chirurgia*). MATERIA MEDICA: animals (SEXTUS PLACITUS, *De medicina ex animalibus*).

.35 ——, MS Rawlinson D.251 (15th c). Astrological miscellany (in English).

    f. 57. PROGNOSIS: ZODIAC-BLOODLETTING-MAN.

125.1 OXFORD, England, PEMBROKE COLLEGE, MS 10 (14th c). Medical miscellany.

    f. 85v. ANATOMY: diagram showing sense centres (folio inserted in an antidotary).

.2 ——, (no shelf number) (14th c). *Breviarium Bartholomei expositus per Johannes Mirfeldus*.

    f. 17. DIAGNOSIS, PHARMACY: UROSCOPY flask, medicine bag, pot, clyster (four marginal sketches).

126.1 OXFORD, England, ST. JOHN'S COLLEGE, MS 86 (14th c). JOHN ARDERNE, *Liber medicinarum*.

ff. 1–53 *passim*. MATERIA MEDICA, SURGERY, DISEASED members. MEDICATION. PHARMACY (marginal sketches of herbs, instruments, etc.).

.2 ——, MS 178 (13th c). Miscellany (in Latin and French).

ff. 143–220v *passim*. PROGNOSIS: ZODIAC-MAN. MATERIA MEDICA: animals (LEO FORTISSIMUS, *Bestiarium*).

127.1 PADUA (Padova), Italy, BIBLIOTECA PINALI (Medical Faculty) (no shelf number) (14th c). Medical miscellany (in Italian).*

f. 1. PROGNOSIS: ZODIAC-BLOODLETTING-MAN. Fifteen CAUTERY-MEN; one CAUTERY-WOMAN (for each figure, two cautery irons and explanatory text).

128.1 PADUA (Padova), Italy, BIBLIOTECA DEL SEMINARIO VESCOVILLE, MS 194 (14th c). DIOSCORIDES, *Materia medica* (in Greek).*

ff. 1–200v. MATERIA MEDICA: herbs.

129.1 PADUA (Padova), Italy, UNIVERSITY (Biblioteca Universitaria), MS 604 (15th c). ROLANDUS PARMENSIS, *Chirurgia* (in Latin and Italian).*

ff. 1–55 *passim*. MATERIA MEDICA: herbs. BLOODLETTING-MAN (f. 47).

130.1 PARIS, France, BIBLIOTHÈQUE DE L'ARSENAL, MS 979 (16.B.L.) (14th c). Medical miscellany.

f. 1. AUTHOR: reading (MUNDINUS DE FORO JULIO, *Synonima*).

.2 ——, MS 1025 (14th c). Medical miscellany.

f. 1. AUTHOR, DIAGNOSIS: RICARDUS ANGLICUS does UROSCOPY for bed-patient (*Practica*).

.3 ——, MS 1031(81.S.A.L) (14th c). Pseudo-APULEIUS, *Herbarium*; SEXTUS PLACITUS, *De medicina ex animalibus*; Pseudo-DIOSCORIDES, *De herbis femininis*.

ff. 1–74. AUTHOR: holding plant. MATERIA MEDICA: herbs and animals.

.4 ——, MS 2510(133.S.A.F.) (13th c). ALDOBRANDINO DA SIENA, *Le régime du corps* (in French).

ff. 1–61 *passim*. REGIMEN: collecting and consuming food and drink, sleeping, bathing; *coitus*. BLOODLETTING: doctor bleeds patient's arm; doctor cups patient's back; patient with feet in leech-pond. DISEASE: people displaying ailments.

.5 ——, MS 2894 (15th c). ALDOBRANDINO DA SIENA, *Le régime du corps* (in French).

ff. 1–129 *passim*. AUTHOR: with book. Four TEMPERAMENTS. PROGNOSIS: ZODIAC-MEN. DISEASE: men and women displaying ailments. DIAGNOSIS: doctor does UROSCOPY. BLOODLETTING: doctor bleeding patient's arm; doctor cupping patient. BLOODLETTING-MAN. REGIMEN: people consuming food and drink, *coitus*. PHARMACY: men with mortar and pestles, pharmacy jars, etc.

.6 ——, MS 2895 (15th c). Medical miscellany; miniatures in LANFRANCUS MEDIOLA-NENSIS, *Chirurgia* (in French).

ff. 1–244 *passim*, 247, 286. SURGERY: instruments in text. BLOODLETTING-MEN.

.7 ——, MS 5062 (16th c). AEGIDIUS ROMANUS, *De regimine principium* (in French).

f. 149v. PHARMACY: street scene showing apothecary shop.

.8 ——, MS 5196 (15th c). VALERIUS MAXIMUS, *Memorabilia*.*

f. 257. DIAGNOSIS: doctor taking PULSE of female bed-patient.

131.1 PARIS, France, UNIVERSITY (Bibliothèque de la Faculté de Médecine) MS 2046(32) (14th c). Medical miscellany.

ff. 1–390v *passim*. AUTHOR: HIPPOCRATES lecturing to five students (*Aphorismi*); HIPPOCRATES with book, expounds (*Prognostica*; *De regimine acutorum morborum*); GALEN and HALY ABBAS with books, expound (*Commentarium super tegni Galeni*); GALEN (or JOHANNITIUS) expounds (*Isagoge ad tegni Galeni*).

.2 ——, MS 5119(171) (13th c). AVENZOAR, *Theisir*.

f. 3. AUTHOR: Avenzoar sits at lectern with open book, in king's presence.

132.1 PARIS, France, BIBLIOTHÈQUE MAZARINE MS 3599 (c. 1300). Medical miscellany.

ff. 65v–116v *passim*. PHARMACY: doctor directs assistant, with mortar and pestle (*Pomum ambre*). TEACHING: doctor expounds; doctor expounds to six students (*Liber de conferentibus et nocentibus*). BLOODLETTING: cupping glasses in text (ALBUCASIS, *Chirurgia*). DISEASE: woman holding hands to her fractured skull: nude female (ALBUCASIS, *Chirurgia*). PROGNOSIS: ZODIAC-BLOOD-LETTING-MEN (Anonymous text on veins, etc). ANATOMY: nude man holding apple (Adam?), faces a bone-man (Anonymous text on veins, etc.).

133.1 PARIS, France, BIBLIOTHÈQUE NATIONALE, MS Allemand 124 (c. 1500). Astro-logical-medical miscellany (in German).*

ff. 162v, 168, 172v. BLOODLETTING-MEN; BLOODLETTING-WOMAN.

.2 ——, MS Ang. 25 (c. 1400). GUY DE CHAULIAC, *Chirurgia* (in English).*

ff. 2, 75–172v *passim*. AUTHOR: Guy de Chauliac holding arm of nude patient. SURGERY: instruments.

.3 ——, MS Arab (ten detached folios) (13th c). DIOSCORIDES: *Materia medica* (in Arabic).*

ff. 1–10. MATERIA MEDICA: herbs.

.4 ——, MS Arab 2850 (12th c). DIOSCORIDES, *Materia medica* (in Arabic).*

ff. 1 ff. *passim*. MATERIA MEDICA: herbs.

.5 ——, MS Arab 2964 (1199). Anonymous antidotary (in Arabic).*

pp. 22, 27. MEDICATION: antidote for snake bite discovered by Andromachus.

.6 ——, MS Arab 5847 (1237). AL-HARIRI, Assemblies (in Arabic).*
   f. 122v. OBSTETRICS: woman in childbirth, attended by two midwives.

.7 ——, MS Fr. 218 (15th c). BARTHOLOMAEUS ANGLICUS, *De proprietatibus rerum* (in French).*
   f. 56. ANATOMICAL DISSECTION: 'surgeon of the long robe' incises cadaver, four others discuss.

.8 ——, MS Fr. 396 (15th c). GUY DE CHAULIAC, *Chirurgia* (in French).
   ff. 1–80v *passim*. AUTHOR: Guy de Chauliac lecturing to five students. ANATOMICAL DISSECTION: Guy at lectern directing four surgeons who incise cadaver. CLINIC, DIAGNOSIS: Guy diagnoses patients with diseased arm, hand, thigh, knee (Fig. 4). ORTHOPAEDICS: Guy and two assistants reducing elbow dislocation, patient with dislocated knee.

.9 ——, MS Fr. 623 (15th c). MATTHAEUS PLATEARIUS, *Circa instans* (in French).
   ff. 23–183 *passim*. AUTHOR, PHARMACY: Matthaeus writing, woman and boy compounding medicines from herbs. MATERIA MEDICA: herbs, animals and minerals, with action scenes.

.10 ——, MSS Fr. 1309–1312 (15th c). MATTHAEUS PLATEARIUS, *Circa instans* (in French).
   ff. 1–63 *passim*. MATERIA MEDICA: herbs, animals and minerals, with action scenes.

.11 ——, MS Fr. 1313 (14th c). PETRUS DE EBULO, *De balneis Puteolanis* (in Latin and French).
   ff. 1v–35. BATHING: health-bathers at Puteoli.

.12 ——, MS Fr. 1318 (13th c). ALBUCASIS, *Chirurgia* (in French).
   ff. 3–64. SURGERY: instruments throughout text.

.13 ——, MS Fr. 2030 (1314). HENRI DE MONDEVILLE, *Chirurgia* (in French).
   ff. 1v–29 *passim*. AUTHOR: Henri de Mondeville lecturing to five students. ANATOMICAL DISSECTION: surgeon dissecting skull of cadaver. ANATOMY: skeletons and cadavers showing internal organs.

.14 ——, MS Fr. 9136 (15th c). Medical miscellany; miniatures in MATTHAEUS PLATEARIUS, *Circa instans* (in French).*
   ff. 1–303 *passim*. AUTHOR. MATERIA MEDICA. PHARMACY, etc. (reported similar to MS Fr. 623, q.v.).*

.15 ——, MS Fr. 9137 (15th c). MATTHAEUS PLATEARIUS, *Circa instans* (in French).*
   ff. 1–318. AUTHOR: MATERIA MEDICA. PHARMACY, etc. (similar to MS Fr. 623, q.v.).

.16 ——, MS Fr. 12319 (15th c). MATTHAEUS PLATEARIUS, *Circa instans* (in French).

ff. 40–324v. MATERIA MEDICA: herbs, animals and minerals, with action scenes.

.17 ——, MS Fr. 12320 (15th c). MATTHAEUS PLATEARIUS, *Circa instans* (in French).

ff. 1–242. MATERIA MEDICA: herbs, animals and minerals, with action scenes.

.18 ——, MS Fr. 12323 (14th c). Religious-medical miscellany (in French); miniatures in ALDOBRANDINO DA SIENA, *Le régime du corps*.

ff. 71v–135v *passim*. BATHING. BLOODLETTING. DIAGNOSIS. REGIMEN. MATERIA MEDICA. MEDICATION. MEDICAL MEN (with patients). ANATOMY: doctor, nude man and woman. AUTHOR: presenting to king his book *De pestilence* (see next manuscript).

.19 ——, MS Fr. 12399 (1379). HENRI DE FERRIERES, *Les livres du Roy Modus et de la Royne Ratio, de deduis . . . de pestilence* (in French).

f. 2v. DISEASE: man with pestilence in king's presence ('Modus scet toute medicine . . .').

.20 ——, MS Fr. 19081 (15th c). MATTHAEUS PLATEARIUS, *Circa instans* (in French).

ff. 1–238 *passim*. MATERIA MEDICA: herbs, animals and minerals, with action scenes.

.21 ——, MS Fr. 19994 (1454). Astrological-medical miscellany (in French).

ff. 12v–96 *passim*. REGIMEN: Four TEMPERAMENTS. PROGNOSIS: ZODIAC-MAN. ANATOMY: bone-man. MEDICAL SAINTS: Cosmas with UROSCOPY flask, Damian with medicine jar. AUTHOR (?) in prayer, book on a chair (at beginning of surgical miscellany).

.22 ——, MS Fr. 24249 (15th c). GUY DE CHAULIAC, *Chirurgia* (in French).

ff. 129–315 *passim*. SURGERY: instruments in text.

.23 ——, MS Gr. 36 (15th c). Medical miscellany (in Greek).

ff. 3v–203v *passim*. MEDICAL SAINT: Pantaleon with pen. AUTHOR: HIPPOCRATES holding glass of medicine (extracts from his works). DISEASE: impotent patient, doctor writing on scroll. MATERIA MEDICA: man collects fruit, amidst herbs and animals (illustrating a prescription).

.24 ——, MS Gr. 247(Suppl.) (11th c). NICANDER, *Theriaca* (in Greek).

ff. 2v–48v *passim*. MATERIA MEDICA: herbs and animals (for antidotes), with action scenes (e.g., serpents attacking men). PHARMACY: man with mortar and pestle, vase for liquid.

.25 ——, MS Gr. 1180 (15th c). Astrological-medical miscellany (in Greek).*

f. 107. BLOODLETTING-MAN.

.26 ——, MS Gr. 2091 (15th c). Medical miscellany (in Greek); miniatures in DIOSCORIDES, *Materia medica*, fragmentary.*

ff. 113–117v. MATERIA MEDICA: herbs.

.27 ——, MS Gr. 2144 (*c.* 1350). HIPPOCRATIC miscellany (in Greek).

ff. 10v, 11. AUTHOR: 'Hippocrates' enthroned with book showing incipit of *Aphorismi*; 'ALEXIUS APOCAUCHOS' enthroned with the book of JOHANNES ACTUARIUS.

.28 ——, MS Gr. 2155 (14th c). Medical miscellany (in Greek).

ff. 30–278 *passim.* DISEASE: man with apoplexy about to fall. PHARMACY: mortars and pestles and other pharmaceutical implements.

.29 ——, MS Gr. 2179 (10th c). DIOSCORIDES, *Materia medica* (in Greek).

ff. 1–142. MATERIA MEDICA: herbs, occasionally with action scenes.

.30 ——, MS Gr. 2180 (15th c). Astrological miscellany (in Greek).*

f. 108. PROGNOSIS: ZODIAC-WOMAN.

.31 ——, MS Gr. 2182 (1481). DIOSCORIDES, *Materia medica* (in Greek).*

ff. 1–10. MATERIA MEDICA: herbs.

.32 ——, MS Gr. 2183 (15th c). DIOSCORIDES, *Materia medica* (in Greek).*

ff. 1–164 *passim.* MATERIA MEDICA: herbs and animals.

.33 ——, MS Gr. 2243 (14th c). Medical miscellany (in Greek).

f. 10v. CLINIC, DIAGNOSIS, DISEASE, PHARMACY: doctor and assistants with patients, doctor does UROSCOPY, one assistant with mortar and two pestles (Fig. 1; NICOLAUS MYREPSUS, *Antidotarium*).

.34 ——, MS Gr. 2244 (15th c). Anonymous, *Hippiatrica* (in Greek).*

f. 49. VETERINARY MEDICINE: Man leads ailing horse.

.35 ——, MS Gr. 2286 (15th c). DIOSCORIDES, *Materia medica* (in Greek).

ff. 1 ff. MATERIA MEDICA: herbs, animals and minerals.

.36 ——, MS Gr. 2294 (15th c). Medical miscellany (in Greek).

ff. 70–95, 138–257 *passim.* DIAGNOSIS: HIPPOCRATES, GALEN, PAULUS, IANPHROS and others with UROSCOPY flasks (Anon., *On urines*). DISEASES: patients with ailments, some in bed, doctors in attendance; occasional PHARMACY implements. BLOODLETTING. MATERIA MEDICA: herbs and animals, with occasional pharmaceutical implements (DIOSCORIDES, *Materia medica*).

.37 ——, MS Gr. 2419 (*c.* 1450). Astrological miscellany (in Greek).

f. 1. PROGNOSIS: ZODIAC-MAN at centre of zodiac circle.

.38 ——, MS Lat. 6821 (14th c). DIOSCORIDES, *Materia medica* (alphabetical).

ff. 1, 127. AUTHOR: with book, expounds. MATERIA MEDICA: three herbs.

.39 ——, MS Lat. 6823 (14th c). Medical miscellany.

ff. 1–185. AUTHOR: MANFREDUS DE MONTE IMPÉRIALE seated with book, three bring herbs (*De herbis et plantis*); NICOLAUS PRAEPOSITUS expounds to four students (*Antidotarium*). MEDICAL CELEBRITIES: (ff. 1v–2) Avicenna, Johannitius,

Hippocrates, Galen; unidentified, Averrhoes, Bartholomaeus, Porphyry; all with books, expound (MANFREDUS DE MONTE IMPÉRIALE, *De herbis et plantis*). MATERIA MEDICA: herbs, animals and minerals in alphabetical order, with action scenes (from Manfredus).

.40 ——, MS Lat. 6862 (*c.* 900). Medical miscellany; miniatures in Pseudo-APULEIUS, *Herbarium*.

ff. 18v, 20–63 *passim.* PHARMACY: Aesculapius collects herb *vettonica.* MATERIA MEDICA: herbs.

.41 ——, MS Lat. 6884 (14th c). Medical miscellany.

f. 1. DIAGNOSIS, TRANSLATOR: Constantinus Africanus in monk's garb with UROSCOPY flask (ISAAC JUDAEUS, *De urinis*, translated by Constantinus).

.42 ——, MS Lat. 6888 (14th c). Medical miscellany.

f. IV. BLOODLETTING-MAN (CONSTANTINUS AFRICANUS, *Viaticum*).

.43 ——, MS Lat. 6910.A (15th c). Medical miscellany; miniatures in GUY DE CHAULIAC, *Chirurgia.*

ff. 1–182v. PROGNOSIS: ZODIAC-BLOODLETTING-MAN. SURGERY: instruments.

.44 ——, MS Lat. 6912 (14th c). RHAZES, *Continens*, translated by FERAGIUS (in five volumes).

Vol. I, ff. 1–173; II, ff. 1–246v; III, ff. 1–122; IV, ff. 1–153; V, ff. 1–189 *passim.* AUTHOR, TRANSLATOR: Rhazes presents book to Caliph; Feragius presents book to Charles of Anjou (I, f. IV; V, f. 78v; *passim* in all vols.). DISEASE: patients illustrating ailments, doctors in attendance in some cases. MEDICATION: doctors administering medicines, etc., e.g., CLYSTER (II, f. 134v). REGIMEN: food and drink. TEACHING: doctors expounding. DIAGNOSIS: by UROSCOPY. MATERIA MEDICA: doctors with herbs.

.45 ——, MS Lat. 6916 (14th c). AVICENNA, *Canon.*

ff. 1–329 *passim.* AUTHOR: expounds; Gerardus Cremonensis (translator) and two others with books (f. 1); Avicenna expounds (several miniatures). DISEASE: patients pointing to ailing members. MEDICATION: doctors attending patients.

.46 ——, MS Lat. 6966 (15th c). GUY DE CHAULIAC, *Chirurgia* (preceded by brief *Antidotarium*).

ff. 4, 154v. AUTHOR, MEDICAL CELEBRITIES: Guy de Chauliac points to book on lectern and to 'Galenus,' 'Avicenna' and 'Ypocras' (carrying books), six students seated. PHARMACY: Guy de Chauliac with assistants collecting herbs and using mortar and pestle (Fig. 21).

.47 ——, MS Lat. 6977 (14th c). ELLUCHASEM ELIMITHAR, *Tacuinum sanitatis.*

f. 1. AUTHOR: in monk's garb, with book and UROSCOPY flask (?).

.48 ——, MS Lat. 7056 (*c.* 1300). Medical miscellany.

ff. 87–89. OBSTETRICS: diagram of uterus showing foetal presentations (MOSCHION, *De aegritudinibus mulierum*).

.49 ——, MS Lat. 7138 (15th c). Medical miscellany; miniatures in GULIELMUS DE SALICETO, *Chirurgia*.

ff. iv, 199v–201, 238, 239. SURGERY: instruments in text. ANATOMY: bone-man; disease-man.

.50 ——, MS Lat. 7351 (14th c). Astrological miscellany (in Latin and French).

f. 2. PROGNOSIS: ZODIAC-MAN.

.51 ——, MS Lat. 9331 (15th c). GALENIC miscellany.

ff. 1, 91, 162, 202. AUTHOR: writing (*De ingenie sanitatis*); thinking (*De crisibus*); with book (*De interioribus*); collecting herbs (*De simplicibus medicinalis*).

.52 ——, MS Lat. 9332 (*c.* 800). Medical miscellany; ALEXANDER TRALLIANUS, *Libellum artis medicinae*.

f. 140. AUTHOR: seated, holding medicine case or book.

.53 ——, MS Lat. 9333 (1474). ELLUCHASEM ELIMITHAR, *Tacuinum sanitatis.*[1]

.54 ——, MS Lat. 11226 (14th c). THEODORICUS DE CERVIA, *Chirurgia*.

ff. 1, 24v, 107, 55. AUTHOR: in monk's garb reading. DISEASE: ulcerated face; attendant and mental patient (*mania*). SURGERY: operation for 'fistula' of eye.

.55 ——, MS Lat. 11229 (14th c). Medical miscellany (in Latin and French). BLOODLETTING-MAN.

.56 ——, MS Lat. 14068 (15th c). Astrological miscellany.

f. 195. PROGNOSIS: ZODIAC–MAN.

.57 ——, MS Lat. 14389 (14th c). GALENIC miscellany.

f. 280. AUTHOR: Galen seated with book (*De simplicibus medicinae*).

.58 ——, MS Lat. 15113 (13th c). Medical miscellany.

f. 8v. BLOODLETTING-MAN (with French text).

.59 ——, MS Lat. 15456 (13th c). GALENIC miscellany.

ff. 61, 147v, 186. AUTHOR: expounds (*De ingenio sanitatis*); half-figure of Galen (*De iuvamento anhelitus*); expounds (*De voce et anhelitu*).

.60 ——, MS Lat. 16187 (12–13th c). *Antidotarium*.

ff. 41, 46. PHARMACY: woman holding jar. MEDICAL CELEBRITY: King Mithridates enthroned, illustrating antidote *Mithridatum*.

.61 ——, MS Lat. 17846 (1472). GUY DE CHAULIAC, *Chirurgia.**

ff. 269–275. SURGERY: instruments in text.

[1] Topics, text and illustrations are almost identical with those of MS Lat. Nouv. Acquis. 1673, q.v.

.62 ——, MS Lat. Nouv. Acquis. 1673 (14th c). ELLUCHASEM ELIMITHAR, *Tacuinum sanitatis*.

ff. 1–103 *passim*. AUTHOR: enthroned, with book. MATERIA MEDICA, DIAETICA: herbs, grains, meats, etc., in process of collection or preparation by doctors, cooks, etc. PHARMACY: implements, apothecary shop, etc. DISEASE: man vomits (f. 89). REGIMEN: sleep; bathing; man and woman in bed (*coitus*). PAEDIATRICS: mother nurses baby, nurse holds baby (f. 90).

.63 ——, MS Suppl. Turc. 693 (1465). CHARAF ED-DIN, *Chirurgia* (in Turkish).[1]*

ff. 17–201 *passim*. SURGERY: CAUTERY at or near diseased organs; masculinization of hermaphrodite; suturing ear; use of cannula; circumcision; castration; amputation instruments; amputation of finger; tracheotomy. BLOODLETTING: by cupping; by leeches (f. 80v, retracting leech from throat); by incision. DENTISTRY: instruments. MEDICATION: by CLYSTER (patient on his back). OBSTETRICS: midwife delivers child; evacuation of placenta. ORTHOPAEDICS: reduction of fractures and dislocations; traction machine.

134.1 PARIS, France, BIBLIOTHÈQUE STE-GENEVIEVE, MS 588 (13th c). Saints' lives (in French).

ff. 136v, 173v. MEDICAL SAINTS: SS. Cosmas and Damian; St. Pantaleon.

.2 ——, MS 1028 (15th c). BARTHOLOMAEUS ANGLICUS, *De proprietatibus rerum* (in French).*

f. 61v. DISEASE: old man with staff beseeches aid of doctor.

.3 ——, MS 1029 (14th c). BARTHOLOMAEUS ANGLICUS, *De proprietatibus rerum* (in French).

ff. 32v, 120–265 *passim*. ANATOMY: doctor examines nude man. MATERIA MEDICA: herbs, animals and minerals. PROGNOSIS: Caladrius bird perches on bed of patient (f. 147).

.4 ——, MS 2235 (13th c). PETRUS HISPANUS (Pope John XXI), *Thesaurus pauperum*.

f. 3. AUTHOR, TEACHING: lectures to four students.

135.1 PAVIA, Italy, UNIVERSITY (Biblioteca Universitaria), MS 130.E.31 (14th c). Anonymous herbal.*

ff. 1–130 *passim*. MATERIA MEDICA: herbs.

136.1 PERUGIA, Italy, BIBLIOTECA COMUNALE (AUGUSTA), MS 316(E.64) (15th c). Surgical miscellany (in Italian).

f. 20v. SURGERY: instruments in text (LANFRANCUS MEDIOLANENSIS, *Chirurgia*).

---

[1] Our data is from Pierre Huard and Miro Grmek's photoreproductions in *Le Premier Manuscrit Chirurgical Turc* (Paris, 1960).

137.1 PISA, Italy, UNIVERSITY (Biblioteca Universitaria), MS 735(R.99) (14th c). Medical miscellany.

ff. 1–2. SURGERY: eight CAUTERY scenes, with instruments. ANATOMY: diagrams of internal organs; spleen, liver, heart, lungs, genitalia.

138.1 PRAGUE (Praha), Czechoslovakia, METROPOLITAN CHAPTER (Knihovna Metropolitni Kapituli), MS L.IX (15th c). Medical miscellany.
(front guard-sheet). BLOODLETTING-MAN.

.2 ——, MS L.X. (15th c). NICOLAUS BERTRUCIUS, *Collectorium medicinale*.
ff. 1, 219, 228v. AUTHOR, DIAGNOSIS, TEACHING: lectures while holding UROSCOPY flask; takes PULSE of bed-patient. UROSCOPY flask.

.3 ——, MS L.XI (1404). THOMAS DE CANTIMPRÉ, *De rerum natura*.
ff. 22–181 *passim*. MATERIA MEDICA: herbs and animals. PROGNOSIS: Caladrius bird (f. 93v).

.4 ——, MS L.XXXIX (*c.* 1487). Scientific miscellany.
ff. 137, 201v. ANATOMY: human figure, internal organs showing (commentary on ARISTOTLE, *Physica*). PROGNOSIS: ZODIAC-MAN.

139.1 PRAGUE (Praha), Czechoslovakia, UNIVERSITY (Universitni Knihovna), MS I.E.39 (15th c). Miscellany.
f. 245. BLOODLETTING-MAN (*Tractatus de minutione*).

.2 ——, MS III.E.20 (13–14th c). Medical miscellany.
ff. 1, 104, 115v. AUTHOR: HIPPOCRATES (commentary on *Aphorismi*); PHILARETUS (*De pulsibus*); GALEN (*Liber tegni*).

.3 ——, MS VI.Fc.29 (14th c). Medical miscellany.
pp. 89–109 *passim*. SURGERY: thirty-two CAUTERY scenes. ANATOMY: three wound-men; artery-man; vein-man; bone-man; muscle-man; nerve-man (Pseudo-GALEN, *Figura incisionis, Historia arteriorum*).

.4 ——, MS X.A.4 (14–15th c). THOMAS DE CANTIMPRÉ, *De rerum natura*.
ff. 1–225 *passim*. AUTHOR: with book. MATERIA MEDICA: herbs and animals. PROGNOSIS: caladrius bird (f. 92). MEDICATION: man binds herb (*sponsa*) on leg for snake bite (f. 185v).

.5 ——, MS XI.E.5 (15th c). Medical miscellany.
ff. 44v–45. DIAGNOSIS: UROSCOPY flasks.

.6 ——, MS XIII.F.29 (15th c). Medical miscellany (in Latin and German); miniatures in HEINRICH VON PFALZPEUNT, *Bindarznei*.
ff. 70–83 *passim*. SURGERY: instruments and bandages.

.7 ——, MS XIV.A.15 (14th c). THOMAS DE CANTIMPRÉ, *De rerum natura*.

ff. 3–147 *passim*. MATERIA MEDICA: herbs and animals. DIVINE HEALING: Christ(?) at bedside of patient. PROGNOSIS: Caladrius bird. MEDICATION: application of herb (*sponsa*) to leg wound.

.8 ——, MS XVII.D.10 (15th c). Astrological-medical miscellany.

ff. 41–101 *passim*. PROGNOSIS: ZODIAC-MAN. BLOODLETTING-MEN. BLOODLETTING: with cups and leeches. DIAGNOSIS: UROSCOPY flasks. ANATOMY: diagrams of internal organs, including stomach and heart.

140.1 ROME, Italy, ARCHIVIO DI STATO, MS. S. Spirito 1 (14th c). *Regula Hospitalis S. Spiritus in Saxia de Urbe*.

ff. 1–248 *passim*. HOSPITAL: life of the Hospitalers, with occasional scenes of sick-care.

141.1 ROME, Italy, BIBLIOTECA ANGELICA, MS 1474(V.2.11) (13th c). PETRUS DE EBULO, *De balneis Puteolanis*.

ff. 2–19. BATHING: scenes at baths of Puteoli.

142.1 ROME, Italy, BIBLIOTECA CASANATENSE, MS 163(D.II.7) (15th c). Herbal miscellany (in Italian).

ff. 1–90v. MATERIA MEDICA: herbs.

.2 ——, MS 208(A.II.14) (14th c). Medical miscellany; miniatures in ALBUCASIS, *Chirurgia*.

ff. 1, 3–78 *passim*. AUTHOR, SURGERY: ALBUCASIS applies cautery iron to patient's arm while assistant heats another cautery iron; instruments throughout margins of text; operation on patient's head. BLOODLETTING: bleeding patient's arm. ORTHOPAEDICS: reducing dislocated shoulder.

.3 ——, MS 459(A.I.20) (*c*. 1400). ELLUCHASEM ELIMITHAR, *Tacuinum sanitatis*.[1]

.4 ——, MS 1167 (15th c). Astrological-medical miscellany (in Italian).

f. 159v. BLOODLETTING-MAN.

.5 ——, MS 1382(A.II,15) (*c*. 1300). Medical miscellany; miniatures in ROLANDUS PARMENSIS, *Chirurgia*.

ff. 2–25 *passim*. DIAGNOSIS, SURGERY: Hippocrates directs UROSCOPY, forges cautery irons; trephines; nineteen CAUTERY scenes in which Hippocrates points out places on humans for cauterization. AUTHOR: ROLANDUS lectures to students (f. 3). SURGERY: Rolandus examines skull fracture (Fig. 63); probes skull fracture; operates on skull fracture; examines wounded nose; removes arrow from patient's skull; operates on skull; probes wounded neck; treats arm wound; replaces liver exposed through wound in patient's side; places

---

[1] This MS is similar to Paris, BN, MS Lat. Nouv. Acquis. 1673, q.v.

slit cat on patient's wounded intestine (Fig. 80); operates for scrotal hernia with patient on slanting board head downward (Fig. 81B); operates for stone while two assistants hold patient's legs apart (Fig. 82A). ORTHOPAEDICS: Rolandus reduces dislocated jaw (Fig. 78); reduces cervical dislocation; sets broken arm.

.6 ——, MS 4182 (c. 1400). ELLUCHASEM ELIMITHAR, *Theatrum sanitatis*.[1] (Fig. 23)

143.1 ROME, Italy, BIBLIOTECA LANCISIANA, MS LXXV.I.5(121) (1360). AVICENNA, *Canon*.

ff. 1v–353 *passim*. AUTHOR: bearded Avicenna in classical Roman dress. TEACHING: Avicenna with four students; doctors argue. CLINIC: assistants with mortar and double pestle; with scales; doctors instruct and medicate patients (f. 114); medical men and patients (very small, beautiful miniatures throughout).

144.1 ROME, Italy, BIBLIOTECA NAZIONALE CENTRALE VITTORIO EMANUELE II, MS 200 (15th c). Medical miscellany.

f. 77. BLOODLETTING-MAN.

145.1 ST. GALL (Sankt Gallen). Switzerland, STIFTSBIBLIOTHEK, MS 754, (1466). Medical miscellany (in German).*

p. 164. MATERIA MEDICA: herb 'agrimonia.'

.2 ——, MS 760 (15th c). Astrological-medical miscellany (in German).*

pp. 4–128 *passim*. REGIMEN. BLOODLETTING. TEMPERAMENTS.

3. ——, MS 827 (1425). Astrological-medical miscellany.*

p. 262. BLOODLETTING-MAN.

146.1 ST. GALL (Sankt Gallen), Switzerland, VADIANISCHE BIBLIOTHEK, MS 430 (15th c). Surgical miscellany; miniatures in GUY DE CHAULIAC, *Chirurgia*.

ff. 1, 12. AUTHOR, DIAGNOSIS: holds medicine jar; holds UROSCOPY flask.

.2 ——, MS 431 (1465). Medical miscellany.

ff. 4, 129, 177, 264, 345v. AUTHOR, DIAGNOSIS: HIPPOCRATES with UROSCOPY flask (CONSTANTINUS AFRICANUS, commentary on HIPPOCRATES, *Aphorismi*); HIPPOCRATES holds medicine glass (*Prognostica*); does UROSCOPY (*De regimine acutorum*); GALEN with UROSCOPY flask (two scenes, *Liber tegni*).

.3 ——, MS 433 (1465). PETRUS DE TUSSIGNANO, *Super nono Almansor*.

f. 1. AUTHOR, DIAGNOSIS: does UROSCOPY for bed-patient.

.4 ——, MS 436 (15th c). PETRUS HISPANUS, *Thesaurus pauperum* (followed by prescriptions).

[1] Topics, text and illustrations in this MS are similar to those in Paris, BN, MS Lat. Nouv. Acquis. 1673, q.v.

ff. 1 *passim*, rear guard-sheet. DISEASE: patient with staff beseeches doctor (Petrus?) for aid; patient vomits. MATERIA MEDICA: herbs (f. 20v).

147.1 SALZBURG, Austria, STIFTSBIBLIOTHEK ST. PETER, MS a.VII.12 (*c.* 1400). Astro-logical-medical miscellany (in German).*

f. 123v. BLOODLETTING-MAN.

148.1 SAN MARINO, California, USA, HUNTINGTON LIBRARY, MS HM.64 (15th c.). Medical miscellany (in Latin and English).

ff. 8v–47v *passim.* BLOODLETTING-MAN. PROGNOSIS: two ZODIAC-MEN. DIAGNOSIS: UROSCOPY flasks.

.2 ——, MS HM.19079 (1100). Herbal (in English).

f. 223v. MATERIA MEDICA: marginal sketch of herb.

149.1 SEVILLA, Spain, BIBLIOTECA COLUMBINA, MS 5.2.19 (15th c). *La Cirogia delli Cavalli* (in Spanish).*

f. 3v. VETERINARY MEDICINE: veterinarian displaying object removed from horse's foot.

150.1 SIENA, Italy, BIBLIOTECA COMUNALE, MS L.VII.7 (14th c). AVICENNA, *Canon.*

f. 1. AUTHOR, DIAGNOSIS, TEACHING: Avicenna with UROSCOPY flask; doctor expounds.

.2 ——, MS L.VII.18 (14th c). MANFREDUS DE MONTE IMPÉRIALE, *De simplicibus.*
ff. 214v–220. MATERIA MEDICA, DIAETICA: herbs, grain, fruit.

151.1 SOISSONS, France, MS 50 (15th c). Pseudo-APULEIUS, *Herbarium*; Pseudo-DIOSCO-RIDES, *De herbis femininis*; SEXTUS PLACITUS, *Medicina ex animalibus.*
ff. 4–61 *passim.* MATERIA MEDICA: herbs and animals.

152.1 STOCKHOLM, Sweden, KUNGLIGA BIBLIOTEKET, MS X.84 (14th c). AVICENNA, *Canon.**

ff. 1–200 *passim.* DISEASE: patients exposing diseased members.

.2 ——, MS X.118 (1412). JOHN ARDERNE, *De arte phisicale et de cirurgia* (a scroll with unnumbered illustrations in a central column and in the side margins).
Central column, positions 1, 3, 4, 7, 21. ANATOMY: vein-man; bone-man; nerve-man; sagittal sections with posterior and anterior unions, internal organs showing, surgical instruments alongside. Central column, positions 2, 5, 6. SURGERY: instruments and operation for *fistula in ano*. Central column, positions 8–20. OBSTETRICS: woman in childbirth, nurse; diagrams of uterus showing foetal presentations.
Side margins. DIAGNOSIS, DISEASE, MEDICATION, PHARMACY: spirited human figures illustrating ailments of all kinds with occasional pharmaceutical

implements and UROSCOPY flasks; patients CLYSTERED and CATHETERIZED; extraction of arrows; priest praying for patient.[1]

153.1 STUTTGART, West Germany, WÜRTTEMBERGISCHE LANDESBIBLIOTHEK, MS HB.XIII.2 (15th c). RUDOLF VON EMS, *Wilhelm von Orleans* (in German).*

f. 105v. MEDICATION: doctor gives bed-patient medicine through a tube.

.2 ——, MS Med. et Phys. Fol. 30 (15th c). Astrological-medical miscellany.*

f. 200v. BLOODLETTING-MAN.

154.1 THORN (Torun), Poland, UNIVERSITY (Biblioteka Uniwersytecka), 1506 edition of ULRICH BINDER (or PINDER), *Epiphanie medicorum* with three cut-out miniatures pasted over printed illustrations.

ff. 1, 4, 86. AUTHOR: expounds. DIAGNOSIS: doctor with UROSCOPY flask; doctor takes PULSE.

155.1 TÜBINGEN, West Germany, UNIVERSITÄTSBIBLIOTHEK, MS M.d.2 (*c.* 1500). Astrological-medical miscellany (in German).*

f. 12v. PROGNOSIS: ZODIAC-MAN.

.2 ——, MS Berlin Lat. Fol. 219 (1304). Medical miscellany; miniatures in HENRI DE MONDEVILLE, *Anathomia.*[2]

ff. 78–87. ANATOMY: marginal sketches of skeletons and various organs.

.3 ——, MS Berlin Or. Fol. 91 (15th c). ALBUCASIS, *Chirurgia* (in Arabic).[3]

156.1 TURIN, Italy, BIBLIOTECA NAZIONAL.[4]

157.1 TURIN (Torino), Italy, BIBLIOTECA REALE (Biblioteca Sua Maesta), MS N.129 (15th c). Anonymous, *Antidotarium.*

ff. 13v–52. MATERIA MEDICA: herbs and animals.

158.1 UTRECHT, Holland, BIBLIOTHEEK DER UNIVERSITEIT, MS 1356 (15th c). GUY DE CHAULIAC, *Chirurgia.*

ff. 1–275 *passim.* SURGERY: instruments in text.

[1] For a photofacsimile of the scroll, with the text in English translation, see Sir D'Arcy Power, *De Arte Phisicali et de Cirurgia of Master John Arderne, Surgeon of Newark,* in Research Studies in Medical History, No. 1, Wellcome Historical Medical Museum (London, 1922).

[2] This MS was formerly in the East Berlin Deutsche Staatsbibliothek.

[3] For photoreproductions of miniatures and details concerning illustrated ARABIC manuscripts of Albucasis, the older works by Johannis Channing, Lucien Leclerc, Ernst Gurlt and Karl Sudhoff are still useful, but for additional manuscripts and new data works such as the following are indispensable: Pierre Huard and Mirco Grmek, *Le Premier Manuscrit Chirurgical Turc* (Paris, 1960) with many photoreproductions and a brief list of manuscripts (p. 57); Sami Hamarneh, 'Drawings and Pharmacy in al-Zahrawi's 10th-Century Surgical Treatise,' *United States National Museum, Bulletin 228* (1961) with valuable photoreproductions and list (p. 85) of little-known manuscripts.

[4] Numerous illustrated manuscripts, destroyed in a disastrous fire, are described and photoreproduced in part, in Piero Giacosa, *Magistri Salernitani nondum editi* (Rome, etc., 1901).

159.1 VALENCIA, Spain, UNIVERSITY (Biblioteca Universitaria), MS 860 (138) (*c.* 1495). RAYNALDUS DE VILLANOVA, *Super balneis Puteoli.**
 ff. 2–38. BATHING: the baths at Puteoli.

160.1 VATICAN CITY, BIBLIOTECA APOSTOLICA VATICANA, MS Barb. Lat. 160 (11th c). Medical miscellany; miniatures in Pseudo-APULEIUS, *Herbarium.*[1]
 ff. 8–14. MATERIA MEDICA: herbs, with animals illustrating uses. AUTHOR: GALEN(?) (f. 66v, beginning of *De methodo medendi*, book II).

.2 ——, MS Barb. Lat. 311 (15th c). Medical miscellany.
 ff. 26–58. BATHING: scenes at baths of Puteoli (PETRUS DE EBULO, *De balneis Puteolanis*).

.3 ——, MS Barb. Lat. 341 (1552). JOHANNIS BADIANUS' translation of an Aztec herbal.
 ff. 1–63. MATERIA MEDICA: 204 herbs and trees.

.4 ——, MS Borgh. Lat. 353 (14th c). MESUE, *Graoadin.*
 f. 1. DIVINE HEALER: Christ, the source of healing, giving benediction,

.5 ——, MS Chigi F.IV.65 (14th c). Medical miscellany; miniatures in ALBUCASIS, *Chirurgia.*
 ff. 3–55 *passim.* SURGERY: instruments throughout text.

.6 ——, MS Chigi F.VII.158 (15th c). DIOSCORIDES, *Materia medica* (alphabetically arranged illustrations, without text).
 ff. 1–97v. MATERIA MEDICA: herbs, animals and minerals, with realistic action scenes (Fig. 19); interspersed with them are full-page illustrations of MEDICAL CELEBRITIES: Greek, Roman and Muslim medical men, usually collecting herbs.

.7 ——, MS Chigi F.VII.159 (15th c). DIOSCORIDES, *Materia medica* (in Greek).[2]
 ff. 13–239. MATERIA MEDICA: herbs, animals and minerals with action scenes. AUTHOR, MEDICAL CELEBRITIES: (ff. 233–236v are identical with Vienna, NB, MS Med. Greek 1, ff. 2v–6v, q.v.) (Fig. 18). ANATOMY: two nude eunuchoid figures (at end of MS).

.8 ——, MS Chigi F.VIII.188 (15th c). SIMON JANUENSIS, *De simplicibus medicinae.*
 ff. 1–197 *passim.* MEDICAL CELEBRITY: Dioscorides(?) holding lumps of *aurum*, *argentum*. MATERIA MEDICA: herbs, animals and minerals with action scenes (especially collecting minerals).

[1] Loren MacKinney, 'Medical Illustrations in Medieval Manuscripts of the Vatican Library,' *Manuscripta*, 1959, 3, 3–18, 76–88, has details for this and other manuscripts.
[2] This MS is similar to the sixth-century Greek Dioscorides at Vienna, MS Med. Greek 1.

.9 ——, MS Ottob. Lat. 2110 (14th c). Medical miscellany; miniatures in PETRUS DE EBULO, *De balneis Puteolanis*.

ff. 1–34(25–59) *passim*. BATHING: the baths of Puteoli.

.10 ——, MS Pal. Lat. 1066 (1424). Miscellany; miniatures in THOMAS DE CANTIMPRÉ, *De rerum natura*.

ff. 1–192 *passim*. MATERIA MEDICA: herbs, animals and minerals.

.11 ——, MS Pal. Lat. 1094 (14th c). GALENIC miscellany.

f. 1. DIAGNOSIS: doctor (Galen?) does UROSCOPY (*De elementis*).

.12 ——, MS Pal. Lat. 1304 (14–15th c). Medical miscellany.

ff. 35v, 37v, 68–69v (83–84v). DIAGNOSIS: UROSCOPY flasks (GUALTERUS AGILON, *De urinis*). OBSTETRICS: diagrams of uterus showing foetal presentations (MOSCHION, *De aegritudinibus mulierum*).

.13 ——, MS Pal. Lat. 1369 (1444). Astrological-medical miscellany.*

f. 148. BLOODLETTING-MAN.

.14 ——, MS Pal. Lat. 1709 (15th c). Astrological-medical miscellany.

ff. 44v–45. BLOODLETTING–MAN.

.15 ——, MS Reg. Lat. 214 (9–10th c). Religious miscellany, with marginal additions.

f. 10v. MATERIA MEDICA: herb *vettonica*.

.16 ——, MS Reg. Lat. 222.IV (12–13th c). CONSTANTINUS AFRICANUS, *De gradibus*.

f. 103. Woman's head symbolizing *Medicina*.

.17 ——, MS Ross. 379 (14th c). PETRUS DE EBULO, *De balneis Puteolanis* (in Latin and Italian).

ff. 13–47. BATHING: baths at Puteoli (Fig. 94B).

.18 ——, MS Ross. 458 (14th c). Medical miscellany; miniatures in CONSTANTINUS AFRICANUS, *Viaticum*.

ff. 1, 18v. DISEASE: patient kneels before doctor; patient holds flask.

.19 ——, MS Ross. 1067 (15th c). JOHANNES RUELANT, *De herbis et aliis medicinis*.

ff. 1–159. MATERIA MEDICA: herbs and animals, with action scenes.

.20 ——, MS Ross. 1101 (15th c). JACOPO DE FILIPPE, *Materia medica* (in Italian).

ff. 1–196v *passim*. PHARMACY, MATERIA MEDICA: herbs; animals; utensils.

.21 ——, MS Urb. Lat. 234 (15th c). HALY ABBAS, *Liber regalis*.

ff. 1, 162v. AUTHOR: Haly Abbas (or Stephen of Antioch, the translator) confers with royal patron.

.22 ——, MS Urb. Lat. 236 (14th c). Medical miscellany.

f. 1. AUTHOR: GALEN with book (*De ingenio sanitatis*).

.23 ——, MS Urb. Lat. 238 (15th c). SERAPION, *Breviarium*.

ff. 1–92 *passim*. AUTHOR: with Gerardus Cremonensis, the translator. DISEASE:

patients pointing to their ailments. AUTHOR expounding (*De simplici medicina*).

.24 ——, MS Urb. Lat. 240 (14th c). AVICENNA, *Canon* (books I, II, IV; see MS Urb. Lat. 241 for books III, V).

ff. 2–458 *passim*. AUTHOR: Avicenna; Gerardus Cremonensis, the translator; and others with books (ff. 2, 6, 143, 277). ANATOMY: patients demonstrating nerves, veins, arteries. DISEASE: doctors and patients illustrating ailments (*passim*). DIAGNOSIS: doctors taking PULSE; doing UROSCOPY. OBSTETRICS: midwife explaining childbirth. REGIMEN: exercise, old age, the four seasons. PROGNOSIS: caladrius bird perched on patient's wrist.

.25 ——, MS Urb. Lat. 241 (14th c). AVICENNA, *Canon* (books III, V).

ff. 2–422 *passim*. AUTHOR: Avicenna; Gerardus Cremonensis, the translator; and others with books (ff. 2, 6, 409v). ANATOMY: doctor and students with skull and other organs (f. 2, in lower margin). DISEASE: patients or doctors demonstrating ailments (*passim*). MEDICATION: doctor places slit rooster on patient's head (f. 30). ANATOMY, TEACHING: use of internal and external organs in demonstrating to students (*passim*). DIAGNOSIS: doctor does UROSCOPY (f. 255v). OBSTETRICS: pregnant woman (f. 330v). PHARMACY: doctors or pharmacists compound medicines (ff. 364–408v) (Figs. 24–25).

.26 ——, MS Urb. Lat. 242 (15th c). MESUE, *Grabadin*.

facing f. 1. AUTHOR, PHARMACY: Mesue with book, pharmacist with implements.

.27 ——, MS Urb. Lat. 243 (15th c). SERAPION, *Liber aggregationum*.

facing f. 1. AUTHOR, MEDICAL CELEBRITIES: Serapion presents book to Dioscorides, Hippocrates and Galen.

.28 ——, MS Urb. Lat. 246 (15th c). MUNDINUS DE LENTIIS, *Anatomia*.*

f. 248v. ANATOMY: diagram of eye.

.29 ——, MS Urb. Lat. 250 (15th c). THEOPHRASTUS, *De plantis*.

ff. 3–188 *passim*. MATERIA MEDICA: herbs.

.30 ——, MS Urb. Lat. 252 (14–15th c). LORENTIUS RUSIUS (Lorenzo Rusio), *Liber mareschalciae*.

f. 2. VETERINARY MEDICINE: veterinarian applies plaster to horse's back, groom attends.

.31 ——, MS Urb. Lat. 746 (12th c). MACER FLORIDUS, *De viribus herbarum*.

ff. 30, 31, 32. MATERIA MEDICA: herbs.

.32 ——, MS Urb. Lat. 1354 (16th c). *Herbarium* (in Italian).*

ff. 3–34. MATERIA MEDICA: herbs.

.33 ——, MS Urb. Lat. 1398 (15th c). Astrological miscellany.

f. 10v. PROGNOSIS: ZODIAC-MAN.

.34 ——, MS Vat. Lat. 2375 (14th c). GALENIC miscellany.

ff. 17v–479 *passim*. AUTHOR: Galen and other doctors (at the beginnings of treatises).

.35 ——, MS Vat. Lat. 2378 (14th c). GALENIC miscellany.

f. 1. AUTHOR: with book (*De ingenio sanitatis*).

.36 ——, MS Vat. Lat. 2382 (14th c). GALENIC-HIPPOCRATIC miscellany.

ff. 1, 15, 63v. AUTHOR: Galen (*De differentibus febrium*; *De regimine sanitatis*; *De voce et anhelitu*).

.37 ——, MS Vat. Lat. 2411 (*c.* 1300). AVICENNA, *Canon* (book II).

f. 1v. ANATOMY, BLOODLETTING-MAN with parts of body captioned.

.38 ——, MS Vat. Lat. 4425 (14th c). Medical miscellany; miniatures in RHAZES, *Almansor*.

ff. 182v, 234v. AUTHOR: Rhazes with book, two enthroned women. DISEASE: man's profile opposite text on head ailments.

.39 ——, MS Vat. Lat. 4427 (14th c). AVICENNA, *Canon*.

ff. 1, 46. AUTHOR: Avicenna with book. DISEASE: woman's head.

.40 ——, MS Vat. Lat. 4467 (12th c). ALBUCASIS, *Chirurgia*.

ff. 1–32 *passim*. AUTHOR, SURGERY: Albucasis performs head operation; Albucasis with book expounds (f. 25v); instruments throughout text.

.41 ——, MS Vat. Lat. 4468 (14th c). GULIELMUS DE SALICETO, *Chirurgia*.

ff. 1–35 *passim*. AUTHOR, SURGERY: Gulielmus probes patient's leg wound. AUTHOR (ff. 1v, 35). DISEASE: patient with nasal fracture; with ailing throat.

.42 ——, MS Vat. Lat. 4471 (14th c). BRUNO LONGOBURGENSIS, *Chirurgia*.

ff. 1, 23. AUTHOR, SURGERY: Bruno performs skull operation, doctors and assistants stand by; Bruno expounds.

.43 ——, MS Vat. Lat. 4473 (12th c). ROLANDUS PARMENSIS, *Chirurgia*.

ff. 22, 60v. PHARMACY: prescriptions written on dimly outlined flasks.

.44 ——, MS Vat. Lat. 4476 (15th c). MARCUS BENZARUS, *Herbarium*.

ff. 1–52 *passim*. MATERIA MEDICA: herbs, animals and minerals, with action scenes. MEDICATION: patient CLYSTERED (f. 44).

.45 ——, MS Vat. Lat. 4804 (1363). GUY DE CHAULIAC, *Chirurgia* (in Provençal).

ff. 1–240 *passim*. AUTHOR: LECTURES to three students. ANATOMICAL DISSECTION: doctor directs surgeon, cadaver on trestle (f. 8). MEDICATION: doctors prepare to treat chest; arm; leg (Fig. 89B). SURGERY: instruments in text. DIAGNOSIS, PHARMACY: doctor does UROSCOPY as assistant compounds medicines (f. 223).

.46 ——, MS Vat. Greek 284 (10th c). Miscellany of materia medica (in Greek).

ff. 2–284v *passim*. MATERIA MEDICA: herbs and animals.

.47 ——, MS Vat. Greek 1613 (*c.* 1000). *Menologion* of Basil II (in Greek).

f. 152. MEDICAL SAINTS: Cosmas and Damian receive UROSCOPY flask(?) from heaven.

161.1 VENICE (Venezia), Italy, BIBLIOTECA NAZIONALE MARCIANA, MS VI. 59 (2548) (1419). BENEDICTUS RINIUS, *De simplicibus.*

ff. 1–458 *passim.* AUTHOR: enthroned lectures. MATERIA MEDICA: herbs.

.2 ——, MS VII.13(3090) (14th c.). Surgical miscellany; miniatures in *Chirurgia cauterium secundum Rogerium, Brunum et Rolandum.*

ff. 22v–23v. CAUTERY: doctors cauterize; CAUTERY-MEN.

.3 ——, MS VII.16(2862) (14th c.). Medical miscellany.

ff. 1, 33, 43, 57. AUTHOR, TEACHING: GALEN expounds to six students (JOHANNI-TIUS, *Isagoge in tegni Galieni*). DIAGNOSIS: caricature figure holds aloft UROSCOPY flask (HIPPOCRATES, *Prognostica*). AUTHOR, DIAGNOSIS: THEO-PHILUS PROTOSPATHARIUS holds UROSCOPY flask (*De urinis*); PHILARETUS takes PULSE (*De pulsibus*).

.4 ——, MS VII.32(3023) (14th c.). Surgical miscellany; miniatures in ALBUCASIS, *Chirurgia.*

ff. 2–40 *passim.* SURGERY: instruments throughout text. ORTHOPAEDICS: traction machine for reducing vertebral dislocations. ANATOMY: BLOODLETTING-MAN, internal organs showing.

.5 ——, MS 265(1677) (15th c.). THEOPHRASTUS, *De plantis.*

f. 1. AUTHOR: bust of Theophrastus.

.6 ——, MS 318(1960) (14th c.). Medical miscellany.

ff. 1, 54. AUTHOR: AVERRHOES lectures to three students (*Colliget*); AVICENNA with book (*De naturalibus*, book VI).

.7 ——, MS 320(1937) (14th c.). Medical miscellany.

ff. 1–103 *passim.* AUTHOR: King Almansor expounds to RHAZES who holds book (*Almansor*); RHAZES with book (*Almansor*); RHAZES lectures to three students (*Liber divisionum*). AUTHOR: ALBUCASIS expounds (*Chirurgia*). SURGERY: instruments throughout text of Albucasis; head operation. OBSTETRICS: diagrams of uterus showing foetal presentations (MOSCHION, *De aegritudinibus mulierum*). ORTHOPAEDICS: traction machine (Albucasis).

.8 ——, MS 536(1999) (14th c.). Medical miscellany.

ff. 25–28. CAUTERY, MEDICAL CELEBRITIES: 'Aristotle,' 'Apollonius,' etc. cauterize.

.9 ——, MS Greek 92 (11th c.). DIOSCORIDES, *Materia medica* (in Greek).*

ff. 1 ff. *passim.* MATERIA MEDICA: herbs.

162.1 VERCELLI, Italy, BIBLIOTECA CAPITOLARE, MS 202 (9th c.). ISIDORUS HISPALENSIS, *Etymologiae.*

f. 91v. MEDICAL CELEBRITY: 'Apollo Medicus' (at beginning of book IV, *De medicina*).

163.1 VICENZA, Italy, BIBLIOTECA COMUNALE BERTOLIANA, MS G.24.25 (13th c). GARIO-PONTUS, *Passionarius*.

f. 10. ANATOMY: diagrams of uterus.

164.1 VIENNA (Wien), Austria, KUNSTHISTORISCHES MUSEUM, MS (14th c). ELLUCHASEM ELIMITHAR, *Tacuinum sanitatis*.*

ff. 1ff. MATERIA MEDICA, DIAETICA, REGIMEN: herbs, animals and minerals, with action scenes.

165.1 VIENNA (Wien), Austria, ÖSTERREICHISCHE NATIONALBIBLIOTHEK, Incunabula 9.A.3 (1484). AVICENNA, *Canon*.

f. 1. AUTHOR: (miniature).

.2 ——, MS Med. Greek 1 (*c*. 510). DIOSCORIDES, *Materia medica* (in Greek).

ff. 2v–6v, 12–483 *passim*. AUTHOR, MEDICAL CELEBRITIES: Chiron, Moschion, Pamphilos, Dioscorides, Galen, Zenocrates, Sextus Niger, Heraclides, Mantias, Nicander, Rufus, Cratevas, Apollonius and Andicas; Dioscorides receives mandragora from Euresis; Dioscorides, Cratevas the illustrator, and Sophia with mandragora; Dioscorides presents book to patroness Juliana Anicia. MATERIA MEDICA: herbs and animals.

.3 ——, MS 86 (15th c). CELSUS, *De medicina*.

f. 1. AUTHOR, DIAGNOSIS: Celsus takes boy's PULSE.

.4 ——, MS 93 (13th c). Pseudo-APULEIUS, *Herbarium*; SEXTUS PLACITUS, *De medicina ex animalibus*; Pseudo-DIOSCORIDES, *De herbis femininis*.

ff. 2–133 *passim*. AUTHOR, MEDICAL CELEBRITIES: 'Ipokrates'; 'Apuleius Plato'; Centaur; 'Omerus' and 'Mercurius'; 'Achilles'; 'Plato' (i.e., Pseudo-Apuleius) with book; 'Dioscorides' with book. MATERIA MEDICA: herbs and animals, with action scenes. PHARMACY: implements. MEDICATION, DISEASE: simples and compounds applied to patients (Figs. 26, 39, 41); PAEDIATRICS: doctors treating children (Figs. 27, 42); DIAGNOSIS: doctor taking PULSE; BATHING. OBSTETRICS: woman in childbirth (Fig. 92).

.5 ——, MS 1462(A.F.10) (13th c). GALEN, *De tyriaca*; *Antidotum* (in Arabic).

ff. 2v–31 *passim*. PHARMACY: doctors preparing and applying theriacs for snake bite. MEDICAL CELEBRITIES: Galen, Andromachus and other theriac experts (f. 31).

.6 ——, MS 2280 (13th c). Medical miscellany.

ff. 1–89 *passim*. AUTHOR, DIAGNOSIS, TEACHING: AVERRHOES with UROSCOPY flask (*Colliget*); AVENZOAR lectures (*Theisir*); MAIMONIDES with UROSCOPY flask (*De dieta*); SERAPION (*Aggregationes*). BATHING: king with book instructs assistant attending man in tub (AVERRHOES, *Colliget*). DIAGNOSIS: AVERRHOES with UROSCOPY flask examines kneeling patient; examines bowl of stool; ponders hygienic problem (*Colliget*); AVENZOAR with UROSCOPY flask (*Theisir*). DISEASE: haemorrhoids; bed-patient (AVERRHOES, *Colliget*); patient dicusses internal ailment with doctor (AVENZOAR, *Theisir*). MATERIA MEDICA: AVERRHOES with herb (*Colliget*).

.7 ——, MS 2284 (14th c). Medical miscellany.

f. 1 AUTHOR, DIAGNOSIS: AVICENNA does UROSCOPY (*Canon*).

.8 ——, MS 2286 (14th c). RHAZES, *Almansor*; *Liber divisionum*.

ff. 1, 75. AUTHOR: with book; expounds.

.9 ——, MS 2294 (14th c). GALENIC miscellany.

f. 123. AUTHOR: Galen expounds (*De accidenti et morbo*).

.10 ——, MS 2301 (14th c). Surgical miscellany.

ff. 1, 31, 87. AUTHOR: BRUNO LONGOBURGENSIS expounds (*Chirurgia*); GULIELMUS DE SALICETO expounds (*Chirurgia*); ALBUCASIS with scroll (*Chirurgia*).

.11 ——, MS 2315 (13th c). HIPPOCRATIC-GALENIC miscellany.

ff. 1–187v *passim*. AUTHOR, TEACHING: Hippocrates dictating *Aphorismi* and lecturing to six students; Galen lecturing to five students (f. 145, *Liber tegni*). DIAGNOSIS: doctors performing UROSCOPIES (Hippocrates, *Aphorismi*; *Pronostica*). DISEASE: doctor with 'spasmus' patient (Hippocrates, *Aphorismi*); doctors examine patient's chest (Hippocrates, *Pronostica*; *De regimine acutorum*). MEDICATION: doctor and assistant holding jars, bed-patient; doctor with jar, bed-patient with flask (Hippocrates, *De regimine acutorum*). REGIMEN: three at table preparing food (Galen, *Liber Tegni*).

.12 ——, MS 2320 (14th c). Medical miscellany.

ff. 4, 18v, 30, 136. AUTHOR: GALEN and JOHANNITIUS arguing (*Isogoge ad tegni Galeni*); THEOPHILUS performing UROSCOPY (*De urinis*); HIPPOCRATES lecturing to four students from *Aphorismi*; GALEN lecturing (*Liber tegni*). DIAGNOSIS: doctor feeling patient's head, assistant taking PULSE (f. 91v, HIPPOCRATES, *Pronostica*); doctor feeling patient's head and chest, assistant holding UROSCOPY-flask carrier (f. 219v, HIPPOCRATES, *De regimine acutorum*).

.13 ——, MS 2328 (14th c). HIPPOCRATIC miscellany.

f. 1. AUTHOR: does UROSCOPY (*Aphorismi*).

.14 ——, MS 2381 (14th c). ALBUCASIS, *Chirurgia*.

ff. 2–62 *passim*. SURGERY: instruments throughout text.

.15 ——, MS 2396 (*c.* 1400). ELLUCHASEM ELIMITHAR, *Tacuinum sanitatis*.[1]

[1] Similar to Paris, BN, MS Lat. Nouv. Acquis. 1673, q.v.

.16 ——, MS 3085 (15th c). Astrological-medical-literary miscellany (in German).

    ff. 28–31 *passim*. REGIMEN: Four TEMPERAMENTS. BLOODLETTING-MAN with ZODIAC signs.

.17 ——, MS 5264 (15th c). Medical miscellany (in Italian).*

    ff. 4v–112 *passim*. MEDICAL CELEBRITIES: circle of nine famous medical men (JOHANNES CADAMOSTO, *Herbarium*). MATERIA MEDICA: herbs, in alphabetical order (JOHANNES CADAMOSTO, *Herbarium*). MATERIA MEDICA, DIAETICA: herbs, animals and minerals, with action scenes (ELLUCHASEM ELIMITHAR, *Tacuinum sanitatis*).

.18 ——, SERIES NUOVA, MS 2641 (14th c). ALBUCASIS, *Chirurgia*.

    ff. 4v–76v *passim*. SURGERY: Muslim doctors CAUTERIZING. OBSTETRICS: Muslim midwives delivering infants in various presentations (Fig. 91C). SURGERY: woman with imbedded arrow to illustrate extraction. BLOODLETTING: by incision and cupping. ORTHOPAEDICS: woman examines man's thigh; patient on traction machine.

.19 ——, SERIES NUOVA, MS 2644 (c. 1300). ELLUCHASEM ELIMITHAR, *Tacuinum sanitatis*.[1]*

.20 ——, MS Pal. 276 (14th c). Medical miscellany; miniatures in Pseudo-APULEIUS, *Herbarium*.*

    ff. 1–18. MATERIA MEDICA: herbs.

166.1 VIENNA (Wien), Austria, SCHOTTENKLOSTER, MS 53.h.9 (15th c). Astrological-medical miscellany.*

    f. 343v. BLOODLETTING-MAN.

167.1 WARSAW (Warszawa), Poland, NATIONAL LIBRARY (Biblioteka Narodowa), MS (formerly Danzig, Poland, City Library, MS 2310) (1467). THOMAS VON BRESLAU (Bishop of Sarepta), *Mihi competit* (*Tractatus de defectu capillorum*, etc.).

    ff. 2v, 3. BLOODLETTING-MAN. DIAGNOSIS: author does UROSCOPY.

.2 ——, MS (formerly Pelplin Seminary, MS Cim. 43/79) (13th c). Medical miscellany.

    f. 50v. AUTHOR, TEACHING: lectures to two students (AVICENNA, *Canon*).

168.1 WASHINGTON, D.C., USA, FREER GALLERY OF ART, MS 30.76 (1315). AL-JAZARI, *Automata* (in Arabic).

    detached folio. BLOODLETTING: automatic device for measuring the amount of blood extracted (Fig. 59).

.2 ——, MS 32.20–22, 38.1, 43.2.a–b, 47.5, 53.91 (eight detached folios from Istanbul, Turkey, Sancta Sophia (Aya Sofya) Library, MS 3703, q.v.).

[1] Reported to be similar to Paris, BN, Lat. Nouv. Acquis, 1673, q.v.

169.1 WEIMAR, East Germany, LANDESBIBLIOTHEK, MS F.59 (14th c). Medical miscellany.

ff. 1, 35, 53. AUTHOR, DIAGNOSIS: MESUE with UROSCOPY flask (*De simplicibus medicamentis*). MATERIA MEDICA, REGIMEN: ISAAC JUDAEUS collects fruit (*De dietis universalibus*). DIAGNOSIS: ISAAC JUDAEUS does UROSCOPY; takes PULSE (*De urinis*).

WIEN, see VIENNA.

170.1 WOLFENBUTTEL, West Germany, HERZLICHEN BIBLIOTHEK, MS 1.8. Aug. 2°(1615) (14–15th c). AVICENNA, *Canon*.

f. 3. AUTHOR, DIAGNOSIS: with UROSCOPY flask.

.2 ——, MS 8.7. Aug. 4°(2973) (*c.* 1500). Astrological-medical miscellany.

ff. 125–126v, 139, 140v. REGIMEN: FOUR TEMPERAMENTS. BATHING, BLOOD-LETTING: couple in tub eating and drinking, others bled by cupping. MEDI-CATION: doctor administers CLYSTER to bed-patient, UROSCOPY-flask carrier on wall.

.3 ——, MS 18.2. Aug. 4°(3133) (15th c). Astrological-medical miscellany.

f. 110. ANATOMY, BLOODLETTING-MAN: with ZODIAC signs, internal organs exposed.

.4 ——, MS 18.18. Aug. 4° (15th c). Astrological-medical miscellany (in German).

f. 124v. PROGNOSIS: ZODIAC-MAN with captions of four temperaments in margins.

.5 ——, MS 20.16. Aug. 4°(3245) (15th c). Astrological-medical miscellany (in German).

f. 69. BLOODLETTING-MAN.

.6 ——, MS 79. Aug. 2°(2778) (15th c). Herbal-animal miscellany (in German).

ff. 1–174 *passim*. MATERIA MEDICA: herbs and animals.

.7 ——, MS 81.4. Aug. 2°(2794) (14th c). Medical miscellany.

f. 231. BLOODLETTING-MAN: with points for cupping.

.8 ——, MS 85.2. Aug. 2°(2855) (15th c). Medical miscellany.

f. 104. BLOODLETTING: doctor bleeds arm of bed-patient.

.9 ——, MS Helmstadt 760(696) (15th c). Astrological-medical miscellany.

f. 130v. PROGNOSIS: ZODIAC-MAN.

WROCLAW, see BRESLAU.

171.1 WURZBURG, West Germany, UNIVERSITY (Universitätsbibliothek), MS M.ch.F.106 (14–15th c). Astrological-medical miscellany.*

f. 85. BLOODLETTING-MAN.

.2 ——, MS M.ch.F.150 (15th c). THOMAS DE CANTIMPRÉ, *De rerum natura*.

ff. 49v–211v. MATERIA MEDICA: herbs and animals (including monsters).

.3 ——, MS M.ch.F.265 (15th c). CONRAD VON MEGENBERG, *Buch der Natur* (in German).

ff. 36v–208v. MATERIA MEDICA: herbs and animals.

.4 ——, MS M.ch.Q.30 (15th c). Medical miscellany; miniatures in ALBERTUS MAGNUS, *De secretis mulierum*.

ff. 258v, 259. ANATOMY: male and female figures showing internal organs.

.5 ——, MS M.p. Med. F.2 (14th c). Medical miscellany.

f. 5. AUTHOR: GALEN presents book to 'Nero'; Galen and two students approach king.

172.1 YORK, England, CATHEDRAL, MS XVI.E.32 (1414). Astrological-medical miscellany (in English).

ff. 21, 108v, 166. ANATOMY: marginal sketches of tongues. PROGNOSIS: ZODIAC-MAN. DIAGNOSIS: UROSCOPY flasks.

SELECT BIBLIOGRAPHY

Works especially useful for their reproductions of miniatures are starred.

* American Institute of the History of Pharmacy, *Calendars*. Madison, Wisconsin, 1958 ff.

* *American Professional Pharmacist*. New York, 1935 ff.

Arderne, John, *Treatises of Fistula in Ano, Haemorrhoids and Clysters*. Edited by D'Arcy Power. Early English Texts Society, Original Series, No. 139. London, 1910.

* *De Arte Phisicali et de Cirurgia of Master John Arderne, Surgeon of Newark*. Edited and translated by D'Arcy Power. Wellcome Historical Medical Museum. Research Studies in Medical History, No. 1. London, 1922.

* Artelt, Walter, 'Bilderatlass zur Geschichte der Medizin', *in* Paul Diepgen, *Geschichte der Medizin*, II (2). Berlin, 1949.

* ——, *Kosmas und Damian, die Schutzpatrone der Ärzte und Apotheker; eine Bildfolge.* Frankfurt, 1954.

* Bettman, Otto, *A Pictorial History of Medicine*. Springfield, Ill., 1956.

* Bober, Harry, 'The Zodiacal Miniatures of the *Très Riches Heures* of the Duke of Berry—Its Sources and Meaning', *Journal of the Warburg and Courtauld Institutes*. 1948, *11*, 1–34.

Bogoiavlenskii, N. A., *Old Russian Medical Practice, XI–XVIII Centuries*. Moscow, 1960 (In Russian).

Bond, W. H., *Supplement to the Census of Medieval and Renaissance Manuscripts in the United States and Canada*. New York, 1962.

* Boussel, Patrice, *Histoire Illustrée de la Pharmacie*. Paris, 1949.

* Büchthal, Hugo, 'Early Islamic Miniatures from Baghdad,' *Journal of the Walters Art Gallery*. 1942, *5*, 18–39.

* Campbell, Eldridge and James Colton (Translators), *The Surgery of Theodoric*, 2 vols., New York, 1955, 1960.

Castiglioni, Arturo, *A History of Medicine*. Translated by E. B. Krumbhaar. New York, 1941.

Celsus, *De medicina*. 3 vols., Edited and translated by W. G. Spencer. Loeb Classical Library. London, 1935–1938.

* *Ciba Symposium*. Basle, 1951 ff.

* *Ciba Symposia*. Summit, New Jersey, 1939 ff.

* Cooper, Douglas, *The Courtauld Collection*. London, 1954.

SELECT BIBLIOGRAPHY

Corner, George W., 'Salernitan Surgery in the Twelfth Century,' *British Journal of Surgery*. 1937, *25*, 84–99.

De Ricci, Seymour and W. J. Wilson, *Census of Medieval and Renaissance Manuscripts in the United States and Canada*. 3 vols., New York, 1935–1940.

★ Diepgen, Paul, *Geschichte der Medizin*. 2 vols., Berlin, 1949.

Duffy, John, *The Rudolph Matas History of Medicine in Louisiana*. 2 vols., Baton Rouge, Louisiana, 1960, 1962.

★ Ettinghausen, Richard, *Arab Painting*. Cleveland, Ohio, 1962.

★ Dumesnil, René, *Histoire Illustrée de la Médecine*. Paris, 1935.

★ Ferchel, Fritz, *Illustrierte Apotheker-Kalendar*. Berlin, 1925.

Frederick II, *The Art of Falconry, being the De Arte Venandi cum Avibus of Frederick II of Hohenstaufen*. Edited and Translated by Casey A. Wood and F. Marjorie Fyfe. London, 1943.

★ Giacosa, Piero, *Magistri Salernitani nondum editi*. Torino, 1901.

Griffenhagen, George, 'Tools of the Apothecary,' *Journal of the American Pharmaceutical Association*. Practical Pharmacy Edition. 1956, *17*, 810–813.

Gruner, O. Cameron, *A Treatise on the Canon of Medicine of Avicenna*. London, 1930.

Hamarneh, Sami, 'Drawings and Pharmacy in al-Zahrawi's 10th Century Surgical Treatise,' U.S. National Museum (History and Technology). Bulletin 228, 1961, pp. 81–94.

★ Hein, Wolfgang-Hagen, *Illustrierte Apotheker-Kalendar*. Essen, 1954–56.

★ ——, *Die Deutsche Apotheke Bilder aus ihrer Geschichte*. Stuttgart, 1960.

Hill, Boyd, *Fünfbilderserie in Medieval Anatomy* (Unpublished Ph.D. Dissertation, University of North Carolina) Chapel Hill, 1963.

★ Holländer, Eugen, *Die Medizin in der klassischen Malerei*. Berlin, 1913.

★ ——, *Die Karikatur und Satire in der Medizin*. Stuttgart, 1921.

Horine, B. F., 'An Epitome of Ancient Pulse Lore,' *Bulletin of the History of Medicine*. 1941, *10*, 216–235.

★ Huard, Pierre Alphonse and Mirko Drazen Grmek, *Le premier manuscrit chirurgical turc, rédigé par Charaf ed-Din (1465) et illustré de 140 miniatures*. Paris, 1960.

Jones, W. H. S. (ed. and trans.), *The Medical Writings of Anonymous Londinensis*. Cambridge, 1947.

★ *Journal of the American Pharmaceutical Association*. Practical Pharmacy Edition. Easton, Pennsylvania, 1912 ff.

★ Kauffmann, C. M., *The Baths of Pozzuoli*. Oxford, 1959.

★ Kilgour, Frederick G., 'Medicine in Art,' *What's New*. 1960, *3*, 104.

★ Koning, D. A. Wittop, (ed.), *Art and Pharmacy*. 2 vols. Deventer, 1950, 1958.

Kühn, C. G., *Claudii Galeni Opera omnia*. 20 vols., Medicorum Graecorum Opera quae extant. Lipsiae, 1821–1833.

* Laignel-Lavastine, M., *Histoire générale de la Médecine, de la Pharmacie, de l'Art Dentaire et de l'Art Vétérinaire*. 3 vols., Paris, 1936–1949.

* Leersum, E. C. van and W. Martin, *Miniaturen der lateinischen Galenos-Handschrift der kgl. öffentl. Bibliothek in Dresden*. Codices graeci et latini photographice depicti. Supp. VIII. Leiden, 1910.

McCullough, Florence, *Medieval Latin and French Bestiaries*. Chapel Hill, North Carolina, 1960.

MacKinney, Loren C., *Early Medieval Medicine with Special Reference to France and Chartres*. The Hideyo Noguchi Lectures, The Johns Hopkins University. Baltimore, 1937.

* ——, 'Childbirth in the Middle Ages, as Seen in Manuscript Illustrations,' *Ciba Symposium*. 1960, *8*, 230–236.

* ——, 'Double-pestle Action in Medieval Miniatures,' *Journal of the American Pharmaceutical Association*. Practical Pharmacy Edition. 1961, *NS1(3)*.

——, 'Medical Ethics and Etiquette in the Early Middle Ages,' *Bulletin of the History of Medicine*, 1952, *26*, 1–31.

——, 'Medical Illustrations in Medieval Manuscripts of the Vatican Library,' *Manuscripta*, 1959, *3*, 3–18, 76–88.

——, 'Medieval Medical Miniatures in Central and East European Collections,' *Manuscripta*, 1961, *5*, 131–150.

——, 'Medieval Surgery,' *Journal of the International College of Surgeons*. Hall of Fame Lecture. 1957, *27(3)*, 393–404.

* ——, 'A Thirteenth Century Medical Case History in Miniatures,' *Speculum*, 1960, *35*, 251–259.

* ——, 'Tranquillisers before the Modern Era,' *Chemist and Druggist*. 1960, *173* (Special Issue), 766–771.

* ——, 'What Did Medieval and Early Modern Illustrators Think Hippocrates Looked Like,' *News* (University of Kansas Medical Center), 1960.

MacKinney, Loren and Thomas Herndon, 'American Manuscript Collections of Medieval Medical Miniatures and Texts,' *Journal of the History of Medicine and Allied Sciences*, 1962, *17(2)*, 284–307.

Moorat, S. A. J., *Catalogue of Western Manuscripts on Medicine and Science in the Wellcome Historical Medical Library*. London, 1962.

* *M D Medical Newsmagazine*. New York, 1957 ff.

Monumenta Germaniae Historica. Auctorum Antiquissimi. XII, 191 ff.

* Netter, F. H., *The Ciba Collection of Medical Illustrations*. Summit, New Jersey, 1948.

* New York Academy of Medicine, *Illustration Catalog*. Boston, 1960.

Olivieri, A., 'Indice de' Codici Greci Bolognesi,' *Studi Italiani di filologia classica*. 1895, 3, 387–495.

* Pächt, Otto, 'Early Italian Nature Studies and the Early Calendar Landscape,' *Journal of the Warburg and Courtauld Institutes*. 1950, 13, 13–47.

* Pedrazzini, Carlo, *La farmacia storica ed artistica Italiana*. Milan, 1934.

* Peters, Hermann, *Aus Pharmazeutischer Vorzeit in Bild und Wort*. 2 vols., Berlin, 1899–1910.

* ——, *Pictorial History of Ancient Pharmacy*. Translated by Dr. William Netter. Chicago, 1889.

* Pierpont Morgan Library. (Various Catalogues of Exhibitions). New York, 1938 ff.

Pohl, Hans, *Ein Pseudo-Galen-Text aus dem frühen Mittelalter, betitelt 'De pulsis et urinis omnium causarum' aus der Handschrift Nr. 44 der Stiftsbibliothek zu St. Gallen*. Inaugural-Dissertation. Leipzig, 1922.

* Proskauer, Curt, *Iconographia Odontologica*. Berlin, 1926.

* *Rassegna Medica*. Convivium Sanitas. 1959, 36, 169 ff.

* Richter, Paul, *L'Art et la Médecine*. Paris, 1902.

Sarton, George, *Introduction to the History of Science*. 3 vols., Baltimore, 1927–1948.

* Schering Corporation, *Medicine and Pharmacy: An Informal History*. 3 vols., Bloomfield, New Jersey, 1955–1956.

* Schöne, Hermann (ed.), *Apollonius von Kitium; illustrierter Kommentar zu der hippokratischen Schrift*. Leipzig, 1896.

Sharpe, William, 'Bede, De minutione sanguinis sive de phlebotomia,' *Quarterly of Phi Beta Pi Medical Fraternity*. 1955–56, 52, 85–87.

Shelley, Harry, 'Cutting for the Stone,' *Journal of the History of Medicine and Allied Sciences*, 1958, 13, 50–67.

Sigerist, Henry, *Studien und Texte zur frühmittelalterlichen Rezeptliteratur*. Leipzig, 1923.

* Singer, Charles, 'The Herbal in Antiquity,' *Journal of Hellenic Studies*. 1927, 47, 1–52.

* ——, 'Thirteenth Century Miniatures Illustrating Medical Practice' *Proceedings of the Royal Society of Medicine*, 1915–1916, 9(2), 29–42.

Strong, George, *Medieval Medical Costumes as Seen in Miniatures* (Unpublished M. A. Thesis, University of North Carolina). Chapel Hill, 1961.

Stubbs, S. G. B. and E. W. Bligh, *Sixty Centuries of Health and Physic; the Progress of Ideas from Primitive Magic to Modern Medicine*. London, 1931.

* Sudhoff, Karl (ed.), *Studien zur Geschichte der Medizin*. 22 vols., Leipzig, 1907–1934.

* *Sudhoff's Archiv für Geschichte der Medizin und der Naturwissenschaften*, Leipzig and Wiesbaden, 1907 ff.

SELECT BIBLIOGRAPHY

Tabanelli, Mario, *Albucasi: un chirurgo arabo dell' alte medio evo*. Florence, 1961.

Temkin, Owsei, 'Geschichte des Hippokratismus im ausgehenden Altertum,' *Kyklos*, 1932, *4*, 1–80.

Thorndike, Lynn, *A History of Magic and Experimental Science During the First Thirteen Centuries of Our Era*. 2 vols., New York, 1923.

—— and Pearl Kibre, *A Catalogue of Incipits of Mediaeval Scientific Writings in Latin*. Cambridge, Mass., 1937.

* Urdang, George, *The Spuibb Ancient Pharmacy*. New York, 1940.

Weedeon, F. R. and A. P. Heusner, 'A Clinical-Pathological Conference from the Middle Ages,' *The Bulletin* (University of North Carolina School of Medicine), 1960, *8*(2), 14–20.

* Weindler, Fritz, *Geschichte der Gynäkologisch-Anatomischen Abbildung*. Dresden, 1908.

White, T. H., *The Book of Beasts*. New York, 1954.

Wickersheimer, Ernest, 'Note sur les oeuvres médicales d'Alphane, Archevêque de Salerne,' *Janus*, 1930, *34*, 273–278.

Wiedemann, E. and F. Hauser, 'Über Schalen, die beim Aderlass verwendet werden, und Waschgefässe nach Gazarî,' *Sudhoff's Archiv für Geschichte der Medizin und der Naturwissenschaften*, 1919, *11*, 22–43.

Zimmerman, Leo and Ilza Vieth, *Great Ideas in the History of Surgery*. Baltimore, 1961.

Fig. 3. A Three-Bed Hospital

193

Fig. 5. Byzantine Uroscopy

194

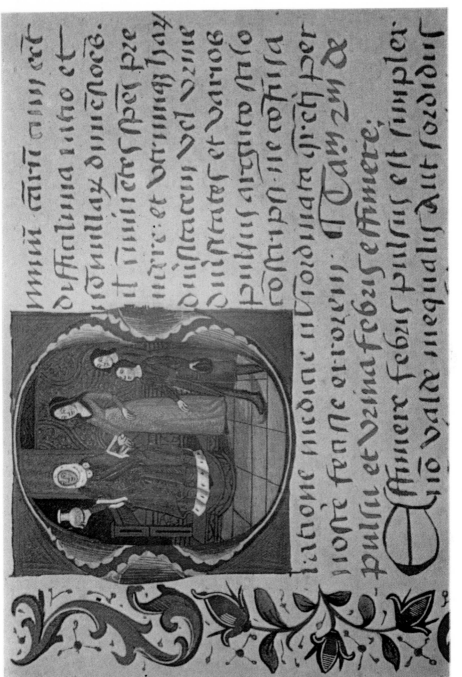

Fig. 14. Galen Does a Woman's Uroscopy and Pulse

Fig. 21. Pharmacy in a Surgeon's Office

196

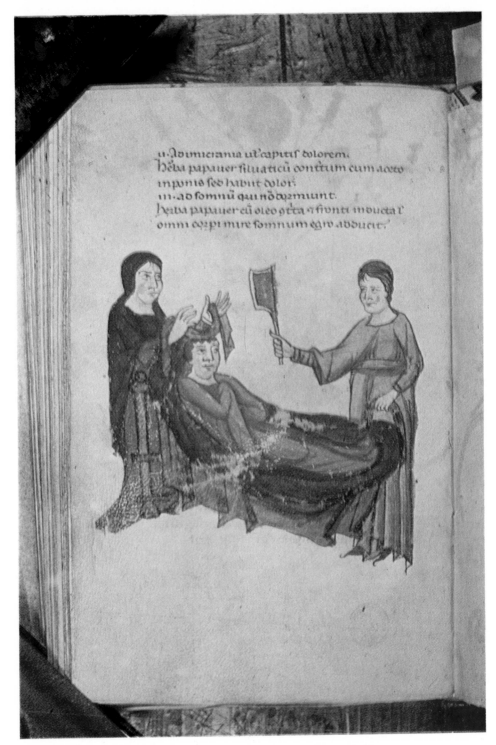

Fig. 32. A Headache and Insomnia Remedy

Fig. 35. Realistic Publicizing of a Purgative-Emetic

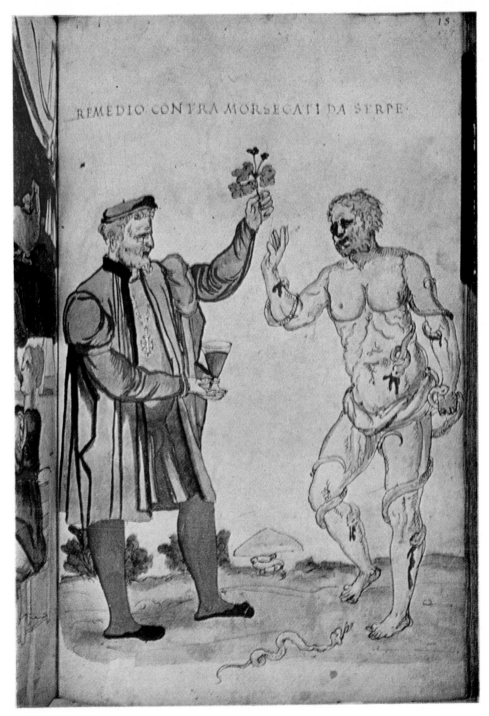

Fig. 38. A Late Dramatization of Snake Bite

Fig. 42. A Soothing Inhalant for Babies

Fig. 45. Cautery Points and Cauterizing

Fig. 54. Bleeding a Man

202

que roues enfans sil nont · iij · ans
passes · ne soient pas ventousse le
grant besoing ne leur fait faire ·
Li · xi · chapitres des sansues ·

ous d
ues sa
non · d
il y a
vne u
mere
sansu
es qu
sunt
xvm

meules licorne dient li philo
sophe · z pour cognoistre les qu
les sont bonnes z les queles si
ventueuses · si vous endrons a
q auicenes en dit · Il dit q cele

Fig. 58. Leeching

203

Fig. 61. Examining Wounds on the Head and Arms

204

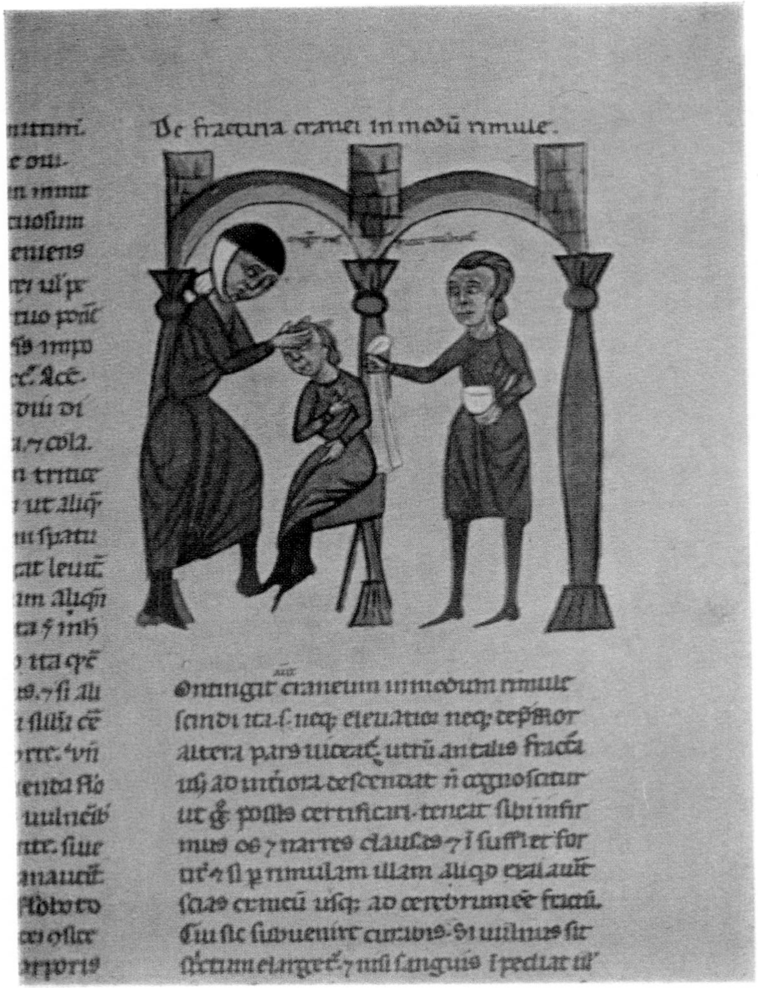

Fig. 63. Surgical Examination of a Fractured Cranium

Fig. 82A. Operation for Bladder Stones. The Celsan Operation

Fig. 66. A Cranial Incision to Drain a Fracture

Fig. 77. Operating on the Upper Arm

ncai o piaco tag acceptt nic
lavatim. quu quater uel pluuer
coler in accellare.

P omnium ttc lune c sir cc lu
na tu x. vics accipiat vi. ccte
las cc rudice spade keata radii
tapham agsti. alia vic v. aliar.
a sic nct, ao finc lune. cuius vic
mimucto una. Ce si li in u valiui.

Fig. 73. Medicating and Operating for Scrofula

Fig. 81B. Treatment of Scrotal Hernia. By Surgical Operation

208

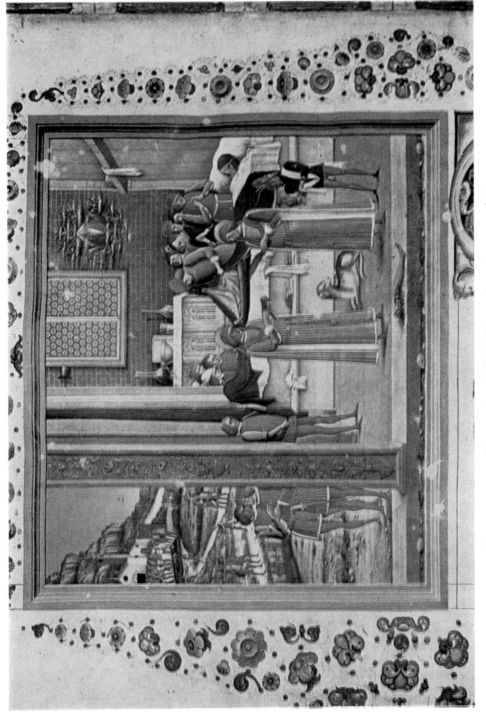

Fig. 90. Grafting a New Leg in Place of an Amputated One

209

Fig. 91A. Reducing Dislocated Vertebrae. Reduction by Jolting on a Ladder

Fig. 1. A Byzantine Diagnostic-Pharmaceutical Clinic

Fig. 2. A Western Out-Patient Clinic

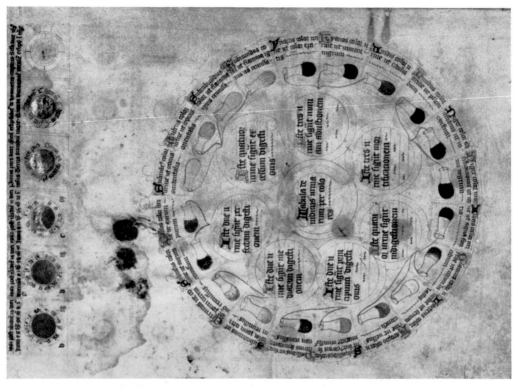

Fig. 6. Western Uroscopy Chart

Fig. 4. Preliminary Examinations in a Surgeon's Office–Clinic

Fig. 8. Constantinus Africanus does Uroscopy for Women and Men

Fig. 7. Delivering a Urine Flask at a Diagnostic Clinic

Fig. 9. A Physician makes a Careful Inspection of Urine

Fig. 10. Uroscopy in a Clinic

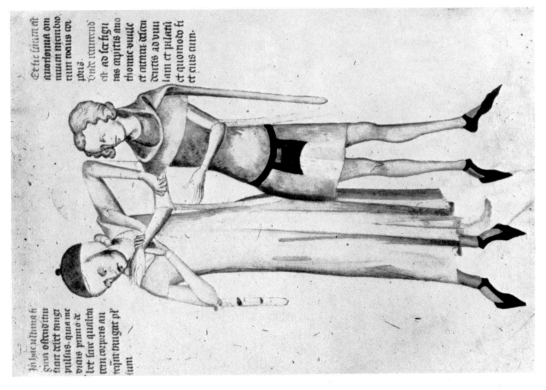

Fig. 12. Taking the Pulse at the Brachial Artery

Fig. 11. Taking the Pulse of a Bed-Patient

Fig. 13. Taking a Woman's Pulse

Fig. 15. A Medieval Comic: The Ape doctors a Man

216

Fig. 16. Prognosis of Death by the Caladrius Bird

Fig. 17. Diagnosis-Prognosis by Astrology

Fig. 19. A Crowded Page from a Pictorial Materia Medica

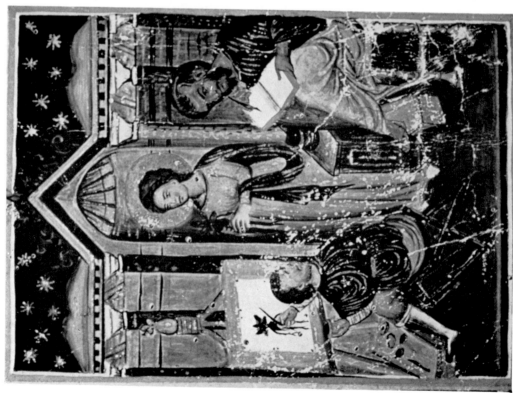

Fig. 18. The Fathers of Western Pharmacopoeia at Work

Fig. 22. A Physician and Assistants prepare a Prescription

Fig. 20. Collecting Medicinal Herbs

Fig. 24. A Pharmacist or Physician rolling Pills

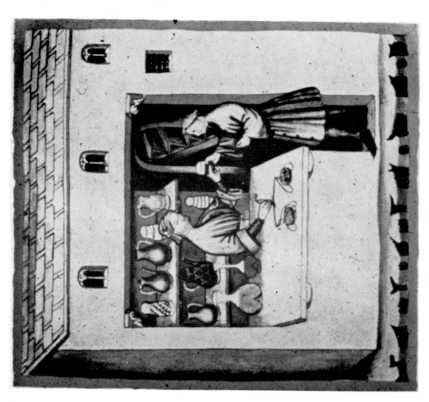

Fig. 23. A Pharmacist dispenses Syrup for Coughs

Fig. 25. A Patient taking
a Cough Drop

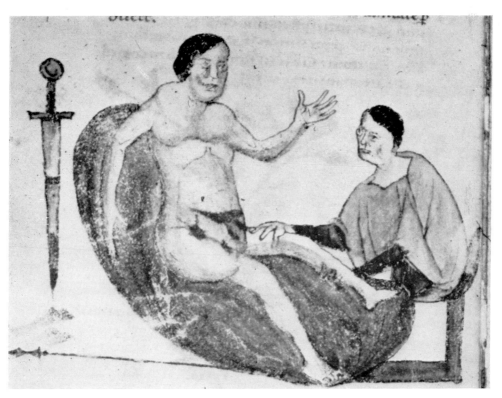

Fig. 29. Ointment for a Sword Wound

Fig. 27. A Herbal Fomentation for a Child's Internal Pain
and a Herbal Potion for Nausea

Fig. 26. Ointment of Pig Dung and Herb Scelerata for Scrofula

222

Fig. 30. An Ointment for Arthritis

Fig. 28. The Eagle Remedy for Poor Eyesight

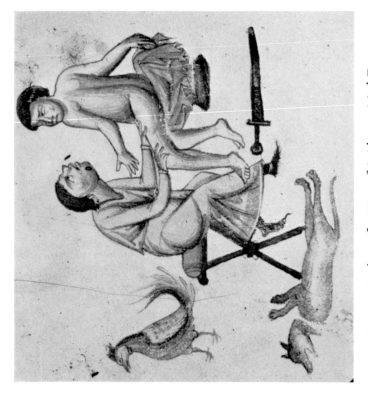

Fig. 33. Verbena for Bite of Spider or Mad Dog

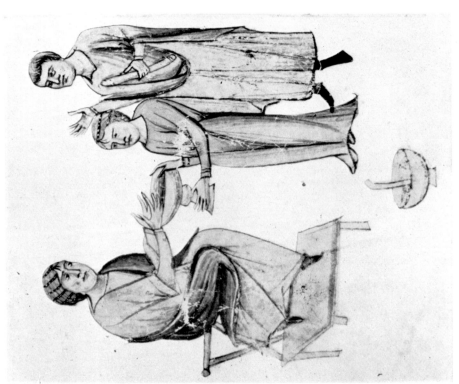

Fig. 31. A Face-Wash for Women's Freckles

224

Fig. 36. Dramatizing a Cure for Insanity

Fig. 37. Dramatizing a Cure for Snake Bite

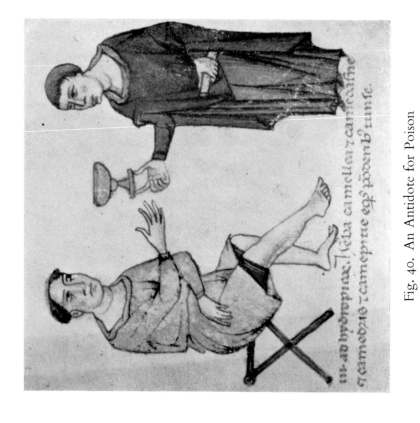

Fig. 40. An Antidote for Poison

Fig. 34. Purging with an Enema (Clyster)

226

Fig. 41. Potions of Gladiola and Goats' or Asses' Milk for Internal Pains

Fig. 39. Curing Lunacy with a Sprig of Peony, and Sciatica with Peony Root

227

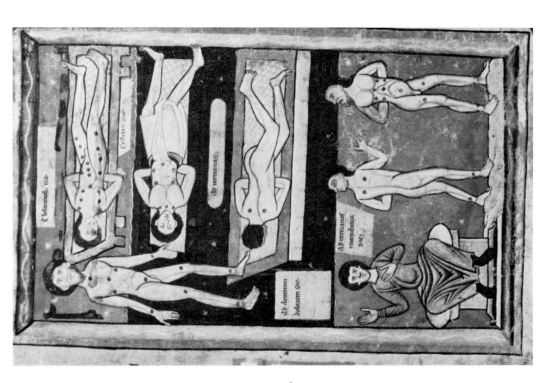

Fig. 44. Cautery Points and Famous Healers

Fig. 43. Cautery Points shown on Human Figures

228

Fig. 46. Heating the Cautery Iron

Fig. 51. Cautery 'of the Entire Body'

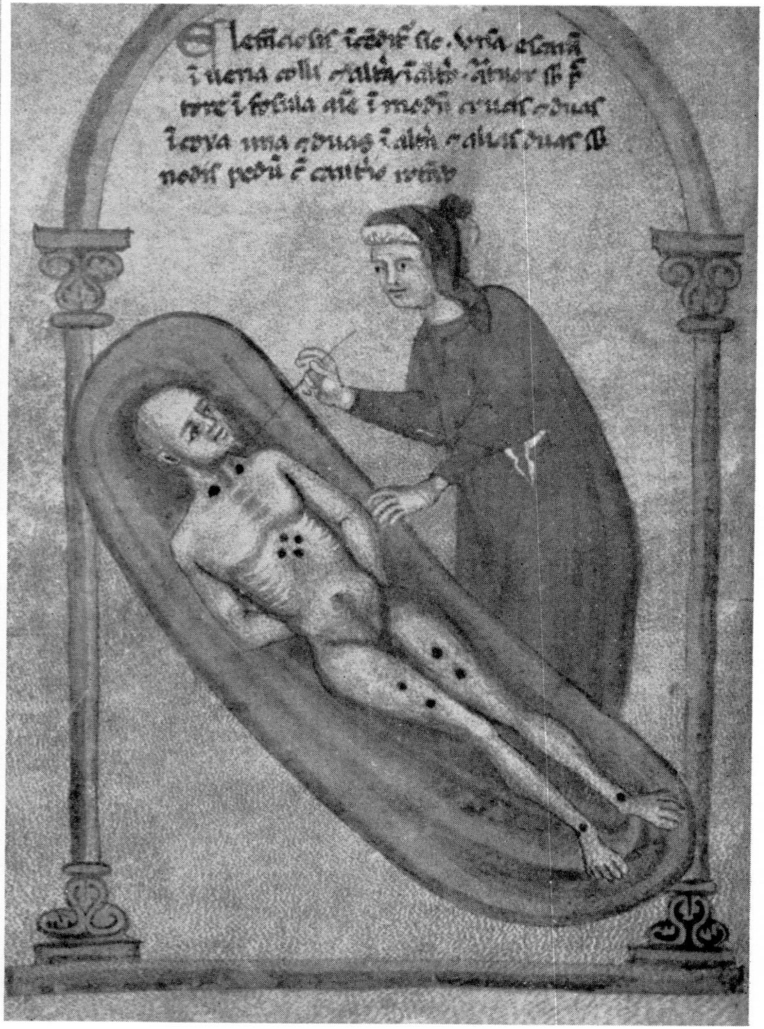

Fig. 48. Cauterizing for Elephantiasis

Fig. 47. Three Cautery Victims Approach the Ordeal

Fig. 50. Surgery and Cautery

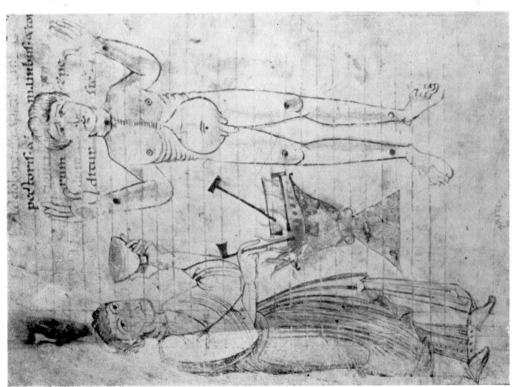

Fig. 49. A Physician about to Cauterize and Causticize

231

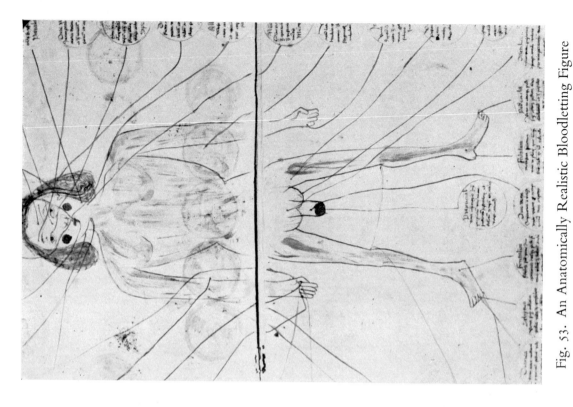

Fig. 53. An Anatomically Realistic Bloodletting Figure

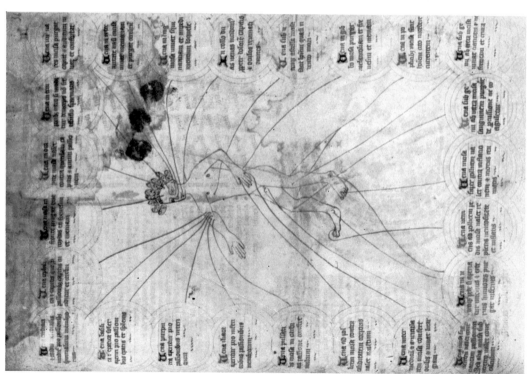

Fig. 52. An Annotated Bloodletting Figure

Fig. 55. Bleeding a
Woman

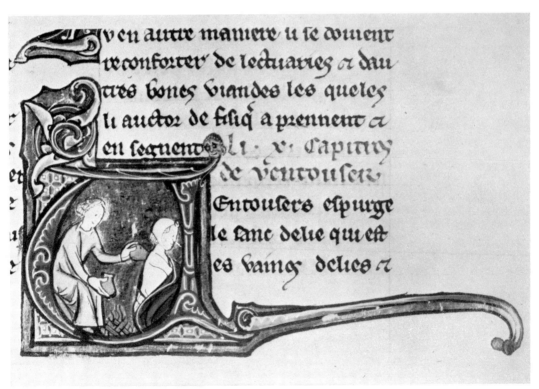

v en autre maniere il se coment
reconforter de lectuaries a dau
tres bones viandes les queles
li auctor de fisiq a prennent a
en seruents li x capitus
de ventouser

Entousers espurge
le sanc delie qui est
es vaines delies a

Fig. 56. Cupping

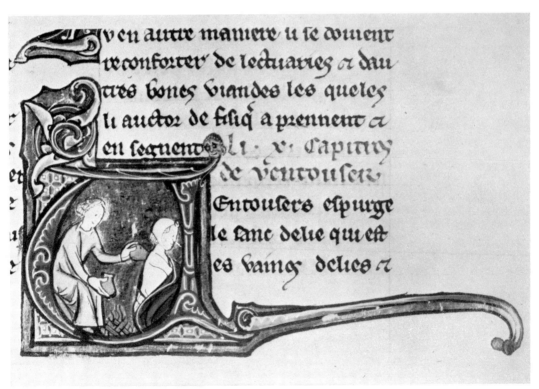

233

ولإبرازلكذلك طلاهالبائنة وتسمن دوغا وكأثالانواقرة وبثأوتسرريع البيد وتستكانق تكمصرحا عجمروشئت الكاناوبض بالعزالضوري حلاراضحا

Fig. 59. An Arabic Measuring Instrument used in Bloodletting

Fig. 57. Cupping in a Bath House

Fig. 64. Surgical Exploration of a Fractured Cranium

Fig. 60. Surgical Instruments

235

Fig. 67. Suturing a Superficial Head Wound

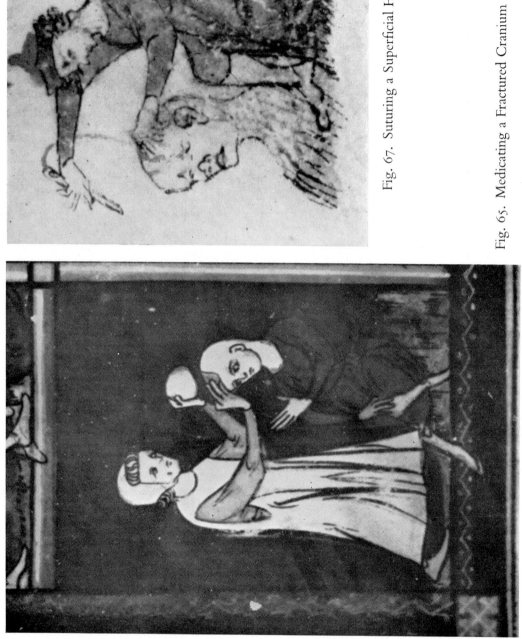

Fig. 65. Medicating a Fractured Cranium

236

Fig. 62. A Head Wound from a Brawl

Fig. 68. Mania Cured by Head Surgery

Fig. 70. A Late-Medieval Operation for Cataract

Fig. 69. Early-Medieval Operations for Cataract and Nasal Polyps

Fig. 71. Cutting and Cauterizing a Facial Fistula

Fig. 72. Ligaturing a Cut Vein in the Neck

Fig. 75. Extraction of a Barbed Arrow from the Arm

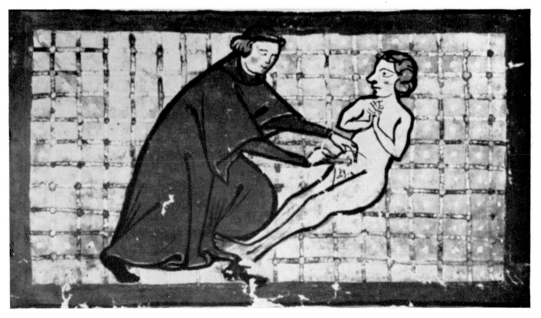

Fig. 79. Operating on an Abdominal Fistula

Fig. 76. Extraction of Missile Weapons from the Body

Fig. 74. Extraction of a Barbed Arrow from the Face

241

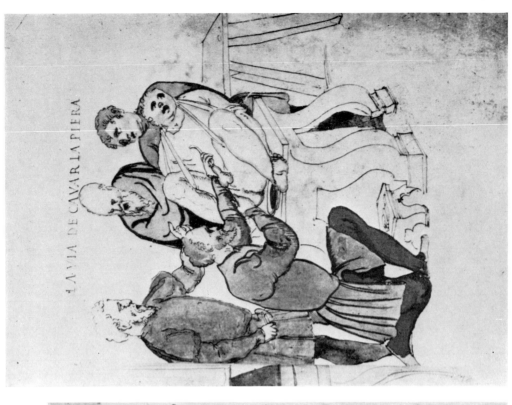

Fig. 82b. Operation for Bladder Stones. An Improved Early-
Modern Operation

Fig. 78. Setting a Fractured Arm

242

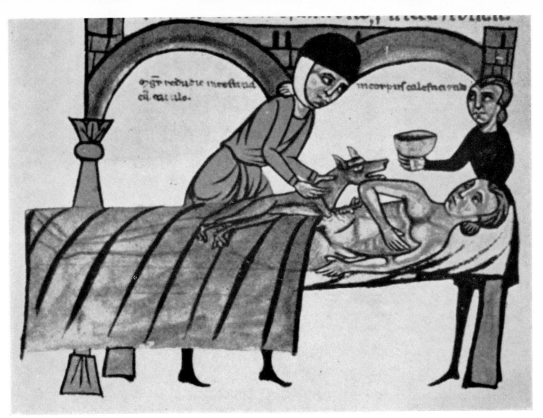

Fig. 80. Preliminary Treatment of Intestines Protruding from a Wounded Abdomen

Fig. 81A. Treatment of Scrotal Hernia. By Medication and a Truss

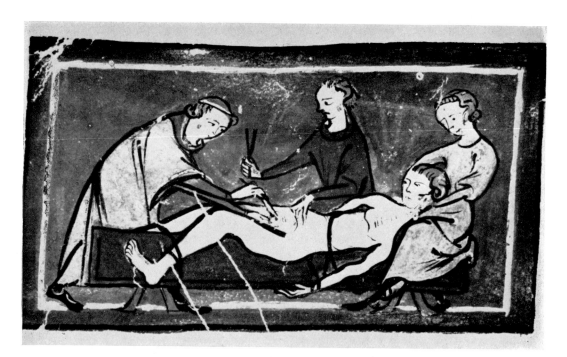

Fig. 81c. Treatment of Scrotal Hernia. By Surgical Operation

Fig. 84. Excising Cancer of the Penis

Fig. 85A. Circumcision of Christ. In a Miniature

Fig. 83. Early-Modern Catheterization for Urinary Obstruction

245

Fig. 87A. John Arderne's Operation for Anal Fistula. Preliminary
Probing

Fig. 85B. Circumcision of Christ. In an Altar Painting

Fig. 86. Removal of Hemorrhoids

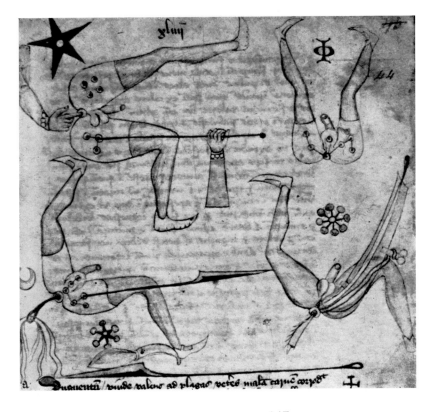

Fig. 87B.
John Arderne's
Operation for
Anal Fistula.
Operational
Procedure

247

Fig. 89B. Surgical Examination of Legs. For Ulcers

Fig. 88. Incising a Thigh: Preparation of Herbal Medicines

248

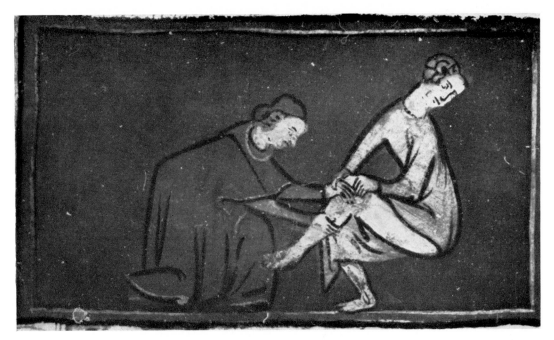

Fig. 89A. Surgical Examination of Legs. For Cancer

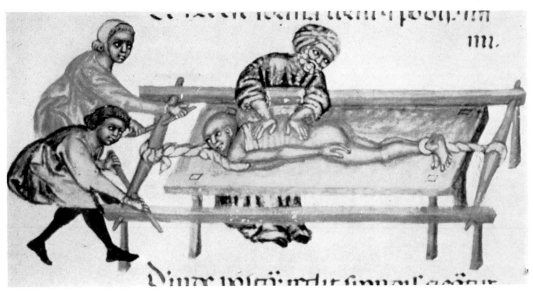

Fig. 91C. Reducing Dislocated Vertebrae. Reduction, in the Moslem Middle Ages, by Hand-Pressure

Fig. 92. Midwives Hastening a Slow Delivery

Fig. 91B. Reducing Dislocated Vertebrae. Reduction by Traction and Pressure on the Spine

Fig. 91D. Reducing Dislocated Vertebrae. Reduction by Classical-Medieval Methods

Fig. 96. An Autopsy

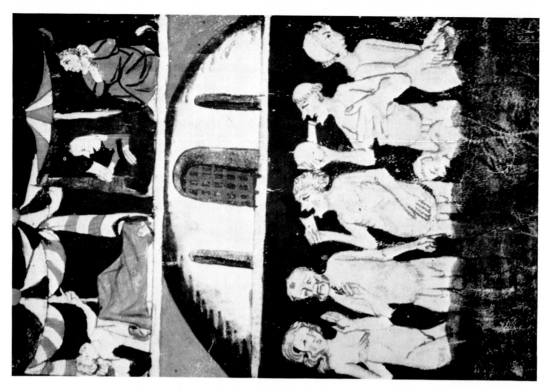

Fig. 94B. Mixed Nude Bathing

Fig. 94A. A Medical Bath

Fig. 93. Inhaling Tranquillizing Fumes for Toothache

Fig. 95. Veterinary Treatment of Dogs

INDEX

The figures in italics indicate page numbers in Part I. Figures in roman type refer to the index numbers of the manuscripts listed in Part II, and to the illustrations.

INDEX

INDEX

INDEX

INDEX

INDEX

INDEX

Made and printed in Great Britain by William Clowes and Sons Ltd., London and Beccles